Animals in Migration

Also by Robert T. Orr

THE ANIMAL KINGDOM

Animals
In Migration

ROBERT T. ORR

THE MACMILLAN COMPANY

COLLIER-MACMILLAN LTD., LONDON

CONTENTS

v

PREFACE

Man has been aware of the phenomenon of migration for thousands of years. Many explanations have, therefore, been proposed to account for these periodic appearances and disappearances of certain kinds of organisms. Some were founded on superstition, others belonged to the world of fantasy, but few were in any way related to facts. The appearance of migrating salmon, eels, and other fishes, the arrival of waterfowl in the autumn or of songbirds in the spring were accepted like the seasons. Only in the last few decades has there been any concerted effort to understand these population movements and determine the causes as well as the means by which they are effected. As in many other fields of scientific endeavor more has been learned about migration in the last quarter of a century than in all of previous recorded history. Even so only a start has been made in this field.

Since there tends to be a separation of those studying the same subject but with entirely different groups of organisms, the purpose of this book is to gather together under one cover most of the basic principles and recent discoveries on population movements in general. Mammalogists, ornithologists, herpetologists, ichthyologists, entomologists, and zoologists specializing in invertebrates each tend to stay within their own field of study and restrict their activities to those organisms with which they are most familiar. This may be necessary but it can also result in a loss of perspective. The modern ethologist is more inclined to work with principles that may be common to many groups of animals. This integration of information covering a broad spectrum of taxa is just as essential in analyzing migratory behavior. For example, celestial orientation is used by invertebrates, fishes, and amphibians as well as by birds. Olfactory orientation in travel is just as important to certain insects as to some mammals. The reason a monarch butterfly travels south in

ix

autumn may not be very different from the reason a hermit thrush does the same thing. However, the truth or falsity of such an assumption can be determined only by careful comparative analysis of the factors involved in each of the species.

Many references are given in this book and many have been consulted because of the extent of the fields that have been covered. I appreciate assistance given me by many persons. For the use of certain pictures I want to thank Basic Books, Inc.; Bird-Banding; Mr. Dan Bleitz, Bleitz Foundation, Hollywood; British Museum of Natural History, London; Mr. Rex Burress, Oakland Park Department; Canadian Wildlife Service; Dr. Nathan W. Cohen, University of California Extension, Berkeley; Dr. Lauren R. Donaldson, College of Fisheries, University of Washington; Dr. Earl S. Herald, Steinhart Aquarium, California Academy of Sciences; The Ibis; Idaho Fish and Game Department; Dr. Joseph Hall, San Francisco State College; Houghton Mifflin Co.; Mr. Richard Jennings, formerly of Stanford Research Institute; University of Kansas, Museum of Natural History; Dr. George E. Lindsay, California Academy of Sciences; The Macmillan Co.; Mr. Anthony Mercieca, San Diego; Dr. Dietland Müller-Schwartze, Utah State University; National Aeronautics and Space Administration; Norske Videnskaps-Akademi i Oslo; Oceans Magazine; Oregon State University Press; Pacific Discovery; Point Reyes Bird Observatory; Dr. Thomas C. Poulter, Stanford Research Institute; Mr. Lewis S. Rose, California Academy of Sciences; Dr. Edward S. Ross, California Academy of Sciences; Dr. E. G. Franz Sauer, Zoologisches Forschungsinstitut und Museum Alexander Koenig, Bonn, Germany; W. B. Saunders Co.; Mr. Vincent Serventy, Hunter's Hill, N.S.W., Australia; Dr. Walter A. Sheppe, University of Akron, Ohio; Mr. John H. Tashjian, Oakland; Mr. Cornelius G. Willis, Sierra Madre, California and the University of Wisconsin Press.

I am greatly indebted to those persons who enabled me to go to certain areas extremely important in the migratory patterns of some species. I am especially grateful to Mr. and Mrs. Kenneth K. Bechtel and the Belvedere Scientific Fund, whose generosity made it possible for me to visit St. Paul Island in Bering Sea and Point Barrow, Alaska, and to Mr. and Mrs. Lawrence C. Kuebler of Bonita, California, whom I accompanied to Scammons Lagoon, Isla Raza, and other localities in Baja California that are important to migrant species. I wish to thank Dr. George E. Lindsay, Director of the California Academy of Sciences, for the opportunity to visit many areas, especially in western North America, that were vital to gathering data for this book, and particularly for the chance to observe and photograph migrating gray whales.

Charlotte Dorsey typed the manuscript, checked the references, and assisted in the proofreading. Joy Bailey Osborne critically read the manuscript and contributed her services to compiling the index. Dorothy B. Orr critically read the edited copy and assisted in the proofreading. Dr. Lawrence C. Binford checked numerous scientific names of birds and proofread sections relating to avian migration. Jean Firby completed the final indexing and Jacqueline Schonewald assisted in the proofreading.

INTRODUCTION

Filtered sunlight shines through more open parts of the forest and on patches of the stream whose clear water, augmented by the autumn rains, flows swiftly past. In deeper parts of this watercourse, where the bottom may still be seen, worn and weary salmon hold their places in the current with almost imperceptible effort. For the most part they remain in the shadows cast by tall cedars, firs, and hemlocks, but their shabby appearance gives them away. In the sea some weeks ago they were flashes of silver and dark steel gray. The scales they possessed as fingerlings were still nearly all present in orderly rows, each showing rings of growth that had been added at regular intervals since hatching. Now great patches of scales and even skin are gone, with the white flesh standing out in stark contrast to other parts of the body. Their tails, too, are white, and on some there are long naked stripes running the length of the back. Sometimes one fish moves upstream and then returns, as though to encourage others. It is really not doing it for this purpose, however, as each salmon is stimulated to perform the way it does by various hormones which the body has built up for this return to these waters of its birth and, finally, its death.

Autumn has also had its effect on the surrounding forest. The vine maples have turned yellow, orange, and pink. The dogwoods are a deep red, and their leaves keep falling gently to the ground. The rich covering of humus on the forest floor gives forth a pleasant, earthy odor, and the underground mycelial strands of fungi are rapidly producing buttons that almost overnight spring up in the form of those fruiting bodies that we call toadstools and mushrooms.

These are not the only manifestations of mid-October in the Cascades. From their hiding places deep in fissures and burrows in the ground, some species of salamanders are coming out. Many have rested quietly in the cool, damp earth since the previous spring, as their thin, moist skin is unable to resist the desiccating effect of summer above ground. Somehow now an awareness of the increase in moisture has stimulated them to move to the surface, where they will remain until next year. During the daylight hours they will be hidden under logs and other debris of the forest floor. When they first emerged, their bodies were quite thin from many months of lack of food and liquid. Their water uptake, though, is very rapid, and within a few days body weight will be back to what it was the previous winter.

As the season progresses, some kinds of salamanders will move to nearby ponds or streams, while others will seek moist chambers in the ground or even holes in trees. There the eggs of a future generation will be deposited by the female. When the rains of the following spring gradually diminish and summer is but a few weeks off, these troglodytes will move once again to their subterranean homes.

As the salmon force their way up the waters of the McKenzie past Limberlost and the salamanders slowly come to the mossy surface of the forest floor, many changes are also evident in the bird life. During spring and summer, the voices of warblers, vireos, flycatchers, and many other nesting species echoed through the woods. This chorus has long ceased, and those responsible for it are mostly gone, except for the permanent residents like jays, chickadees, and nuthatches. Many other birds, however, are now passing through as transients. Some, like the hermit thrushes, kinglets, and fox sparrows, are members of species that also nested here last summer, but they are representatives from Canada and Alaska. They have finished their nesting season, and the long summer days of the far northern latitudes have diminished to brief periods of daylight followed by long nights. This reduction in day length has somehow stimulated their southward movement. They will stay here in Oregon only a few days to replenish their source of energy in the form of fat and then move on farther south, some to California and Arizona, others to Mexico, Central America, and even farther. There the days are longer and warmer and food is more easily obtained.

The behavior of the salmon, the amphibians, and the birds in this tiny area in the mountains of western Oregon is repeated all over the northern part of the world each autumn, and is a manifestation of the same phenomenon. In many respects they are governed by the same basic factors.

As far back as we can go in recorded history there is evidence that man has been aware of this seasonal appearance and subsequent departure of certain kinds of animals. Many superstitions developed to account for these regular occurrences and the absences of various animals, but the real reasons were mostly obscure. No doubt such movements were more readily understood by tribes distant from the equator because of the marked seasonal variations and the effect of these changes upon their own bodies. We know that certain aborigines in North America engaged in migration. For some, especially in the West, it was an altitudinal movement to higher mountains in summer and a descent to low country for the winter period. There were plains tribes that regularly moved north and south in summer and winter with the great herds of bison upon which they depended for food and clothing. In eastern Canada we learn that the Micmacs lived in the woods in winter, where they hunted moose, caribou, and porcupines. When spring came, they moved to the seacoast and lived on shellfish.

Modern man, in general, is less aware of the phenomenon of migration. He relies on cultivated plants and domesticated animals for food and tends to live in large communities and metropolitan areas where the seasonal movements of animals are not easily seen. Still, there are scientists who are devoting their lives to this subject and even governmental agencies whose function it is to study migration. Several factors are responsible for this. One of these is man's insatiable desire for knowledge. Why does a bird in autumn fly from the prairies of North America to the pampas of the Argentine? How can it accomplish such a remarkable feat? How is it guided, and what stimulus induces the return flight? Similar questions arise regarding the movements of whales, seals, marine turtles, fishes, as well as many invertebrate organisms. We are slowly learning some of the answers, but the number of problems that remain unsolved is still great.

1

POPULATION MOVEMENTS

Animal populations are never static; therefore the continual changes to which they are subject have played an important part in evolutionary history. These changes result from many variable factors in the environment as well as within the organisms themselves. Environmental changes are constantly occurring and acting as selective forces upon genetic mutations. This not only serves to bring about adaptive modifications in morphological structure and physiological behavior, but has resulted in the development of population mobility in numerous kinds of organisms.

Such population mobility has enabled many species to expand their ranges seasonally, to occupy different environments at different times during the life cycle, to reduce periodic population pressures from within, to escape from unfavorable environmental conditions of both regular and irregular occurrence, and to expand into previously unoccupied geographical areas. Population movements, therefore, may be divided into several different categories. The first of these, and the one with which this book is primarily concerned, is migration.

MIGRATION

The term *migration* has been used very loosely by many writers. Some years ago Walter Heape, in his interesting book *Emigration, Migration and Nomadism*, major types of population movements.[1] He vements of regular periodicity in h or hatching. *Emigration* permanent nature. is followed

More recently the terms *anastrophic* and *diasporic* were proposed to distinguish true migration from other kinds of population movements.[2] The first of these means to retrace one's steps, and the second refers to dispersion or the dispersal of organisms. Migration, therefore, is a periodic phenomenon involving a round trip that may be of seasonal occurrence, or may require a lifetime to complete. It is engaged in by many kinds of organisms ranging from microplankton to whales and is governed by numerous factors. This compulsive movement has evolved in many ways and is a type of behavior that functions for the preservation of the species.

One of the simplest types of migratory patterns is seen in certain planktonic organisms that rise to the surface of the sea at night and sink to greater depths by daylight. This sort of cyclic movement is often of a more seasonal nature in freshwater microorganisms living in lakes and ponds. Seasonal changes in temperature as well as other environmental factors cause a periodic shift from deeper to shallower water, followed by a subsequent return to the depths.

There are other marine organisms, including segmented worms and some kinds of fishes, whose migrations are based upon lunar periodicity. Palolo worms of the genus *Eunice* occurring in tropical parts of the Pacific and Atlantic oceans, as well as certain amphipods, move to reproductive situations under lunar influence. There are fishes such as the grunion (*Leuresthes tenuis*) that exhibit a similar monthly behavior at certain times of the year.

The movements of certain insects are of a seasonal nature and are determined to a large extent by the availability of food. Those of the monarch butterfly (*Danaus plexippus*) are a good example. These butterflies depend upon milkweed (*Asclepias*) for food for the larvae. In autumn they move southward to spend the winter in favorable climatic areas. When spring comes, there is a northward exodus to where the necessary food plant grows.

Many fishes, both fresh- and saltwater species, move to very specific breeding areas, which may or may not be far _____ _____ the feeding grounds. Generally such movements a_____ vidual members of the popul____ ever, this requires a full *diadromous* fishes water, attaining maturity in one and breeding in the other. Those that reproduce in freshwater river systems, move to the sea to attain maturity, then return to the home stream to spawn are referred to as *anadromous* species. Pacific salmon of the genus *Oncorhynchus* are a good example. The reverse type of movement is made by *catadromous* fishes such as freshwater eels of the genus *Anguilla*. These eels breed in the sea and die, and the young, after one to three years, migrate back to the streams from which their parents came. There they remain for some years until sexually mature, at which time they too migrate to the sea and ultimately, if successful, arrive at the spawning area, reproduce, and die.

The migrations of amphibians are basically of a seasonal nature. Because of the necessity of having a moist or wet environment in which to deposit the eggs, and because fertilization in essentially all members of this group is external, males and females of many species tend to aggregate at ponds or streams at some time during the year, depending upon the rainy season and climatic conditions. After the reproductive season there is a dispersal to other areas.

The best-known reptilian migrants are the marine turtles, of which there are several species inhabiting the tropical and subtropical seas of the world. These reptiles lay their eggs on the beaches of remote oceanic islands, and though only the females go on land, the males may also migrate to the adjacent shores. This is not an annual migration on the part of individual females, however, but takes place every two or three years.

The best-known migrants of all are to be found among birds that live away from the equatorial regions of the world. In this group the movements are seasonal and for the most part in a generally north-south direction. Wintering occurs closer to the equator, and in spring, as the weather becomes more favorable, there is an exodus toward the poles. The extent of movement on the part of migratory species ranges from extremes such as the migration of the arctic tern (*Sterna paradisaea*), which may nest in the Arctic and winter in the Antarctic, thereby making an annual round trip of about twenty-two thousand miles, to local spring and fall movements of quail merely up and down a mountain slope.

The migrations of mammals are mostly on a seasonal basis. The principal mammalian migrants are certain species of insectivorous bats, cetaceans, pinnipeds, and some large herbivores. As with birds, the distances vary greatly with the species. The migrations of whales may involve thousands of miles of travel annually, whereas those of certain

large herbivores merely entail a descent from a high summer range to a
lower winter range that may be but a few miles distant.

IRRUPTIONS

There are occasions when a large part of an animal population rather
suddenly moves far out of its normal range. Such a movement is often
referred to as an irruption.

Irruptions are primarily associated with animals living in areas of
climatic extremes. Arctic and subarctic species are most often affected,
and to a lesser extent desert species. Cyclic fluctuations are essentially
unknown in tropical or subtropical regions. This appears to be related
to the numbers of species involved in northern ecosystems as contrasted
with those closer to the equator. Northern communities are formed of
relatively few plants and animals, and a change in one may effect a
change in a number of others. During peak vegetational years in the
Arctic, rodents and hares are abundant, and so are the carnivores that
prey upon them. When there is a decline in the quantity or, as is more
often the case, the quality of the food, the dependent herbivore population undergoes a decline, which is followed by a similar decline in the
carnivores that feed upon them. The reduction in numbers of herbivores
may be brought about by such factors as starvation, a cessation in
reproduction, disease, predation, and emigration.

One of the best-known examples of a mammal that exhibits a cyclic
population fluctuation and irrupts when the peak is reached is the brown
lemming (*Lemmus trimucronatus*) of the Arctic. These animals have a
three- to four-year population cycle. During this time their numbers
build up to a maximum and then crash. The latter results in part from
mortality by disease and predation, as well as from reduced reproduction, but it is also effected in a given area by a large number of individuals moving out and traveling overland. What induces lemmings to
start moving out of their home area is not known, but it is correlated
with stress produced by an excessive number of individuals. Food may
still be abundant, but the lemmings cease to feed. Death ultimately
comes as a result of drowning in rivers, lakes, and even the sea, on occasions, as well as from exhaustion, predation, and disease. Some do not
engage in this mass movement and survive to start the cycle over again.

Irruptions are of more common occurrence among birds than mammals because of their greater mobility. This is especially true of species

that inhabit cold regions, either in the far north or in high mountains. Such birds as snowy owls, Clark's nutcrackers, crossbills, and waxwings irregularly exhibit this type of population movement. The snowy owl (*Nyctea scandiaca*) nests in the arctic tundra of North America and winters in southern Canada. In years when lemmings and hares, upon which owls depend largely for food, are scarce there is a movement south into the United States. These birds at such times have been reported as far south as Georgia and California. This, however, is not a regular periodic movement and does not occur within the lifetime of most snowy owls.

Some of the best examples of irruptions have occurred a number of times in the Pallas' sandgrouse (*Syrrhaptes paradoxus*), a member of the order Columbiformes to which the pigeons belong, but which superficially resembles a gallinaceous bird. This species lives on the steppes of central Asia, but in certain years when there are particularly severe winters it undergoes a spectacular mass movement. At least seven irruptions were recorded in the nineteenth century, but the three largest occurred in 1863, 1888, and 1908. During some of these emigrations, sandgrouse flew to northern and western Europe. They were recorded in Norway, Scotland, and Ireland, and even tried to breed in these places, but none became established. In the 1908 invasion some sandgrouse reached Siberia and northern China.

The Clark's nutcracker (*Nucifraga columbiana*) of the mountains of western North America is another species that has irregular movement in certain years to areas outside of its regular range. This montane species is largely dependent on stored seeds of several species of pines and firs for winter food supply. In some years there are noticeable seed shortages among these conifers, and this appears to be responsible for nutcracker irruptions. According to Davis and Williams, six such irruptions have occurred in California since 1898.[3] Each of these has taken place during a poor seed year that followed several years of high seed production. The abundant food supply may have been responsible for a buildup in the populations of those species dependent on the seeds for food. When the scarcity occurred, nutcrackers were forced to seek food elsewhere at lower levels. They were seen at these times in such unusual places as the desert and the seacoast.

The closely related nutcracker of northern Asia (*Nucifraga caryocatactes*) is also noted for irruptions similar to those of its North American coun-

---

[3]Davis, J., and L. Williams. 1957, 1964.

terpart. These birds depend largely on the seeds of the Arolla pine (*Pinus cembra*) in Siberia. As the seed years of the pines build up, the nutcracker population increases. Seed years are followed by a drastic decline in seed production. When this occurs, the nutcrackers move out of the Arolla pine forests of northern Asia and fly west to Europe, some even reaching the British Isles. Major invasions by nutcrackers have occurred in the winters of 1883–1884, 1891–1892, 1903–1904, 1913–1914, and 1931–1932.

Somewhat similar irruptions, as a result of poor seed years in coniferous trees, occasionally take place among red crossbills (*Loxia curvirostra*). Crossbills, as their name implies, have the mandibles crossed, and this unique arrangement enables them to pry open the scales of pine and spruce cones to obtain the nuts. During poor seed years in the mountains of northern Europe as well as North America, since this is a Holarctic species, crossbills often wander in flocks far outside their regular range. Occasionally they will stay for a year or more in a new area and even breed there before leaving.

Another bird noted for its occasional sporadic movements in certain winters in the Bohemian waxwing (*Bombycilla garrulus*), which is also Holarctic in occurrence. Waxwings feed to a large extent on berries in northern Europe, Siberia, and northern North America. Flocks of waxwings, even under favorable winter conditions, tend to be nomadic, but in years of food scarcity, great irruptions may take place, and large numbers invade regions where the species does not regularly occur. Lincoln mentions the greatest invasion of Bohemian waxwings that ever occurred in the history of Colorado.[4] This took place in February, 1917, when an estimated ten thousand birds invaded the city of Denver.

The Bohemian waxwings of northern Europe and Siberia also engage in considerable nomadic wandering each winter but show a rather definite major ten-year irruption cycle. On these occasions they move in great numbers into middle and western Europe. These irruptions occur when a population peak has been reached. A great many of the birds that emigrate never return to their place of origin.

The budgerigar (*Melopsittacus undulatus*) of Australia and the thick-billed parrot (*Rhynchopsitta pachyrhyncha*) of North America are examples of birds of arid lands that invade new areas when the food supply becomes low. The budgerigar in general inhabits the dry interior of Aus-

[4]Lincoln, F. C. 1950.

A large flock of budgerigars (*Melopsittacus undulatus*) at Zanthus Dam, Australia. *Photograph by Vincent Serventy.*

tralia, where it occurs in large flocks. When conditions are favorable, the population of these parakeets increases rapidly. Subsequent periods of food scarcity or drought may induce extensive movements, and the species may invade the coastal plains.[5] This again is an instance of invasion induced by environmental conditions that occur only in particular years.

In North America the thick-billed parrot is an inhabitant of the table-land of Mexico. There are some years, however, when large numbers of these parrots move out of their normal range and even invade the moun-

[5]Serventy, V. 1965.

tains of southern Arizona, where they may remain for a year or so. This movement may be stimulated by food scarcity.

A. C. Bent has summarized the recorded invasions by this species into the Chiricahua Mountains of southern Arizona.[6] In June, 1900, a small group comprising nine or ten individuals was noted. The species was next seen in August, 1904, when a flock of seven hundred to one thousand parrots was reported. The last positive records were between September, 1917, and March, 1918, when groups numbering up to 250 individuals were periodically noted.

In Africa the occurrence of drought may also cause certain birds to move considerable distances. Moreau mentions an extensive movement of finch larks (*Eremopterix verticalis*) and pipits (*Anthus novaeseelandiae*) in August, 1964, into southern Zambia, where they had never been recorded before, following a drought in Bechuanaland.[7] Queleas (*Quelea quelea*), which are weaver finches that occur in vast flocks in certain parts of Africa, are dependent upon seeds in the dry season. When the rains come and the dropped seeds germinate, their local food source is temporarily gone and they move into other areas where earlier rains have already produced crops with available seeds.

The goshawk (*Accipiter gentilis*) in North America periodically moves south into northern United States from the Canadian provinces. Although it is migratory to some extent, little is known of its habits in this regard. Mueller and Berger observed and banded goshawks on 953 autumn days from 1950 through 1964 north of Milwaukee, Wisconsin, on the western shores of Lake Michigan.[8] This locality is more than ninety miles south of the breeding range of this hawk. In the eleven years prior to 1961, twenty-seven goshawks were trapped. Of this number 89 percent were juvenals. Eleven birds were trapped in 1961, of which 92 percent were juvenals. Following this there was a marked increase in the number of goshawks trapped in 1962 and 1963, with a corresponding decline in the percentage of immature birds. The total taken in 1962 was thirty-two and in 1963 was twenty-six. Fifty percent of these were adults in these years.

It was suggested that the rise in the number of goshawks noted from 1961 through 1963 was associated with a decline in the population of varying hares (*Lepus americanus*) and ruffed grouse (*Bonasa umbellus*) in

[6]Bent, A. C. 1940.
[7]Moreau, R. E. 1966.
[8]Mueller, H. C., and D. D. Berger. 1967b.

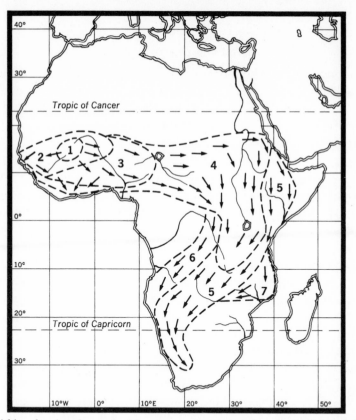

Map of Africa showing the gradual increase and spread of the migratory locust (*Locusta Migratoria*) between 1928 (1) and 1934 (7).

central Canada and the upper Great Lakes area. Varying hares reached a population peak in 1959 in parts of Ontario and in 1961 in Alberta. A decline soon followed. In Michigan the decline began in the winter of 1960–1961. Similarly the ruffed grouse population peaked in the fall of 1961 and then declined sharply. These two species form a major part of the food of the goshawk, and their decline in numbers was followed by an expanded southward movement of the hawks.

The age composition of the autumn-captured birds during non-irruption years is believed to result from forcing the young of the year to search for territory. The adults are normally resident, but the young, unable to find suitable territories within the breeding range, are forced southward in winter. The increase in proportion of adults during the invasion years is attributed to low reproductive success in the years 1962 and 1963, combined with a high population and food scarcity.

Irruptions are by no means limited to vertebrates. Such phenomena occur in a number of kinds of lower organisms but are best known per-

haps among insects. The movements of locusts in both the Old and the
New World are well known. In western North America the grasshopper
Melanoplus mexicanus may, in years when food is abundant, produce migratory forms which will move out of the areas where they were hatched.
They fly in great masses to new regions where they devour all the available vegetation. There are also so-called migratory locusts (*Locusta
migratoria*) in Asia and especially Africa that undergo enormous mass
movements in years when the population has reached a peak. Some may
breed in the new territory, but few return to where they hatched. There
are even records of migratory locusts having been found as much as
1,200 miles at sea. The desert locust (*Schistocerca gregaria*) of North
Africa and southwest Asia may have two breeding seasons a year, each
of which is correlated with rain in two different regions. These locusts,
however, truly migrate from one breeding area to the other and back.

We find true migration occurring in the monarch butterfly (*Danaus
plexippus*), but in certain other butterflies there are definitely irruptive
movements. The latter is true of the California tortoise-shell (*Aglais
californica*) of western North America. Members of this species feed on
shrubs of the genus *Ceanothus*. In years of a peak population they are so
numerous that the caterpillar larvae defoliate most of the host plants.
The adults then begin to move in great numbers to other regions where
the food plants are available. At times the traveling butterflies become
so abundant that the highways are covered with myriads of bodies hit
by passing automobiles.

The painted lady (*Vanessa cardui*), which is a nearly cosmopolitan
species of butterfly, shows some remarkable emigrations in parts of the
world. Some of these are seemingly triggered by food scarcity, whereas
others seem to be influenced by climate. In western North America
this species depends largely upon thistles and mallows as host plants for
the larvae. During years when the painted lady population is high and
the food plants scarce, great mass movements occur, principally to the
north. Some individuals fly to Canada and east as far as Newfoundland,
according to Williams.[9] In late March and early April, 1968, such a
movement of these butterflies occurred on the Pacific coast of North
America. Great numbers of painted ladies were observed flying west
and north in the southwestern desert areas of Arizona and southeastern
California. Some were even noted as far south as Kino Bay in Sonora,
Mexico. The movement continued north from southern California, and

[9]Williams, C. B. 1958.

The painted lady butterfly (*Vanessa cardui*). *Photograph by Edward S. Ross.*

on April 9 in Golden Gate Park, San Francisco, the writer was able to count hundreds within a few minutes passing over the roof of the California Academy of Sciences. This continued all day long, and it was estimated that hundreds of thousands, if not millions, passed over San Francisco on this day. The day was warm, with the temperature close to 80° Fahrenheit by midday. The flight was generally to the north. During the previous two weeks, painted lady butterflies had been noted occasionally but in smaller numbers. The day was cold and foggy on April 10, and essentially none were seen in Golden Gate Park. This movement was known to extend as far north as southern Oregon. Skiers noted painted lady butterflies in the Sierra Nevada at elevations of eight to ten thousand feet during this period. In southeastern United States this species fails to show such irruptive behavior.

In Europe the painted lady breeds as far north as Scotland and in some years may be found in Finland and Iceland. These individuals do not overwinter in these northern countries but move south in autumn. The southern movement from northern and central Europe results in the invasion of Africa by large numbers of these butterflies. They may move to tropical equatorial regions when they breed during the winter season. In the spring these individuals of southern origin begin to move northward. Some may end up in the British Isles and Scandinavia by the following June. The species is capable of very extensive flights, and individuals have been found more than one thousand miles at sea in the mid-Atlantic Ocean. These movements might be regarded as truly migratory, but they are irregular and unpredictable.

Similar movements of painted ladies are known to occur in parts of Asia and in Australia. On the latter continent it is believed that in certain years some make a flight of about twelve hundred miles across the open sea to New Zealand. Likewise, the little sulphur butterfly (*Eurema lisa*) has occasionally been known to fly in mass from the east coast of the United States to Bermuda, a distance of at least six hundred miles.

Many kinds of moths that breed in Asia, North Africa, and southern Europe also make extensive invasions to the north during the warmer parts of the year. The convolvulus moth (*Herse convolvuli*) is one of these. During most years it appears as far north as England, and reaches the Shetland Islands and Iceland on occasions. The death's head hawk-moth

The black witch (*Erebus odora*), a moth of the family Noctuidae. *Photographed in San Francisco, California, in August 1964 by Edward S. Ross.*

(*Acherontia atropos*) has a similar movement and may even invade Scandinavia. Although this species produces pupae in many parts of northern Europe, it is questionable if any of these survive north of southern Spain and south Italy.

In the Western Hemisphere a number of kinds of moths also invade areas far north of their regular breeding range in certain years. One of these is a member of the family Noctuidae known as the black witch (*Erebus odora*). It is a tropical species that may occasionally wander as far north as Canada and south to South America. It has even been found on Tristan da Cunha, which is in the center of the South Atlantic, two thousand miles east of South America.

INVASION AND DISPERSAL

There are types of slower population movements responsible for distributional modifications in the ranges of species that are in many instances correlated with climatic or other environmental changes. It is only ten or twelve thousand years since the end of the last glacial period, yet great adjustments have been made in the ranges of many terrestrial vertebrates of the Northern Hemisphere in that time. Skulls of such arctic mammals as collared lemmings (*Dicrostonyx hudsonius*) found in Pennsylvania in sinkholes have been shown to be no more than about twelve thousand years old. Today this species ranges no farther south in eastern North America than Ungava and Labrador. Parts of southeastern Alaska that were covered with glacial ice up to a few thousand years ago are now forested and inhabited by forest-dwelling animals. Within the past half century numerous species of birds and mammals have extended their ranges northward in North America, Europe, and Asia, and changes can be observed from year to year. Some are natural, and others have been influenced by man, directly or indirectly.

The story of the invasion of the Western Hemisphere by the cattle egret (*Bubulcus ibis*) is a remarkable example of dispersal by an avian species. The cattle egret, or buff-backed heron, as it is also known, was endemic to Africa and Eurasia until the early part of the twentieth century. It is a bird that commonly associates with large herbivorous mammals and feeds to a considerable extent on insects and other small creatures that these animals disturb as they move about. Cattle egrets often perch on the backs of the large herbivores. Such a sight is common in parts of Africa.

Just when this species arrived in the New World is not exactly known, but most of the important records have recently been summed up by Dr. Carl L. Hubbs of the Scripps Institution of Oceanography.[10] There are some early sight records, reputedly of this species, for northern South America between 1877 and 1882. It was also reported in British Guiana and Surinam in 1911–1912. Dr. Alexander Wetmore documented its occurrence in Colombia in 1916 or 1917. The arrival of this species in the Western Hemisphere is considered to be natural and a result of transatlantic flight. Recently the transatlantic movement of another related species, the little egret (*Egretta garzetta*), was reported by Downs.[11] An individual of this species that was banded in Spain was subsequently captured on the island of Trinidad.

Since the establishment of the cattle egret on the east coast of South America, either in the latter part of the nineteenth or early part of the twentieth century, the species has spread rapidly over parts of that continent and into Central America. Cattle egrets were first seen in the United States in Florida in 1941 or 1942. Since then they have spread north, east, and west. The species is now known as far west as California and Baja California. As further proof of its ability to travel long distances over the ocean in its dispersal activities, cattle egrets have been recorded by K. C. Lint between Cocos and Clipperton islands in the eastern Pacific Ocean about 920 kilometers west of Central America, and in the Galapagos Archipelago by Lévêque, Bowman, and Billeb.[12]

The little blue heron (*Florida caerulea*), formerly regarded as a species of eastern United States, Mexico, and Central and South America, has recently expanded westward in North America and has been observed a number of times in the past several years as far west as California.

The story of the starling (*Sturnus vulgaris*) in North America dates back to the year 1890, when sixty individuals were released in Central Park in New York City. These birds bred successfully, and within a few years some of them began to emigrate to other areas. By 1900 they were established in Connecticut and New Jersey. In less than fifty years the species had moved across the entire continent and was recorded in California in the 1940's. Today they occur in that state by the millions.

The English or house sparrow (*Passer domesticus*), which was originally native to Europe, North Africa, and western Asia, has gone with man

[10]Hubbs, C. L. 1968b.
[11]Downs, W. G. 1959.
[12]Lint, K. C. 1962; Lévêque, R., *et al.* 1966.

2

THE REASONS FOR MIGRATION

Migration is an adaptive pattern of behavior that has evolved in a number of kinds of mobile organisms. While mobility in itself is essential to migration, not all mobile species are necessarily migratory. Because of the diversified kinds of animals that do have established migratory patterns, it is obvious that this sort of behavior has evolved independently many times and for different reasons. The reasons for these population movements are not the same for all species. Even within a single population a migration in one direction may be for one purpose whereas the return trip may be for a different one. A good example of this is seen in the movements of some whales that come to subtropical or tropical waters to have their young but return to polar seas to feed. For convenience in discussion, however, the proximal causes of migration are grouped here under three categories: alimental, gametic, and climatic. Frequently all three are involved in the migration of a single species.

ALIMENTAL REASONS

The word *alimental* is defined as "having the quality of nourishing or providing the materials for natural growth." The alimental advantages of migration for some species, therefore, are due to a more favorable food supply available throughout the year as a result of seasonal geographic movements. These are not to be confused with irruptions seemingly induced at times by food scarcity, although it is difficult to make any absolute distinction. Irruptions, however, are not of regular occurrence. They may not even occur within the lifetime of many individuals, and they do not involve movements to a specific location.

In most fishes the movement to the breeding ground is definitely gametic, but after reproductive activities have been completed, the

19

migratory movement is basically alimental—back to the feeding grounds. This is likewise true of the movements of sea turtles. Once they have completed the laying of their eggs, there is a return migration to the sea pastures, where they will remain for two or three years.

Seasonal cycles in the availability of food for terrestrial animals become more apparent as the distance from the equator increases. Even on the equator there may be variation in seasonal abundance of food correlated with the wet and dry seasons. While this is insufficient to induce significant population movements, it may be a factor in the breeding cycle. In the Galapagos Archipelago, which extends from the equator to about 2° S. latitude, the rainy season lasts from January to May in the lowlands. This in general is also the breeding season for the endemic finches. It is the time when food is most abundant and conditions are most favorable for the nesting of land birds. On continental land masses in equatorial regions the breeding season for some species also may be correlated with the rainy season, when food is more abundant. Miller found indications of this in his study of the rufous-collared sparrow (*Zonotrichia capensis*) in Colombia.[1] There are two peaks in egg laying with five- to seven-month intervals between. These peaks are correlated with the rainfall cycle in the western Andes.

Most circumpolar birds of northern North America, northern Europe, and northern Asia, a region known collectively as the Holarctic, do not have food available to them in those areas in winter. Mudflats are frozen for waders, ponds and lakes are sealed in ice and therefore unavailable to waterfowl, insect food for such birds as thrushes, warblers, vireos, swallows, and flycatchers is not obtainable, and the annual vegetation essentially disappears. Areas that provided a rich food supply in summer are barren in winter. A movement to more southern regions where there will be sufficient food at this time of year, therefore, becomes imperative for these species as well as for the hawks that prey upon them.

Most boreal species that do not engage in migration, such as woodpeckers, nuthatches, tits, jays, and crossbills, depend on insect larvae or conifer seeds in winter. These are already stored and available to them. A few species, however, do store food items themselves. One of these is the acorn-storing woodpecker (*Melanerpes formicivorus*) of western North America. These birds gather large numbers of acorns in late summer and fall for food for the following winter. Each acorn is inserted into a separate hole drilled in the bark of a dead or living tree. A single

[1]Miller, A. H. 1965.

storage tree may hold many hundreds of acorns. The Lewis' woodpecker (*Asyndesmus lewis*), which also occurs in western North America, has similar storage habits. Another avian species that employs a most unique method of storing food for winter is the gray jay (*Perisoreus canadensis*) of northern North America. Members of this species produce a very sticky mucus on the tongue. This serves to cement food items together in the form of a bolus, which is attached to the branches of trees and stored for winter food. Storage habits, however, are exceptionally rare among birds.

Food would appear to have been a prime factor in the migration of the passenger pigeon (*Ectopistes migratorius*). From what little we know, it seems that these pigeons fed on the fruit and nuts of trees and shrubs. The meat of acorns, beechnuts, and chestnuts was a very important item in their diet, but berries of many kinds as well as seeds of grasses were also consumed. Seasonal movements to areas where there was sufficient food to sustain such an enormous population were essential for survival. Unfortunately these areas were among the first to be colonized by man, who ultimately brought about the extinction of this bird.

Attempts have been made to determine the former migratory movements of the passenger pigeon. The seasonal appearance of this species in many parts of eastern North America was probably better known to the early colonists than that of any other bird. It seems almost inconceivable that this now-extinct pigeon was probably the most abundant bird on earth a little over three hundred years ago. Schorger estimated the population to number three billion, with a possibility of five billion, at the time of the discovery of America.[2] The principal nesting area extended from Wisconsin, southwestern Minnesota, and northeastern Illinois south to Kentucky and east to New England. Many birds, however, bred in southern Canada and in an area extending west across the Mississippi Valley to the Dakotas, eastern Montana, and Kansas as well as east to Pennsylvania and Virginia.

As far as can be inferred from early records, passenger pigeons began moving south in September and congregated on a winter range in southeastern United States that extended from South Carolina to Florida and Louisiana and west to Arkansas and Missouri. The northward movement in spring reached its peak in April but was spread over several months.

The numbers of birds involved in some of these migratory flocks were

[2]Schorger, A. W. 1955.

enormous. One of America's early ornithologists, Alexander Wilson, described a flight that he watched near Frankfort, Kentucky, in which he estimated that 2,230,000,000 pigeons passed over an area one mile wide in a single day.[3] Similar estimates of the great size of migrating flocks were given by other early observers. The flights lasted from dawn to sunset and are said to have nearly darkened the sky at times.

Some good examples of migratory movements for alimental reasons are to be found among gallinaceous birds. In western North America the blue grouse (*Dendragapus obscurus*) is a species of the boreal forests of the major mountain ranges. In late summer, after the young are fairly well grown, small groups gradually move up the slopes, feeding on berries and other suitable food. By late autumn, when the snows come, they are above the general breeding elevation and spend the winter in thick clumps of conifers, especially firs, whose buds they feed upon. The climate is rigorous, and the region may not be suited for grouse reproduction, but a winter food supply is available.

The mountain quail (*Oreortyx pictus*), which may breed in the same general area as the blue grouse in summer in parts of western North America, has a migratory pattern that is the reverse of that of the grouse. After the nesting season the coveys move down the mountain slopes in autumn to the foothills. Since their food is found principally on the ground, they winter below the snow level.

Food is undoubtedly a most important reason for population movements, although it is probable that gametic and climatic factors also enter into the migratory patterns of many species. Among bats there are several North American species that undergo fairly extensive migrations in spring and autumn. All are insectivorous types that do not appear to enter into true hibernation. One of these is the hoary bat (*Lasiurus cinereus*). This is a species that summers in the boreal parts of temperate North America. It is not colonial like many other members of the family Vespertilionidae. In autumn, before the temperatures become too low for flying insects, these bats migrate southward and often coastwise to where the winter climate will be more favorable. Another closely related species, the red bat (*Lasiurus borealis*), also engages in migratory movements. Along the east coast of North America flights of these bats in migration are sometimes seen during the day. In western North America the movements of red bats do not seem to be so extensive. In California, for example, these bats are common in the fruit orchards of

[3]Wilson, A. 1808–1814.

the Sacramento and San Joaquin valleys during the summer, but they migrate from those areas in fall before the leaves have dropped and move to the coast to winter. Here they forage at night for insects when other resident bats are in deep hibernation.

It is significant to note that the only bats on the Galapagos Islands, about six hundred miles off the coast of Ecuador, are the hoary bat and another member of the genus *Lasiurus* that is closely related to if not conspecific with the red bat. Similarly, the only bat in the Hawaiian chain of islands is also a member of this genus, *Lasiurus semotus*. Undoubtedly the migratory movements of these bats have been responsible for their establishment on these islands.

Many of the smaller cetaceans that are coastal in distribution undergo seasonal movements in search of food. Brown and Norris found that

The white-sided dolphin (*Lagenorhynchus obliquidens*). *Photograph courtesy of Steinhart Aquarium, California Academy of Sciences.*

Pacific white-sided dolphins (*Lagenorhynchus obliquidens*) stay inshore during the winter and spring months along the coast of southern California.[4] Here they feed extensively on anchovies (*Engraulis mordax*). In summer and fall the anchovies move much closer to shore and into water that is too shallow for the dolphins. At this time the latter move offshore and feed at sea on the saury (*Cololabis saira*), a schooling fish that occurs in deep water. There is some evidence that the Dall porpoise (*Phocoenoides dalli*) has a similar migratory pattern in this region, as all the winter records are for inshore areas and the summer records are for farther at sea or farther north. Brown and Norris failed to find any indication that common dolphins (*Delphinus delphis*) undergo any seasonal movements. They remain inshore all year round. The movements to sea of the larger and more aggressive Pacific white-sided dolphins may be a decided advantage to the common dolphins, which also feed on schools of anchovies.

The seasonal movements of most large herbivores appear to be motivated by the need for food rather than by the need for shelter or by gametic reasons. Food availability is nevertheless controlled to a large extent by climatic conditions. Extensive migrations involving several hundred miles of travel between the summer and winter range are made by many caribou (*Rangifer tarandus*) in parts of Alaska. The movements of the very large herds living on the uplands between the Yukon and Tanana rivers do not involve any climatic changes, as conditions are essentially the same in both the summer and winter ranges. Those summering on the arctic coast move south for the most part to the northern edge of the taiga in the Brooks Range to winter, but they do not need the shelter of trees. The sedges, willows, birches, and forbs that were available in summer do not provide winter food, so migration to the higher country to the south is necessary. Here lichens are available beneath the snow and are often exposed on windswept ridges.

The seasonal movements of elk (*Cervus canadensis*) in North America, like those of caribou, are motivated by a search for food. Elk frequent high country to a considerable extent during the summer months, feeding largely on grasses but also taking some sedges and herbs. High meadows are favored foraging areas. Most of the Rocky Mountain herds, such as the Selway herd, the Yellowstone-Jackson Hole herd, and those of the Wind River Range and the Big Horn Mountains, move to the

[4]Brown, D. H., and K. S. Norris. 1956.

lowlands after the first autumn snow and seek valleys where they can find grass and willows, which together constitute their most important winter food plants.

In East Africa the wildebeests (*Gorgon taurinus*) of the Serengeti Plains engage in large annual migrations participated in by hundreds of thousands of animals. The movement is to the calving grounds, where food and water are more favorable, and involves a trip of about two hundred miles. Many die en route from natural causes, including predation.

GAMETIC REASONS

We are generally inclined to regard migration as largely a result of alimental and climatic factors. Food becomes scarce at certain times of the year, and the population dependent on it must leave or starve to death. This seems very plausible for species of birds nesting in the Arctic. Here summer climatic conditions provide a means of greatly expanding the range during that season, but a southward migration is necessary for survival as autumn comes, temperatures lower, and food dwindles. The northward extension of the range in summer results in a higher reproductive capacity than would a static range. Suitable areas for reproduction, however, may be a factor responsible for the development of population movements in a number of species. In some instances food definitely plays no part. This is true of the migration of salmon, sea turtles, a number of whales, and certain pinnipeds.

The movements of some species of fish to specific localities to spawn is definitely gametic. Food for the migrant is not involved, nor are environmental conditions on the feeding grounds such that a movement away from there is necessary. Such a migration serves to ensure the perpetuation of the species by bringing both sexes together to effect fertilization of the eggs in an environment suitable for the deposition of the eggs as well as for the survival of the young when they hatch. The movement of Pacific salmon (*Oncorhynchus* spp.) away from their freshwater hatching site and downstream to the sea is basically for alimental reasons. The river systems could not provide them with sufficient food. After spending several years in the ocean, they return to the stream where they hatched solely for reproductive purposes. The environment is not suited to survival of the adults, and no food is taken en route.

The migration of sea turtles to the beaches where the eggs are deposited is gametic in nature. The major types of marine turtles that are found in the oceans of the world are the leatherback, the hawksbill, the ridley, the loggerhead, and the green turtle. Some have developed distinct populations in the Atlantic, Pacific, and Indian oceans. All are believed to migrate and lay their eggs in areas removed from those in which they feed and live during most of their lives. The females, when ready to lay, go to remote sandy beaches, where they bury their eggs in the sand above high tide. Males move to the same areas but usually remain offshore. In the loggerhead turtle (*Caretta caretta*) a female may lay from fifty to one thousand eggs. These hatch in about two months, and the young emerge from the sand and move immediately to the sea.

The migration of some seals and sea lions is primarily for the purposes of reproduction. Some species are pelagic outside the breeding season. Others are restricted largely to coastal areas. In pinnipeds that have developed a social structure there is a movement to specific rookery areas where the young are born and the females are bred. This serves to bring together a population of animals that may be widely spread out through much of the year because of their large numbers, large size, and great food requirements. The sea in the immediate environs probably could not support the nearly two million northern fur seals (*Callorhinus ursinus*) that gather annually on the Pribilof Islands in the Bering Sea. However, during their stay there in the summer breeding seasons, the males do not feed. When the young are weaned, some of the females and immatures move south in the eastern Pacific as far as the coast of southern California. Similar movements to rookery areas to reproduce are engaged in by sea lions and elephant seals of both the Northern and Southern hemispheres.

Each year in December and January there is a major tourist attraction along the Pacific coast near the city of San Diego. On a good afternoon during a weekend or holiday many thousands of persons may be seen on promontories looking out to sea. Others are in small boats or on larger excursion craft labeled "Whale Hunt." The object of these sightseers is the California gray whale (*Eschrichtius gibbosus*), which is moving southward to its calving grounds along the west coast of Baja California. To be out among these giants as they slowly pass by is an experience one does not forget. In southern California gray whales swim southward within several miles of shore. If one approaches quietly and turns off the motor of the boat, they may pass within fifty yards or even stay around for many minutes, sometimes hours. Normally on surfacing they will blow three or four times, then make a deep dive. During the time

Gray whales (*Eschrichtius gibbosus*) migrating southward in winter often travel in pairs as seen here. *Photographed off San Diego, California, January 27, 1967, by Robert T. Orr.*

they are underwater, they may travel up to 1,200 feet, though the distance is usually considerably less.

The surfacing is exciting. Suddenly a yellow gray object, built like a submarine but encrusted with many barnacles and blotched with the scars of others, comes to the surface. Its presence is immediately indicated by the noise of its exhalation as a great mass of spray is shot into the air. The water is mostly from the surface of the sea as the air rushes out of the two blowholes on the top of the animal's head. After a few breaths the dive is indicated by the pitch of the body and the final view of the large tail flukes, tipped up at times almost vertically before sinking down into the sea.

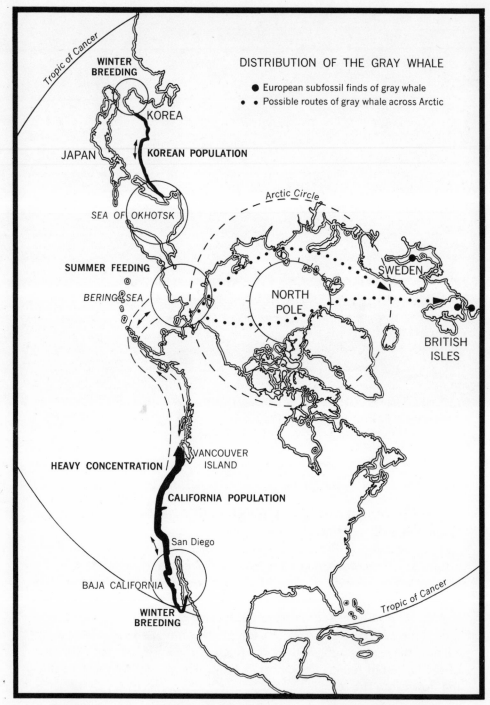

DISTRIBUTION OF THE GRAY WHALE

● European subfossil finds of gray whale
•••• Possible routes of gray whale across Arctic

Tropic of Cancer

WINTER BREEDING

KOREA

JAPAN   KOREAN POPULATION

SEA OF OKHOTSK

Arctic Circle

SWEDEN

SUMMER FEEDING

BERING SEA

NORTH POLE

BRITISH ISLES

HEAVY CONCENTRATION

VANCOUVER ISLAND

CALIFORNIA POPULATION

San Diego

BAJA CALIFORNIA

WINTER BREEDING

Tropic of Cancer

Distribution of the gray whale. (After Gilmore, R. M.: *Oceans Magazine*, 1969)

These whales, whose length may reach forty to fifty feet and whose weight may be as much as thirty tons, were once abundant along the Pacific coast, but whaling activities almost brought about their extinction. In fact, gray whales once occurred also in the Atlantic Ocean, perhaps at a time when there was contact across the Arctic between the North Atlantic and the North Pacific oceans. Today we find a remnant of the Pacific population summering in the Arctic Ocean, the Sea of Okhotsk, the Bering Sea, and the North Pacific. Here for about four months they feed almost continuously on small crustaceans known as krill and develop a large layer of fat or blubber over the body.

In autumn the small Korean population moves down the Asiatic coast, and the now considerably larger eastern Pacific population sets forth for the warm, shallow lagoons along the northwest coast of Mexico, where they begin to arrive by January. One February the writer and several others flew low over Scammon's Lagoon, where the greatest breeding population occurs. There for miles, as we flew a few hundred feet above the water, were females with their calves. For the most part they were well spaced out. The young stayed close to the sides of their mothers and sometimes seemed to rest their heads on the backs of the adults. Near the mouth of the lagoon courting pairs could be seen in the shallow waters.

During their many months of migration as well as in the breeding areas, adults do not appear to feed. They rely for energy upon the enormous fat reserves acquired the previous summer in arctic waters. The young depend upon their mothers' milk and grow rapidly. This is important because they must acquire a layer of blubber for insulation against the cold waters of the north, with which they will soon have to contend.

By March the northward movement of adults and young has begun, and by the middle of April large numbers are passing along the coast of northern California where they can easily be observed from headlands.

A fall and winter migration to subtropical waters to bear young is made by many kinds of large cetaceans. The movement is obviously gametic and climatic. Food is rarely eaten either while migrating or at the calving area where males as well as females gather. Also, the warmer waters protect the young from cold until they have acquired sufficient fat insulation to survive the low temperatures of the polar seas to which they will go. The spring migration, on the other hand, is to Arctic and

The west coast of central Baja California, Mexico, photographed from Gemini V. The land mass extending out into the Pacific Ocean is Punta Eugenia with Cedros Island just beyond on the edge of the cloud area. Scammons Lagoon, the most important calving area for gray whales, is at the north base of the point (lower center of picture). *Photograph courtesy of NASA.*

Antarctic regions where rich food is abundant and the summer periods of daylight permit feeding nearly around the clock.

Essentially no food is found in the stomachs of humpback whales (*Megaptera novaeangliae*) taken off the coast of Australia in winter during the breeding season. During summer in the Antarctic, however, this southern humpback population consumes enormous quantities of euphausiids, copepods, amphipods, pteropods, and other organisms,

Aerial view of a female gray whale and her young in Scammons Lagoon, Baja California, Mexico. *Photographed February 1968 by George E. Lindsay.*

including schools of small fishes. Studies by Best of the sei (*Balaenoptera borealis*) and finback (*Balaenoptera physalus*) whales that migrate northward by the coast of southwest Africa to their breeding areas during the antarctic winter likewise indicate that food is a negligible item at this season of the year.[5] The impulse is basically a gametic one.

CLIMATIC FACTORS

It is almost impossible to separate climatic from alimental and gametic factors influencing the migrations of animals. Food production is very directly dependent upon the climatic environment. When climatic conditions are favorable and food is abundant, reproduction most fre-

[5]Best, P. B. 1967.

quently occurs. It is obvious that freezing winter conditions in the Arctic or Boreal regions of the Northern Hemisphere produce an environment that is unfavorable for many kinds of organisms. The lack of available food in winter as a result of rigorous climatic conditions has undoubtedly been a prime factor in the development of migratory patterns. Conversely, food abundance in warmer seasons of the year has served as an attractant to northward movement.

Many invertebrates, especially insects, have solved the climatic problems presented by winter through the establishment of a period of torpidity, often in a larval state. Dormancy also is employed by amphibians, reptiles, and some mammals. We know of only one species of bird in which true winter dormancy is known to occur. This is the poorwill (*Phalaenoptilus nuttallii*), a caprimulgid species confined to western North America. Individuals have been found in a state of hibernation in the wild. Several other kinds of birds are known to become torpid under certain circumstances, but, so far as is known, they do not use this means to avoid the problems of winter.

The storage of food serves to tide certain warm-blooded vertebrates over the winter period, but this sort of solution is limited primarily to a few rodents, pikas, and several species of birds. It is also employed by some hymenopterous insects in regions where the winter temperatures do not become too low. Some kinds of animals are able to find food throughout the cold winter season. This is true of certain wood-inhabiting invertebrates and those living in ground that is not frozen. Fishes remain active under the ice in water that is close to freezing, but their food consumption under these circumstances is very low, as is their metabolism. In the Arctic, lemmings, voles, and other microtine rodents as well as arctic and varying hares find food in winter. The rodents secure theirs mostly from vegetation beneath the snow while varying hares depend upon bark and twigs. In the mountains farther south fossorial mammals, including insectivores and rodents of certain species, remain active beneath the winter snow because of the presence of a food supply. Carnivorous mammals too, as well as a few birds that prey upon these mammals, remain all winter.

In the Antarctic only the emperor penguin (*Aptenodytes forsteri*) remains all winter. A few birds, such as the antarctic petrel (*Thalassoica antarctica*) and the snow petrel (*Pagodroma nivea*), remain on the edge of the ice pack, but the majority move to temperate and some even to subtropical waters. Likewise, there is a northern movement by some of the pinnipeds as well as the cetaceans. The latter, however, move to their winter breeding areas.

THEORIES ON THE ORIGIN OF MIGRATION

Many theories have been proposed to account for migratory movements. Some have suggested that the last series of glacial periods forced many species to move closer to the equator. Subsequent recession of the polar ice sheet permitted northward movement to the ancestral breeding range, but in winter a southward shift is still required. Since migration is of genetic origin and not necessarily associated with winter in some species, it would appear to have originated independently in different groups of organisms and under different environmental stresses.

The origin of migratory patterns in fishes of the family Salmonidae has been the subject of interesting speculation. All members of the family reproduce in fresh water, in which the family presumably arose. Most of the trout remain in fresh water throughout life, although some do go to sea. The steelhead (*Salmo gairdnerii*) of the Pacific coast of North America is an outstanding example. Spawning occurs in coastal streams, but most of the adult life is spent in the ocean. The cutthroat trout (*Salmo clarki*) and the Dolly Varden (*Salvelinus malma*) are basically freshwater species, but some individuals descend coastal streams to the sea. The Atlantic salmon (*Salmo salar*), which in a sense is a counterpart of the steelhead of the Pacific, behaves like the latter as far as its migratory movements are concerned and, like the steelhead, is capable of spawning in more than one season. The various Pacific salmons of the genus *Oncorhynchus* are mostly marine, except during their early period of life and on their return to fresh water to spawn, after which they die. Nevertheless, even in this group there are exceptions which may remain throughout life in fresh water. The kokanee (*O. nerka kennerlyi*), a form of the sockeye, is a landlocked salmon that matures in fresh water. The Asian masu (*O. masou*) may do the same thing.

This tendency in a basically freshwater group of fishes to migrate to the sea is believed to have arisen during the glacial period, when all the present-day species are thought to have existed. The five species of *Oncorhynchus* in North America, which are the sockeye (*O. nerka*), the coho or silver salmon (*O. kisutch*), the pink salmon (*O. gorbuscha*), the chum salmon (*O. keta*), and the king or chinook (*O. tshawytscha*), have all developed a migratory pattern that takes them to the sea, where they spend several years maturing, before returning to where they were hatched to spawn. Some populations of the sockeye, however, can complete their life cycle in fresh water, and recently silver salmon have been introduced successfully to Lake Michigan. Even so, the landlocked salmon exhibit a pelagic type of schooling unlike that of trout.

In all members of the genus *Oncorhynchus* spawning occurs in streams or rivers, except in the case of the sockeye which usually spawns in lakes. Young chum and pink salmon migrate to the sea at an early age. The coho and sockeye, other than the landlocked kokanee, live a year or longer in fresh water before going to sea. Both undergo a marked physiological and morphological change into what is called a *smolt* before beginning a marine life. Hoar has concluded that in all four of these species which he studied, the evolution of seagoing migration involved three changes: the smolt transformation, increased nocturnal activity, and schooling behavior.[6] The development of the smolt involves a series of changes necessary to resist seawater. Since pink and chum salmon enter salt water at a very early age, the changes necessary to permit them to survive in this environment develop very early. Nocturnal activity implies capability to move at night and to be stimulated by a reduction in light intensity. Salmon have keen eyesight and can see at very low light intensities. Young salmon will surface at night and move with less danger from predators than they would have in the daytime. Schooling is believed to be advantageous to fishes leading a pelagic life.

The ancestral form which came from troutlike salmonids may often have moved downstream in the spring to brackish water in tidal areas, where resistance to salt water developed. Furthermore, schooling may have evolved in order that they might survive in estuaries. Ultimately certain genetic stocks evolved that could move farther into salt water at varying ages, depending on the species, and have a vast source of food available to them during their growing years. This permitted the development of a very large population of large-bodied individuals in these species that would not have been possible in a limited freshwater environment.

Dr. Archie Carr of the University of Florida has done some rather interesting speculating on an island-seeking nesting habit on the part of green turtles.[7] He suggested that it might have developed by the movement of a part of a population from its marine feeding area in algal beds

[6]Hoar, W. S. 1958.
[7]Carr, A. 1967.

along a main shoreline to a nearby sandy-shored island to reproduce. The advantage of this movement might be less predation and possibly a more favorable medium for the incubation of the eggs. Those individuals with the urge to go to such an island to reproduce would have been favored, as would their progeny if this were a genetic trait, over those that bred in less favorable areas. In time, more and more turtles would have possessed this trait, until it had become established for the entire population.

Since marine turtles are a relatively old group of reptiles, there have been many changes in the configuration of the continental masses as well as of oceanic islands since the evolution of the migratory pattern. Subsidence and elevation of land have changed and may have increased the distances involved. As a possible explanation of the migratory pattern of green turtles that leave their marine pastures along the Brazilian coast and migrate to Ascension Island in the mid-Atlantic, at least one thousand miles to the east, Dr. Carr cites the theory of continental drift. Although not espousing this theory, he postulates that in times past a population of South American turtles might have migrated a short distance to the shores of Africa to lay. With the gradual separation of the two continents by drift, the distance became greater and greater, and the navigational problems also increased. These were partly solved by the selection of a point, Ascension Island, on the Atlantic Ridge in mid-ocean as a breeding site. Today this migration is in a sense a vestigial behavioral pattern that lacks much of its original survival value. Another example of such vestigial behavior is seen in the nesting colony on the Aves Islands, southwest of Guadeloupe in the eastern Caribbean. Large numbers of green turtles migrate here to lay their eggs in the sand. The number is so great in proportion to the tiny size of the island that new arrivals dig up eggs that others have laid earlier. En route to the Aves Islands they pass by great expanses of beaches that appear to the human eye to be very suitable as nesting grounds. It is thought that subsidence of the bank on which the Aves Islands are located has proceeded very rapidly and that a chelonian trait that once had great survival value is now operating because adverse selection simply has not had time to eliminate it.

It has been suggested that migration may have arisen in some kinds of birds at a time when certain areas were suitable for occupancy only during the summer season. The movement into these summering areas permitted an expansion of the breeding range of the species. With the onset of winter, a movement toward the equator, where climatic conditions were more favorable at this season, was essential to survival. When conditions changed and climatic conditions became milder in the breeding area, the migratory habit, which had developed as a result of selection, persisted. Of course today we find conditions in the far north that necessitate the southward movement of many birds. These conditions are similar to those that prevailed over much of North America and Eurasia during the Pleistocene glacial periods. However, there are many birds that breed in north temperate latitudes that could probably survive the winter conditions but still move southward. Sometimes their niche is taken over at this season by other species from farther north.

Dr. Richard R. Graber, who has made a number of important contributions to our knowledge of bird migration, found that fall migrants passing through Illinois at night followed a direction somewhat east of south, whereas in the spring their northward movement was east of north.[8] He suggests that many of the fall migrants are probably of southeastern origin. To explain this he cites Lincoln, who suggested that the bobolink (*Dolichonyx oryzivorus*) adheres to the ancestral migration route even though the species has expanded its range to western North America.[9] Populations in the west move east before turning south. A somewhat similar pattern of movement is shown by western populations of the palm warbler (*Dendroica palmarum*). In autumn, western members of this species fly east to the Appalachians before turning south to South Carolina and Florida. A counterpart of the palm warbler is the Nashville warbler (*Vermivora ruficapilla*), which is believed to be of western origin. The eastern race of the Nashville warbler, in flying to its wintering grounds in central and southern Mexico, does not go directly but heads toward Arizona, which is the center of distribution for the *Vermivora* complex of warblers. The eastern route of the palm warbler has the advantage of conserving energy by flying with the wind. This is not true of the western flight of the Nashville warbler, which suffers an energy loss by going against the wind. Both migratory patterns, however, support the theory that some birds at least, even though their ranges have changed greatly, tend to follow the ancestral migratory pattern.

Dr. E. G. Franz Sauer has presented an interesting hypothesis to

[8]Graber, R. R. 1968.
[9]Lincoln, F. C. 1950.

Male golden plover (*Pluvialis
dominica*) near the nest. *Photographed at St. Lawrence Island,
Bering Sea, June 22, 1960, by
E. G. Franz Sauer.*

account for the development of present patterns of migration in the
golden plovers.[10] He assumes that in pre-Pleistocene times a single species
of *Pluvialis* which originated from a tropical or subtropical ancestor
moved northward into Siberia. With the beginning of Pleistocene
glaciation, some plovers moved west along the edge of the tundra toward
Europe, while others moved east toward the Bering Sea. Isolation of
these two populations resulted in speciation, with *P. apricaria* developing
to the west of the Siberian Arctic and *P. dominica* evolving in Alaska.
Subsequently, the latter moved eastward across the American Arctic
and developed into two subspecies, while *P. apricaria*, after the last
glacial recession, moved east across Siberia to contact *P. dominica*. By that
time both were specifically differentiated. The pattern seen in migration
of golden plovers today reflects the history of these movements. Both the
preglacial northward movement and the glacial and postglacial south
and north movements, combined with eastward and westward movements, have resulted in the involved routes shown by the two subspecies
of *Pluvialis dominica* at present.

[10]Sauer, E. G. F. 1963.

The selective significance of migration has been suggested by the work of Österlöf in Sweden on the goldcrest (*Regulus regulus*).[11] This species behaves both as a migrant and as a resident in Scandinavia. The wintering population, however, may suffer great losses from severe cold, and it is estimated that only one-tenth of this resident population survives until spring in Finland. Likewise, in years when the winters are severe farther south, a high mortality is created among the migrants. The balance between the migratory and resident characters in the goldcrest population of Scandinavia, therefore, may be based on the genetic polymorphism which favors the migrants when the northern winters are severe and the residents when severe weather conditions prevail farther south.

[11]Österlöf, S. 1966.

3

INFLUENCE OF ENVIRONMENT

There are many physical and biological factors that are associated with migration. The latter will be considered in subsequent chapters, but first it is well to understand the influence that the environment may have on migratory behavior. Migration itself is predominantly a seasonal phenomenon, so it is not surprising that changes in the physical surroundings associated with the annual cycle of seasons are of prime importance in population movements. It is known that changing day length away from the equator, lunar periodicity, and climate may each in its own way influence migration significantly.

PHOTOPERIODISM

For many years now the daily amount of light received, or, technically, the *photoperiod,* has been regarded as an important causative factor in migration. The first significant experimental studies on the effect of light on migration were carried out by Professor William Rowan in Alberta, Canada.[1] Working with slate-colored juncos (*Junco hyemalis*), he found that when he artificially increased the daily amount of light to which these birds were exposed, the gonads of the male birds could be increased in size in winter, whereas those of the controls remained inactive. Furthermore, he found that when all the birds were released, those whose gonads had increased as a result of a lengthened photoperiod in winter left the area, while the controls did not. He thus suspected that there was a relationship between length of day, gonadal development, and migration. He performed similar experiments with crows (*Corvus brachyrhynchos*). Some of those whose gonads had become enlarged by increased periods of exposure to light moved to the northwest

[1]Rowan, W. 1925, 1926, 1929.

39

in a normal spring migratory pattern, although others went to the south-east and some were sedentary. Castrated individuals either were sedentary or moved to the southeast. This was favorable evidence that gonadal enlargement in the spring might be an important stimulus for northward migration and also might be part of the physiological condition that is necessary for this type of behavior.

Since Rowan's early experiments, many subsequent studies have shown that an increase in gonadal size and activity in many male passerine birds of the Northern Hemisphere is dependent upon an increase in day length in the spring. As the photoperiod increases, there is a general increase in metabolic activity. In many migratory species this is correlated with a marked deposition of fat and with nocturnal restlessness.

Wolfson experimented with a western North American species of junco, *Junco oreganus*.[2] Four subspecies, three of which were migratory and one of which was resident, were maintained in central California within the range of the resident race. It was found that while all four forms may flock together in the wintering area, the male gonads of the resident type recrudesce sooner than those of the migrants. In March, when migration starts, the volume of the testes of the residents averaged two hundred cubic millimeters, and the volume of those of the migrants averaged four cubic millimeters. The migrants, however, had a heavy deposition of subcutaneous and intraperitoneal fat.

Wolfson subjected juncos representing these four populations to increased photoperiods from early December to late January or early February and found that the migratory forms when released began northward migration two months earlier than usual. They also showed some gonadal recrudescence and fat deposition at this time. Migratory birds kept in captivity under natural light until late May or early June showed gonadal recrudescence. This was two months past the time that migration started for wintering birds of the same subspecies in the wild. When released at this late date, however, these birds undertook a northward migration.

Dr. Wolfson concluded that day length is the most important external factor regulating the northward spring migration in this species. Longer days mean longer periods of wakefulness and greater duration of hypothalamus activity. The latter is responsible for increased production of gonadotropic hormones, which in turn stimulate gonadal recrudescence

[2]Wolfson, A. 1940, 1942, 1945.

and fat deposition. Dr. Wolfson (1942, p. 263) states: "Because of these changes, the physiological state prior to migration is so altered from that which prevails in mid-winter that it provides the internal stimulus for the spring migration. The internal stimulus induces the actual migration by releasing the nervous mechanism which controls migratory behavior."

Later Wolfson pointed out some weaknesses in his theories.[3] There are a number of birds that breed in north temperate regions where the day length increases from the winter to the summer solstice, yet they winter near the equator or even in the Southern Hemisphere. The days are of equal length on the equator, and in the Southern Hemisphere the period of day length is decreasing at the time these birds begin migrating northward. He suggests there are other factors in addition to day length, perhaps internal rhythm, that may be of importance. As an example of this, he cites the so-called refractory period in the avian cycle following the reproductive period. During this refractory period, artificially increased photoperiods generally fail to induce gonadal recrudescence, although King, Mewaldt, and Farner were able to induce a gonadal response in white-crowned sparrows (*Zonotrichia leucophrys gambelii*) by photostimulation during the refractory period.[4]

Although more is known about the relationship of day length to migration in birds, there are other animals whose movements also seem to be related in some degree to increasing and decreasing day lengths. Recent studies by Shelbourn have suggested that in chum salmon (*Oncorhynchus keta*) the photoperiod may be a triggering factor in the timing of the migration of the young to the sea.[5] An increase in the photoperiod is associated with increased thyroid activity, which in turn is associated with greater bodily activity in the chum fry. This results in what is termed a migration disposition, which ultimately leads the young to the sea and into schools.

LUNAR PERIODICITY

Among segmented marine worms there are a number of species of polychaetes that periodically produce special reproductive individuals. These are called epitokes, whereas the regular nonsexual forms are

[3]Wolfson, A. 1952.
[4]King, J. R., L. R. Mewaldt, and D. S. Farner. 1960.
[5]Shelbourn, J. E. 1966.

referred to as atokes. An epitoke may be produced from an atoke by budding off or merely by a modification of the body of the atoke. In any event, the epitokous individual has two distinct body parts, with the posterior section much enlarged for the production of eggs or sperm.

These polychaetes live mostly on the bottom of the sea in sand, rocks, or coral. At certain times in the year, the epitokous forms migrate to the surface and swarm as they shed their germ cells. This behavioral pattern has evolved to coincide with lunar periodicity in a number of species, thus ensuring that both sexes will swarm at the same time.

The best-known polychaete migration associated with a particular phase of the moon is that of the Samoan palolo worm (*Eunice viridis*) of the South Pacific Ocean. In the vicinity of Fiji and Samoa the epitokous forms emerge from their burrows and break in half at night during the period of the last lunar quarter in October or November. The posterior portion, which may be male or female, swims to the surface and discharges its sex cells into the water. The inhabitants of these islands have long been aware of this local migration of worms and capture them in quantity for food.

The Atlantic palolo worm (*Eunice schemacephala*) of the West Indies has a somewhat similar cycle. This species, however, swarms during the first or last quarter of the moon in July. It is reported by Clark and Hess to back out of its burrow at three to four o'clock on the morning of the gametic migration and detach the posterior portion of the body so that it is free to swim upward.[6] By dawn, the surface of the sea is a mass of swimming epitokes. Coincident with the rising of the sun, the sex cells are released and fertilization takes place. Growth is rapid, and within three days the larval stage is attained and these young individuals sink to the bottom, where they will remain until they produce epitokes in a future year. The epitokes themselves die after having fulfilled their reproductive function.

A semilunar rhythm is also exhibited by other polychaetes, including Atlantic populations of *Platynereis dumerilii* and *Clunio marinus*. Under laboratory conditions it has been shown that in the former species a monthly reproductive rhythm can be established by artificial nighttime illumination.

Lunar orientation is employed by certain species of amphipods. *Talitrus saltator* and *Orchestoidea corniculata* make use of the position of the moon in order to move toward the waterline on shore. This endoge-

[6]Clark, L. B., and W. N. Hess. 1940.

Grunion (*Leuresthes tenuis*) spawning on a beach. *Photographed at the south end of Mission Bay, San Diego County, California, in May by Anthony Mercieca.*

nous rhythm also enables them to compensate for changes in the position of the moon.[7]

One of the most striking examples of a vertebrate whose population movements are governed by the moon is the grunion (*Leuresthes tenuis*), which occurs in the coastal waters of southern California and north-western Baja California, Mexico. These little smeltlike fish belonging to the silversides family move to shore in large masses for the first three or four nights following either the full moon or the new moon from late February to early September. Then, from one to three hours following the high tide each female comes up on the beach with a large wave, digs a hole by wriggling her body, and deposits her eggs. As she is doing this, the male wraps himself around her and fertilizes the eggs. This all takes but a few moments, and the next wave washes them back to sea and covers the eggs with sand. These eggs do not hatch until they are moistened by the next series of high tides. A related species occurring in the Gulf of California, Mexico, spawns at high tides both day and night.

CLIMATE

The avoidance of unfavorable climatic situations is thought to be one of the major reasons for the evolution of migratory behavior in many kinds of animals. Excessive heat or cold, periods of drought or heavy snowfall, and other unfavorable environmental conditions are thereby avoided by species that do not engage in dormancy or are not adapted to withstand such extremes. It is not surprising, therefore, that climatic changes appear in many instances to trigger population movements.

TEMPERATURE. The environmental temperature is one of the most important physical factors that may stimulate or inhibit migratory behavior. Among fishes, especially freshwater species, movements to the spawning areas generally are seasonal and are frequently associated with rising or falling water temperatures. This is very evident among salmonids. In North America the cutthroat (*Salmo clarki*) and rainbow (*Salmo gairdnerii*) trout are both species that move to the spawning grounds in the spring of the year when the temperature of the water is rising. A reverse of this is seen in the Dolly Varden (*Salvelinus malma*) of the Pacific coast and the eastern brook trout (*Salvelinus fontinalis*) of eastern North

[7]Enright, J. T. 1963.

America. These two species spawn in the autumn, when the water temperature of streams and lakes is declining.

The seasonal northward and southward movement in the ocean of salmon that may bring them closer to the entrance to their spawning streams may be influenced by temperature. It has been noticed that pink salmon (*Oncorhynchus gorbuscha*) are seldom found in the North Pacific when the surface temperatures are less than 5° centigrade or warmer than 12° centigrade. Six to 9° centigrade is most favorable. There are occasions, however, during the coastal stages of their migration to spawning streams in late summer, when they occur in water whose surface temperature may be as high as 15° centigrade.

Among salamanders of many species the lowered environmental temperature, combined with sufficient rainfall, appears to stimulate emergence from the ground in winter and subsequent migration to breeding ponds or streams. Later, as summer approaches and temperatures rise, many of these amphibians move back to subterranean hiding places, where they will remain until the following winter.

Although increasing day length is probably the most important factor governing northward migration of many Northern Hemisphere birds in the spring of the year, temperature also often plays a part. With the daily increase in the photoperiod, there is an average increase in the mean daily temperature. The reverse is true in late fall.

In her very thorough study on song sparrows (*Melospiza melodia*) around Columbus, Ohio, Margaret M. Nice concluded that the most important factors in regulating the song sparrow's behavior are changing day length and changing temperature.[8] Fall migration and winter flocking are stimulated by low temperature, which also inhibits spring migration as well as other activities, including song and nesting. High temperature stimulates spring migration, inhibits fall migration, and stimulates song and nesting activities. These differences in temperature are effective as a stimulus, however, only at the proper season.

The song sparrow, whose range extends from Alaska south to Mexico and across the entire North American continent, may or may not migrate, depending upon environmental conditions. The song sparrows of southeastern Alaska and western British Columbia move south along the Pacific coast each autumn and winter in parts of California. The song sparrows of the Great Basin region likewise move southward to

[8]Nice, M. M. 1937.

warmer areas to pass the winter. On the other hand, the song sparrows living farther south in parts of California, southern Nevada, and Arizona are resident the year round.

Evans' observations on avian migrants in England indicated that in August and September migration was neither more frequent nor more heavy after a marked fall (at least 25° centigrade) in temperature from the previous night.[9] In October and November, however, departure was almost twice as frequent and usually heavier after a decline in temperature. In other areas in the Northern Hemisphere it has frequently been noted that the arrival of a cold front in autumn stimulates the movement of migrants southward. It may have the opposite effect on northbound migrants in spring and cause them to be grounded.

The significance of temperature on migration was stressed by Lincoln, who tried to correlate isochronic lines of migration with particular isotherms and show that the northward movement of birds in spring is associated with an isothermal advance.[10] This phenological theory was applied by Ryder to the northward migration of the Ross' goose (*Chen rossii*), which winters in central California and nests in the Perry River region of north central Canada.[11] The prevailing isotherm in the winter territory of this species in California during January, 1964, was 40° Fahrenheit. The isotherm in the nesting area during June, 1964, was between 30° Fahrenheit and 40° Fahrenheit. During the spring migration from California through Oregon, Montana, and Alberta, reports on 12,531 Ross' geese showed that they arrived at each location en route subsequent to the 32° isotherm. This means that their arrival occurred when the snow was melting and food was available.

The peak of migration in spring for the honey buzzard (*Pernis apivorus*) across the Bosporus in Turkey is late March and early April. On the other hand, peak passage for the same species at Gibraltar occurs in the last week of April and the first week of May. The month difference in time at opposite sides of southern Europe is probably accounted for by temperature differences in the summer range.[12] Buzzards passing north across the Bosporus nest in eastern and central Europe, where it becomes warm early in the season, whereas the Gibraltar migrants are probably destined for Scandinavia, where spring is late.

[9]Evans, P. R. 1966.
[10]Lincoln, F. C. 1939, 1950.
[11]Ryder, J. P. 1967.
[12]Collman, J. R., and J. P. Croxall. 1967.

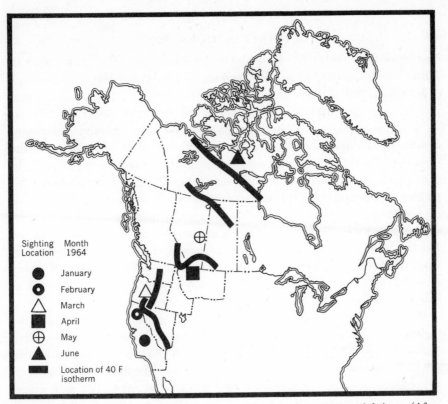

Migration-phenology pattern of Ross' goose, 1964, based on 12,531 sightings. (After Ryder, J. P., 1967)

As a result of a thirteen-year study on the autumn migration of the sharp-shinned hawk (*Accipiter striatus*) at Cedar Grove, Wisconsin, on the western shore of Lake Michigan, Mueller and Berger concluded that the four most important meteorological factors associated with this migration were: (1) wind direction and velocity, (2) cold fronts, (3) decrease in temperature associated with the passage of a cold front, and (4) sunshine.[13] Seventy-three percent of the migrants were recorded within two days of the passage of a cold front, and 69 percent were observed on days when the temperature had dropped within twenty-four hours. Eighty-four percent of the sharp-shinned hawks were seen on days when the sun was shining at least half of the time. Such conditions as these provide updrafts. More than 93 percent of the 17,628 migrant hawks of this species recorded were seen on days when the wind was westerly. Wind from this direction drifts southbound hawks to the

[13]Mueller, H. C., and D. D. Berger. 1967c.

east until they reach the shores of Lake Michigan. They then tend to follow south along the lead line formed by the lake shore.

Edwards and Ritcey found that temperature played an important role in both the autumn and the spring migration of moose (*Alces alces*) in western Canada.[14] Warm weather in autumn delayed movement downward from the high summer range, but early snowfall had the opposite effect and triggered an early migration to the winter range. In the spring the upward migration starts rapidly and is associated with sudden thaws and consequent decrease in depth of the snow. The arrival of a cold spell, however, may slow down the movement.

Similar observations have been made on elk (*Cervus canadensis*) in the Rocky Mountains of western North America. Downward movement from the high summer range usually does not start until the first heavy snowfall. As with the moose, snow is probably as important a factor as lowered temperature, since it acts to cover the food supply.

Water temperatures are thought to play a part in controlling the location of northern fur seals (*Callorhinus ursinus*) in winter in the North Pacific Ocean. They prefer areas along both the Asiatic and American coasts where there is a mixture of cold and warm currents and the temperature of the water ranges from 47° to 54° Fahrenheit. In such places food is most abundant.

WIND. As for the effect of wind on migration, much more is known about its influence on birds than on any other group of migrants. Undoubtedly it plays a part in the migratory movements of butterflies, many of which are frequently blown far off course and even at times out to sea many hundreds of miles. Much remains to be determined, however, regarding wind as a stimulus or inhibitor of the movement of these organisms.

Along the Atlantic coast of North America several observers have noted that onshore winds tend to increase the number of Atlantic salmon (*Salmo salar*) entering the spawning streams. Lorz and Northcote observed the same phenomenon in the kokanee salmon (*Oncorhynchus nerka kennerlyi*) in British Columbia.[15] This species enters the spawning stream at dusk, when the light intensity is low. On windy days, however, there was a movement onshore earlier in the evening and in greater numbers than when it was calm. The observers have suggested that perhaps the

[14]Edwards, R. Y., and R. W. Ritcey. 1956.
[15]Lorz, H. W., and T. G. Northcote. 1965.

wave action produced by the wind carried olfactory clues over a considerably broader front than would occur when the wind was not blowing. Such chemical clues, even though greatly diluted, are important in orientation for this species.

A few kinds of birds, such as some gallinaceous species, migrate on foot, but the great majority of species depend upon flight to take them to their breeding grounds in the spring and back to their wintering area in autumn. As a consequence, wind and air currents play a very important part in their migration. Some knowledge of the degree to which wind affects avian migrants has been obtained by studies made principally at night with radar and also by observing the movements of birds by means of a telescope directed at the moon. Dr. Frank Bellrose, as a result of some years of studying nocturnal migrants with radar in Illinois, concluded that wind direction is more important than sky cover (clear vs. overcast) in determining the magnitude of migration.[16] When winds were favorable in spring, he found no great difference in the numbers of birds migrating on clear nights and overcast nights. The number of migrants was considerably reduced, however, on overcast nights when there were adverse winds, as compared with clear nights with adverse winds. Winds favoring migration in the spring were those blowing toward the north or north-northeast. Unfavorable winds at this season were those blowing to the east, southeast, south, or southwest. In the fall, favorable winds were those blowing to the south and south-southeast. Migration in fall was inhibited by winds blowing to the northwest, north, and northeast. Dr. Bellrose and his associates, however, found that birds will migrate when winds are adverse if they have been grounded by several days of bad weather. Strong favorable winds are selected by waterfowl, whereas small birds prefer favorable winds of low velocity. For waterfowl, wind speeds of over thirty knots per hour are favored, but passerine species prefer winds of less than ten knots per hour. Tail winds present problems and are not favored by many birds. There is always a greater danger in flying with the wind than against it, and when winds become too strong, migration tends to stop. Species that do fly with stronger winds usually proceed at high altitudes. Gliding birds such as eagles, hawks, and vultures generally avoid wind for several reasons. It interferes with thermals, which are essential

16Bellrose, F. C. 1967.

in gaining altitude. Likewise, when these birds glide with the wind, there is the danger of reaching the stalling speed.

There appears to be some difference in the effect of wind on bird migration between spring and fall as well as in different parts of the migratory route. Unfavorable winds seem to have a greater inhibitory effect on migrants in the fall than they do in the spring. This is thought to be a result of a somewhat reduced migratory motivation in the post-breeding period. Lowery and Newman have pointed out that during the autumn migrations in the fall of 1952 and 1953 the flight vectors in the southern part of the data area turned to the north quadrants when the wind blew from the south.[17] This was not true in more northern latitudes, where south winds caused grounding and a cessation of migration temporarily.

In addition to direction of the flow of air, the degree of turbulence is also a significant factor. Raynor proposed that bird migration is accomplished most efficiently in nonturbulent, smooth-flowing air.[18] He also suggested that the presence of this type of air at proper levels is a most important factor in encouraging large night flights by spring migrants east of the Rocky Mountains in North America. He concluded that this may not be true for fall migrants. Lowery and Newman, in their summary of a major series of observations made over the United States and Canada on four successive nights in October by nearly fourteen hundred persons, indicated that stable air aloft may be a requisite also for heavy autumnal migrations.[19]

Though most avian migrants are grounded during periods of strong adverse wind, swifts and swallows appear to be exceptions. These birds depend on insect food taken in the air, and unfavorable weather conditions can greatly affect airborne insects. When flying during periods of wind, these birds move against the air current. It has been suggested that this habit takes them away from cyclone centers.

Ramel made observations on the movements of swifts during a period of one month from mid-August to mid-September at Ottenby Bird Station in Sweden.[20] From August 18 to September 4, which was the migratory period, the north wind blew nearly constantly. Few birds other than swifts or swallows were noted in the air. These birds, how-

[17]Lowery, G. H., Jr., and R. J. Newman. 1955.
[18]Raynor, G. S. 1956.
[19]Lowery, G. H., Jr., and R. J. Newman. 1966.
[20]Ramel, C. 1960.

ever, were noted flying to the north instead of to the south. A total of ten thousand swifts and swallows was recorded going in this direction. The greatest number seen in any one day was two thousand. The specific composition of these countermigrants was as follows: house martins (*Delichon urbica*), over 90 percent; swallows (*Hirundo rustica*), 4 percent; sand martins (*Riparia riparia*), 3 percent; and swifts (*Apus apus*), 2 percent. Only two hundred of the total number of individuals were seen flying in the correct direction, and these were largely house martins. Before and after the period of the north wind, the migration was to the south, and the prevailing winds were from the south and west.

RAIN. The combination of rain and cloudy weather at certain times may produce spectacular results. One such occurrence was reported in Great Britain in early September, 1965.[21] During the last ten days of August the weather had been very cloudy and rainy over Scandinavia. Prior to this a small number of migrant birds had arrived in England, but so far as known, migration across the North Sea essentially ceased with the weather front in Scandinavia and the absence of easterly winds. On August 31 and September 1 conditions in Scandinavia became more favorable for migration, with light winds and clearing skies as a result of rising barometric pressure. This high shifted slowly to the northeast during the early days of September, and the result was a spectacular mass movement of birds from that part of Europe to England. A small number of night migrants, principally whinchats (*Saxicola rubetra*), willow warblers (*Phylloscopus trochilus*), redstarts (*Phoenicurus phoenicurus*), and pied flycatchers (*Ficedula hypoleuca*), was recorded in eastern England. On September 2 a greater number was noted, including, in addition, wheatears (*Oenanthe oenanthe*) and garden warblers (*Sylvia borin*), as well as lesser numbers of other species. On September 3 the number of migrants recorded on the east-facing coast of Suffolk was the greatest concentration ever recorded in Britain. It has been estimated that more than half a million birds arrived on this day along twenty-four miles of coast between Sizewell and Hopton. Very heavy concentrations also occurred in east Norfolk, but they were not as great as in Suffolk. Although at least seventy-eight species were involved, the majority were wheatears, whinchats, redstarts, garden warblers, willow warblers, and pied flycatchers.

Similar great influxes of migrants were recorded along other parts of

[21]Davis, P. 1966.

the east coast of Britain north to Shetland as well as at Helgoland, Germany, and at Vlieland in Holland. It is believed that almost all of these birds were part of a south-southwest-oriented migration from Scandinavia to the Iberian Peninsula that had been disoriented and forced down in great numbers by adverse weather conditions.

As a result of checking the mortality at a television tower near Tallahassee, Florida, during periods of spring and fall migration for eleven years, Stoddard and Norris concluded that on nights when there were early heavy showers, most warblers, vireos, and other small passerines, with the exception of the fringillids and icterids, were grounded.[22] This is a presumption based on the low mortality among these groups on such occasions. The passerine kill on mornings following such weather conditions was found to consist largely of finches, sparrows, and bobolinks. The bobolink is a nocturnally migrating icterid. Water birds did not seem to be affected by rain.

Dr. Graber has presented some interesting data on the effect of cloud cover on nocturnal migrants passing over Illinois in September.[23] Under clear conditions, calling reaches a peak in the predawn hours and appears to be associated with increased density of birds as a result of a reduction in the altitude of flight. When there was heavy cloud cover, Dr. Graber found that calling increased greatly in the early part of the night. If the cloud layer broke, there was a reduction in the number of aural recordings, but this increased when the sky became overcast again. It is believed that the increase in the rate at which call notes are given is correlated with an increase in the possibility of collision.

[22]Stoddard, H. L., and R. A. Norris. 1967.
[23]Graber, R. R. 1968.

4

MIGRATORY DIFFERENCES RELATED

TO POPULATION, AGE, AND SEX

Within some species of animals there may be considerable variation as to the times of migration. This is often associated with age and sex but may also be a character of individuals within a population. Furthermore, in a number of widely ranging species, only certain geographical segments of the population may engage in migration.

DIFFERENCES WITHIN AND BETWEEN POPULATIONS

Within a given population from a specific or limited geographic area, migration, if it takes place, is generally a character of all members of that population. There are exceptions, however, to this general rule.

In the arctic lamprey (*Lampetra japonica*) there are some individuals that are anadromous, whereas others spend their entire lives in fresh water. Heard, who worked on this species in the Naknek river system of southwestern Alaska, found that the majority of the parasitic lampreys in this river completed their life cycle in fresh water and only a few migrated to the sea.[1] No morphological differences were apparent in the adults of the two populations, although the anadromous individuals appeared to be larger than those that remained in fresh water.

Essentially all migratory birds of the Arctic move southward in autumn. Farther south, where climatic conditions are milder and environmental pressures not so great, some individuals of migratory species may remain in the summer breeding grounds unless the winter becomes very severe. This has been observed among many species of birds in North America, a good example being the song sparrow (*Melospiza melodia*). Northern populations are mostly migratory, whereas those

[1]Heard, W. R. 1966.

53

inhabiting the southern part of the range of the species are largely resident. The movements of those that are geographically intermediate may depend upon the severity of the winter. In Europe the common heron (*Ardea cinerea*) is essentially sedentary in Great Britain but migratory in northern and eastern continental Europe. There are a number of passerines that behave in a somewhat similar manner. The robin (*Erithacus rubecula*) is rather sedentary in France, but members of this species farther east in Germany may move as far south as North Africa to winter. Similarly, the chaffinch (*Fringilla coelebs*) is resident the year round in parts of western Europe, whereas in Scandinavia and northeastern Europe it is migratory.

The fact that the northern populations of many Palearctic as well as Nearctic species are migratory whereas those farther south are resident the year round may result in the mingling of migratory and resident populations of the same species in winter in the more southern parts of the range. Along the Pacific coast of North America this commonly occurs among such species as the white-crowned sparrow (*Zonotrichia leucophrys*), song sparrow (*Melospiza melodia*), and fox sparrow (*Passerella iliaca*). Sometimes there is a tendency for more northern populations to migrate farther southward than other populations of the same species. This is seen in the fox sparrow, a Pacific coastal species ranging from Alaska to southern California to winter. Those breeding in the Yakutat region of Alaska winter in central California, and the fox sparrows of extreme southeastern Alaska and northern British Columbia move south to northwestern California, western Oregon, and Washington.

Mewaldt *et al.* made a study of *Zonotrichia leucophrys* along the Pacific coast of North America. Fourteen populations were sampled during the course of two years.[2] These samples were captured in mist nets during the nesting period at localities ranging from Sidney, British Columbia, south to Pismo Beach in southern California. The birds were maintained in cages in San Jose, California. The samples from northern California north to Canada represented *Z. l. pugetensis*, which is a migratory race of white-crowned sparrow. The samples from southern populations represented a nonmigratory race, *Z. l. nuttalli*. In captivity at San Jose the northern birds underwent an extensive prenuptial molt in February and March. The intensity of the molt decreased markedly in birds from farther south, and some from central and southern California did not have any prenuptial molt. This inhibition of molt in nonmigratory

[2]Mewaldt, L. R., S. S. Kibby, and M. L. Morton. 1968.

birds from farther south was presumed to be a result of early gonadal activity. Maximum testicular size was attained in southern birds in March, whereas this did not occur until May in northern populations. Yet both northern and southern populations showed nocturnal restlessness in spring, though it was less pronounced in members of nonmigratory southern populations. Furthermore, in the southern group this developed in March, whereas in the northern migratory birds it did not develop until May. In birds from intermediate areas it was recorded in April.

The existence of nocturnal restlessness in a nonmigratory population is regarded by these workers (1968, p. 29) as an "atavistic remnant of ancestral migratory behavior."

In Europe there is often a noticeable difference in the time that migrants of the same species pass southward to North Africa around the eastern and western sides of the Mediterranean. The golden oriole (*Oriolus oriolus*) presents a good example of this, and its migration is well described by Dr. David Bannerman.[3] Orioles from central Europe begin to move south by late July and August. The passage across the Strait of Gibraltar to Africa is over before mid-September. In the eastern Mediterranean the migration extends from late August to early October, with the peak occurring around mid-September.

AGE AND SEX DIFFERENCES

A great deal remains to be learned about the exact composition of migrant populations. This can be determined accurately only by marking individuals of known age and recapturing them in subsequent seasons. Such procedure for following kokanee salmon (*Oncorhynchus nerka kennerlyi*) has shown that while most individuals return to the spawning stream in their third year, some may be in their second and others in their fourth year.[4]

Among birds there is sometimes a differential in the time that adults and immatures migrate. The Adélie penguin (*Pygoscelis adeliae*), for example, nests all around the shores of Antarctica wherever there are available exposures. By about mid-February these penguins begin moving over the sea ice toward the north. The young of the year depart long before the last of the adults leave. Adults go only as far north as

[3]Bannerman, D. A. 1953.
[4]Lorz, H. W., and T. G. Northcote. 1965.

Adult Adélie penguins (*Pygoscelis adeliae*) jump into the water. The young, readily distinguished by their white throat, do not. *Photograph taken at Cape Hallett Station, Antarctica, February 3, 1965, by Dietland Müller-Schwartze.*

is necessary to provide open sea for feeding purposes during the antarctic winter. This may be anywhere from one hundred to four hundred miles, depending on the extent of the circumpolar ice pack. The young do not make the return migration the following spring but remain in the wintering area until the second year. They may move even farther north than the adults. The southward migration in spring involves hundreds of miles of travel by water and considerable travel on foot across the ice to the nesting area.

Gannets, which are related to another group of sea birds, the boobies, are migratory, but the migratory impulse varies with age. The northern gannet (*Morus bassanus*), which nests in the North Atlantic region from the Gulf of St. Lawrence to the British Isles, may winter in tropical and subtropical waters as far south as North Africa and the Gulf of Mexico. The adults do not migrate in the true sense but rather disperse over the waters fairly near the rookeries. The young, however, have been recorded traveling as far as four thousand miles to the south their first winter. They may remain for two or three years in these warm southern wintering grounds, as they do not breed until they are at least four years of age.

Similar migrations, but to the northward, take place in the Southern Hemispheric forms of gannets. The Cape gannet (*Morus capensis*) of South Africa moves up both the east and west African coasts to sub-tropical waters to winter, and the New Zealand gannet population (*Morus serrator rex*) winters northward off the eastern and southern Australian coast along with the resident form there (*Morus serrator serrator*).

In the latter part of July, 1968, I visited Duck Camp at Point Barrow, Alaska, where one of the most remarkable waterfowl migrations in North America occurs. Extending as a narrow sandspit about six miles into the Arctic Ocean from the northernmost part of the North American

Male king eiders (*Somateria spectabilis*) hanging in front of an Eskimo tent at Duck Camp, Point Barrow, Alaska. *Photographed July 23, 1968, by Robert T. Orr.*

continent, Point Barrow provides a perfect vantage site to observe common eiders (*Somateria mollissima*) and king eiders (*Somateria spectabilis*) starting their migration westward from the Beaufort Sea, along whose shores many breed, to the Chukchi Sea where they are believed to go through the molt before continuing south to the ice-free parts of the Bering Sea to winter. This migration passes Point Barrow early in July. The marked sexual dimorphism in both species makes it easy to determine the sex ratio of the flocks as they pass over the sandspit. Studies have shown that the flocks are composed almost entirely of males from the onset of migration in July until August.[5] Between August 8 and 17, the sex ratio shifts from a preponderance of males to a preponderance of females. The young of the year do not pass by until September. It is of interest to note that Duck Camp has been used by the Eskimos for hunting for at least fifteen hundred years. Remains of primitive weapons have been found in the ancient village of Birnirk dating back to 500 A.D. Even today the natives gather at this locality during these summer months and many of the men spend the day shooting migrant eiders as they pass by. Each tent is a witness to this, with large numbers of ducks hanging outside to be used as food for winter.

In most arctic nesting species of shorebirds, the adults move south first, to be followed later by the immatures. An exception to this, however, is seen in the red-backed sandpiper (*Erolia alpina*) in western North America. Both adults and young of this species drift slowly in the arctic and subarctic regions after the nesting season and later arrive on the wintering grounds on the west coast of North America at the same time.[6]

As a result of observing 17,628 sharp-shinned hawks (*Accipiter striatus*), 2,052 of which were banded, during autumn migration in Wisconsin over a period of thirteen years, Mueller and Berger found that there were two peaks.[7] One occurs in mid-September and is composed mostly of immature birds; the other is in mid-October and consists largely of adults.

These same observers found that goshawks (*Accipiter gentilis*) taken in autumn and winter at Cedar Grove Ornithological Station in southeastern Wisconsin, which is south of the breeding range of the species

[5]Thompson, D. Q., and R. A. Person. 1963.
[6]Holmes, R. T. 1966a.
[7]Mueller, H. C., and D. D. Berger. 1967c.

in that area, were largely immature birds.[8] Furthermore, a careful measurement of 105 individuals taken over a period of thirteen years revealed a significant sex differential among immatures but not adults. Not only were more juvenal males captured, but their migration began before that of juvenal females. Adults of both sexes appeared to migrate at the same time.

A study made on the age and sex of several thousand passerine migrants in the autumn in New Jersey by Murray failed to show any significant difference in this regard.[9] Other observations, however, have shown that in certain species of passerines such differences do exist. Hussell, Davis, and Montgomerie made a study of this in the least flycatcher (*Empidonax minimus*).[10] Between July 25 and October 15, 1965, a total of 222 least flycatchers was captured in Ontario. An age determination was made on 182 of these on the basis of the degree of ossification of the skull. Thirty-one individuals examined between July 25 and August 2 were all adults. Between August 3 and 12, of thirty birds examined, fifteen were adults and fifteen immatures. All of the 119 captured on or after August 13 proved to be immatures. The results clearly indicate that in this species adults migrate before the young. On the other hand, Johnson failed to find evidence of an age differential in the migration of the Hammond's flycatcher (*Empidonax hammondii*) in western North America.[11]

King, Farner, and Mewaldt, in their studies of a migratory race of the white-crowned sparrow (*Zonotrichia leucophrys gambelii*), which breeds in Alaska and western Canada, suggest that adult and immature females may tend to winter predominantly east of the Sierra Nevada of California and in northwestern Mexico.[12] This is south of the wintering area for most of the adult and immature males. Their data were obtained from trapping as well as from museum specimens. In autumn in southeastern Washington there was a steady increase in the number of adult and immature males from the beginning to the end of the migration period. Likewise, in Alaska in the spring the first flocks to arrive were composed exclusively of males, and the first females did not arrive until two weeks later.

[8]Mueller, H. C., and D. D. Berger. 1968.
[9]Murray, B. G., Jr. 1966b.
[10]Hussell, D. J. T., T. Davis, and R. D. Montgomerie. 1967.
[11]Johnson, N. K. 1963.
[12]King, J. R., D. S. Farner, and L. R. Mewaldt. 1965.

In his studies on the snow bunting (*Plectrophenax nivalis*) in Greenland, Tinbergen found a somewhat similar situation. The males arrive in flocks in March and are still in the process of assuming breeding plumage.[13] They remain in these flocks until the latter part of April, at which time the females arrive and pairing takes place.

The males of the long-billed marsh wren (*Telmatodytes palustris*) of North America arrive on the breeding grounds ten days or so before the females, and during this interval they spend much of their time building dummy nests.

Findley and Jones compiled considerable data on the migratory movements of the hoary bat (*Lasiurus cinereus*) in New Mexico and also examined records of this species from other parts of the Western Hemisphere and plotted them for each month.[14] In general they found that females preceded males in the northward spring migration and tended to occupy an eastern summering ground, where they had their young. Most of the males appear to concentrate in western North America. It is noted that, unlike the situation with birds, where the males often arrive first and set up territories, the females are pregnant in their northward flight and in no way dependent upon the males at this season of the year. Most of the males noted with females during the summer are believed to be the young of the year. Sexual segregation in the fall migration and in winter, when most of the hoary bat population is south of the United States except for coastal southern California, has not been demonstrated.

Davis and Hitchcock found that in the common little brown bat (*Myotis lucifugus*) in Vermont the females come out of hibernation in Aeolus Cave between early April and mid-May and migrate to their summer colonies, which may be up to 172 miles distant. The males were found to end hibernation between May 7 and June 7.[15]

Constantine has pointed out that in the guano bat (*Tadarida brasiliensis*) the older bats precede the younger in both sexes in migration.[16] Furthermore, in North America the sexes segregate following mating in Mexico in February and March. The migration is to the north to the United States or to higher elevations. The males migrate to higher,

[13]Tinbergen, N. 1939.
[14]Findley, J. S., and C. Jones. 1964.
[15]Davis, W. H., and H. B. Hitchcock. 1965.
[16]Constantine, D. G. 1967.

cooler areas, while the females summer in hot lowland regions where they have their young.

Migratory differences associated with sex and age are seen in certain kinds of seals and sea lions. The species whose movements of this sort are best known is the northern fur seal (*Callorhinus ursinus*) of the North Pacific Ocean. The majority of these animals breed on the Pribilof Islands, St. Paul and St. George, in the Bering Sea, Alaska.

The adult male fur seals begin to arrive at the islands in late April and reach peak numbers by mid-June. There they haul out on the rookeries. The oldest bulls are the first to arrive. Territorialism is weakly developed at first, and the animals can easily be driven into the water. Within several weeks, however, they become aggressive and defend their territory, in which they will remain without food or water until the end of the breeding season.

The females come to the islands in late June and July. As with the males, the oldest are the first to arrive. They lack any territoriality but have a strong homing tendency. It is believed that females come back to the same spot each year to give birth to their young. Each successful bull gathers a harem of cows, as the females are called. The cows give birth to a single young about two days after coming ashore. The pupping season terminates by about the first of August. The females are bred a few days after the young are born. After the young are a week or so old, the females regularly go to sea but return periodically to nurse their young. Although there are about one and one-half million seals in the area, each female is capable of returning to her own pup. This has been demonstrated by marking them.

Kenyon concluded that the early-arriving bulls remain on their territories an average of 54.4 days.[17] Those that come later in the season may not remain much more than a month. Immature animals arrive at different times based on age and sex, according to Kenyon and Wilke.[18] The youngest males are the last to arrive. Males that are over three years old arrive before mid-July. Three-year-old males arrive in maximum numbers after mid-July. Yearlings and two-year-old males come in large numbers in late July and August. Two-year-old cows first appear in late August but do not reach maximum numbers until October.

[17]Kenyon, K. W. 1960.
[18]Kenyon, K. W., and F. Wilke. 1953.

The breeding females leave the islands sometime between September and December when the pups are weaned. The bulls and bachelors, or nonbreeding males, leave after the adult females but are generally gone before severe winter storms arrive. The young leave the rookeries shortly after the females, but there is no indication that they accompany them.

Outside of the time spent on the Pribilof Islands, the northern fur seals spread out widely over the North Pacific Ocean, but again there are differences associated with sex and age. The adult females seem to go the farthest south. According to Wilke and Kenyon, 98 percent of the fur seals off the California coast in winter are females that are mostly adults.[19] The percentage of females off the coasts of Oregon and Washington is 96 percent, but more of them are immatures. Most of the males and yearlings stay farther north.

Along the Asiatic coast, as along the American coast, females are more abundant farther south and the old males remain in the north. The Asiatic population breeds on Robben Island off Sakhalin and on the Commander Islands.

The California sea lion (*Zalophus californianus*) shows marked sexual difference in migratory behavior within parts of its range (see Chapter 10). Those sea lions breeding on islands along the west coast of Baja California and off southern California gather at the rookeries in June and July, at which time the females give birth to their young and are bred. By late July the males begin to leave, and many are seen farther north in central California.[20] Here the males are found in great numbers by the end of August, and many are seen along the coast of Oregon and Washington, and even as far north as British Columbia. About 80 percent of these northern migrants are fully adult males. The remaining 20 percent are immatures of varying ages but mostly more than one year old. Bartholomew and Hubbs found that the winter population of California sea lions on islands off the west coast of Baja California was characterized by the absence of adult males.[21] Only 11 out of 9,714 sea lions counted in February, 1950, were large males. The rest were females and immatures.

A somewhat similar situation prevails in the southern part of the range of the Steller, or northern, sea lion (*Eumetopias jubata*). Along the central California coast, about two thousand adults of this species gather

[19]Wilke, F., and K. W. Kenyon. 1954.
[20]Orr, R. T., and T. C. Poulter. 1965.
[21]Bartholomew, G. A., Jr., and C. L. Hubbs. 1952.

A large aggregation of male California sea lions (*Zalophus californianus*) at the height of the late summer northward migration. *Photographed August 30, 1963, at Año Nuevo Island, California, by Robert T. Orr.*

on Año Nuevo Island between late May and July. The adult and immature males, except for yearlings and pups, begin to leave in late July and are all gone by the beginning of September. They leave the area and are not found south of it after this time, so it is presumed that they migrate north. The females remain in large numbers with their young and some yearlings until about January, when many leave. They do not all leave, however, as some females with their young can be found there at any time of year. The movement of at least part of the other females and young may be fairly local, as there are hauling-out areas within twenty-five to one hundred miles where they may be seen during the winter and spring months. The males are not in evidence in central California until May, when they begin arriving at the rookery area.

The migration of sea lions away from the rookery where the females and young are may be of adaptive significance to the species involved. Males in both the California and Steller sea lions are between two and three times the size of the females. If they remained in the vicinity of the rookery, there would be competition for food required by the females and young. By moving northward, they are able to spend most of the year in areas where food is available but breeding sites are not. There is one complicating factor that occurs from central California north to Oregon. As the male Steller sea lions move out of their rookeries, their places are taken by northward-migrating male California sea lions. On Año Nuevo Island in 1963, after the summer breeding season was over and essentially all male Steller sea lions had migrated, there was an influx in early September of approximately thirteen thousand

Immature northern elephant seals (*Mirounga angustirostris*) arrive in numbers in the spring after the breeding season is over and the adults have left. *Photographed at Año Nuevo Island, California, by Thomas C. Poulter and Robert T. Orr.*

California sea lions. This only occurs, however, in this area of overlap between the two species and may be a factor limiting the south end of the range to the more northern species.

A rather complicated migratory pattern that is not clearly understood occurs in the northern elephant seal (*Mirounga angustirostris*), at least in the northern part of its range. As pointed out by Radford, Orr, and Hubbs, this species became established or possibly reestablished as a breeding species on Año Nuevo Island along the central California coast in about 1961.[22] Previously, its breeding range had extended from Guadalupe Island off the west coast of Baja California, Mexico, north to the Channel Islands off southern California. Once the central California population became established, a migratory pattern appeared. The breeding season for this species extends from December through February, at which time the island population consists primarily of bulls with harems of cows, unattached bulls, and pups. By March, the bulls and females leave, and immature elephant seals arrive in numbers. The pups, which are weaned when a few weeks old, leave around May. One tagged in March, 1962, when about six weeks old was observed the following September on the Farallon Islands, fifty-five miles to the north. Another pup, tagged in February, 1962, was found at Cape Sebastian, Oregon, on May 30, 1964. This is four hundred miles north of Año Nuevo Island.

The immatures reach a peak in numbers by May and then begin to depart. Their place is taken in summer by adult and subadult males that come in to undergo molt. By late summer the large males leave and again are replaced by immature elephant seals, which remain until the adults arrive for the breeding season in December, and then they leave.

Where the adults go during much of the year is not known, but large bulls have been recorded as far north as British Columbia.

It has been found that in the Southern Hemisphere the humpback whales (*Megaptera novaeangliae*) that first migrate north to the calving grounds are females that are at the end of lactation and will breed that season. They are accompanied by their weaned yearlings. These are followed by immature whales and then by adult males and resting females. The pregnant females are last. On the return trip to the southern summering grounds, the recently bred females are first, followed by

[22]Radford, K. W., R. T. Orr, and C. L. Hubbs. 1965.

immature animals, mature males with nonbreeding females, and finally females with small young.

A somewhat different order of migration appears to take place in the California gray whale, which migrates southward from the Arctic to subtropical breeding areas along the west coast of Mexico, according to studies made by the United States Fish and Wildlife Service. In this Northern Hemisphere species, the pregnant females seem to be the earliest migrants to the calving grounds. They are followed in order by nonpregnant females, adult males, and immature males. On the northward movement in spring there is also a definite segregation by sex, reproductive condition, and age class. The first are the newly pregnant females. These are followed by adult males, anestrous females, immature females, and immature males, with postpartum females and their calves coming last.

Maher and Wilimovsky have tried to work out the migratory pattern of the bowhead whale (*Balaena mysticetus*) in the North Pacific.[23] This species is important to the Eskimos but was almost exterminated by commercial whalers by the early part of the twentieth century. Although the population is increasing, the Eskimos continue to take them. Bowheads enter the Arctic Ocean early in the spring. Their migration takes them northeast along the Alaskan coast. At Point Barrow the first bowheads seen in April are said to be immatures. These seem to be followed by adult males. Adult females with calves are seen from the middle of May until the middle of June.

In the sperm whale (*Physeter catodon*) the females and immature males confine their movements largely to within 40° N. and 40° S. latitude, while the majority of the mature males move into the colder waters to the north and south during the summer season in the Northern and Southern hemispheres. The males return to winter with the females.

[23]Maher, W. J., and N. J. Wilimovsky. 1963.

5

SOME PHYSIOLOGICAL ASPECTS

OF MIGRATION

Many studies have been made in recent years on physiological and bio-chemical changes associated with migration. Some of these are thought to be causative factors, perhaps responsible for seasonal movements, whereas others are obviously the result of such activity. Most of our current information relative to these physiological changes has been obtained from studies on birds, particularly passerine species, and, to a lesser extent, studies on fishes, mainly salmonids.

REPRODUCTION

Migration in many organisms is intimately associated with reproduction and is designed to bring the individual to the breeding ground at the most favorable time of year for this purpose. The close relationship between these two phenomena, therefore, necessitates an understanding of the reproductive cycle in order to relate it properly to the various aspects of migratory behavior.

Some migratory insects have a winter and a summer breeding ground. The painted lady (*Vanessa cardui*) regularly breeds in northern Europe, including the British Isles, in summer, and in northern Africa on the edge of the Sahara Desert in winter. The northern population moves south in autumn, and the African population moves north to Europe in spring. Little is known as yet as to whether the individual survives a round trip. It appears likely that the southbound butterflies are largely if not entirely the progeny of the spring migrants from Africa and that the northbound migrants are the progeny of the autumn migrants from Europe.

The desert locust (*Schistocerca gregaria*) of Africa and Asia has two breeding seasons a year. In Africa breeding occurs from January to June in the northern desert belt. In late spring great flights move south of the Sahara to breed during the monsoon season, and breeding may occur there from July to December, after which time the locusts move north again.

Sometimes reproduction in marine organisms is on a lunar cycle, depending upon the tides or certain phases of the moon. As pointed out previously, a number of kinds of nereid worms and some species of fish adhere to this pattern of reproductive behavior. Such activity, however, is generally limited to a few of the most favorable months of the year.

Among vertebrates in the mid and higher latitudes of both hemispheres, reproduction is generally on an annual cycle irrespective of whether the species migrates or not. The term "annual," however, is used here only in relation to the species and not necessarily to the individual. Pacific salmon (*Oncorhynchus* spp.) migrate upstream from the sea to spawn each year, although each individual participates in this activity only once in its lifetime, which may span three or four years. Eels migrate to the Sargasso Sea each year, but the individual does this once in a lifetime, which may be twenty years. Marine turtles are found each year laying on islands, but individual females participate in this activity but once every two or three years. There are terrestrial reptiles such as some snakes that breed only every other year. This is also true of whales and a few birds. These, however, are exceptions. Reproductive activity for most sexually mature vertebrates is on an annual cycle and is associated with a particular season or seasons of the year. In large herbivorous mammals of the north and north temperate zones, breeding occurs in the fall and the young are born in the spring. Bears breed in summer and the young are born in midwinter.

Most whales have their young in the winter season in tropical and subtropical waters. Breeding occurs at this time as well as during migration. Great variation is exhibited by pinnipeds. The northern elephant seal (*Mirounga angustirostris*) has its young and breeds in midwinter shortly after arriving at the rookery area. The northern fur seal (*Callorhinus ursinus*) has its young and breeds in midsummer. This is also true of the two kinds of sea lions of the Northern Hemisphere (*Zalophus* and *Eumetopias*). In each instance reproductive activity commences almost immediately on arrival at the breeding area.

The movement of some species of freshwater fishes to the spawning ground is associated with rising water temperatures in late spring or early summer, whereas that of others occurs in autumn when tempera-

SOME PHYSIOLOGICAL ASPECTS OF MIGRATION   69

tures decline. The breeding time for most amphibians is the rainy season or, in colder areas, after the winter snow melts.

The very cyclic nature of reproduction led investigators to look for various environmental factors that might be primary instigators. This research has been done largely with birds of the Northern Hemisphere, most of which nest in the spring of the year. Long ago ornithologists began to study the possible relationship of the changing period of day length to reproductive and migratory behavior. This is the one factor in the environment that has a regular annual periodicity. The photoperiod, or length of the period of daylight, at any one locality is the same on a given day each year.

It was first shown that gonadal activity could be induced in the males of certain species of birds in midwinter by subjecting them to increased daily amounts of light.[1] It was also demonstrated that such induced changes were associated with the manifestation of migratory behavior. We know now from numerous subsequent experimental studies that in many circumpolar species of the Northern Hemisphere day length is the primary timing mechanism that initiates gonadal activity. In brief, the light stimulus received by the retina of the eye is relayed to the hypothalamus, which in turn acts upon the anterior lobe of the pituitary. The later produces gonadotropic hormones which stimulate gonadal activity and the production of gonadal hormones. Following the period of reproductive activity there is gonadal regression, which terminates in a refractory period in late fall and early winter. This is a time of physiological rest when the gonads, at least in most species studied, cannot be stimulated by artificially increased daily photoperiods.

This annual cycle in birds is associated with chemical as well as physiological changes. Studies made by Lofts on wintering shorebirds in Africa have shown marked cyclic changes in the disposition of lipids in the testes.[2] This is first indicated by a gradual depletion of lipids in the postnuptial seminiferous tubules. As this occurs, there is a corresponding increase in interstitial lipids. Toward the onset of migration a reverse trend occurs and there is a decrease in the cholesterol-positive lipids in the Leydig cells of the interstitial area. This is accompanied by the beginning of spermatogenesis. By the time the migrants arrive in Europe, spermatozoa are present in the seminiferous tubules and there is further

[1]Rowan, W. 1929.
[2]Lofts, B. 1962.

depletion of the lipid content of the interstitial cells. Earlier Marshall had found that samples of certain passerine species known to winter in Africa and southern Europe had achieved spermatogenesis by the time they arrived in England in April and May.[3] All had a considerable amount of fat remaining which was cholesterol-free.

More recently John and George made a study of the gonads of wintering pied wagtails (*Motacilla alba*) and yellow wagtails (*Motacilla flava*) at Baroda near the Gulf of Cambay in western India.[4] These two species nest widely over the Palearctic during the summer months. Wintering birds arrive at Baroda in October and leave in late March and April. The testes in both species show a minimum weight in October, with a slow increase in size through the winter. From February on, the increase in size and weight becomes more rapid. From October to January the seminiferous tubules contain considerable amounts of cholesterol-positive lipids. In February, however, as the tubules become larger, there is a reduction in their lipid content and an increase in the lipid content of the interstitial cells. By March the tubules are free of lipids, which are present in large amounts in the interstitial cells. By the time migration starts in April, the lipid content of the interstitial cells has decreased and spermatogenesis is well under way.

It has been suggested that the depletion of the lipids from their storage in the interstitial tissue around the onset of the northward spring migration in birds may be the result of their being diverted to the synthesis and secretion of gonadal hormones, or androgens. This has been thought by some to be a possible stimulus to migration, although it has been shown that migratory behavior can develop in castrated individuals.[5] Furthermore, females, as well as the young of many species, also migrate. John and George suggest that migratory behavior as well as testicular rhythm may result from a common trophic hormone of perhaps hypothalamic origin or from one produced by the anterior lobe of the pituitary or some other endocrine gland.

MOLT

In general, most avian migrants in the Northern Hemisphere undergo a complete molt after the breeding season. This is followed by a period of

[3]Marshall, A. J. 1952.
[4]John, T. M., and J. C. George. 1966.
[5]Farner, D. S. 1955.

fairly rapid fat deposition in some species and the development of nocturnal restlessness, or *Zugunruhe*, in those that migrate at night. As will
be seen, the exact relationship between these last two changes is still not
clear. Both are correlated with a decrease in the length of the daily
photoperiod in autumn. In spring there may or may not be a prenuptial
molt in migratory species. If there is one, it is only a partial molt and far
less of an energy drain on the individual than the complete postnuptial
molt.

In many passerine species the annual molt occurs in late summer and
early autumn and is more or less complete by the time migration starts.
It thereby avoids conflict with the energy requirements of migration.
This is especially true of long-distance migrants. Short-distance migrants
tend to have a more extended molt that may continue during fall migration. Dolnik and Blyumental have shown, on the basis of data derived
from 140,000 birds trapped in northern Europe along the Baltic Sea,
that the willow warbler (*Phylloscopus trochilus*), the spotted flycatcher
(*Muscicapa striata*), and the garden warbler (*Sylvia borin*) generally complete their postnuptial molt by late August or early September, when
they start their long migration southward to central or southern Africa.[6]
By this time also large fat reserves have been acquired. On the other
hand, short-distance migrants such as the great tit (*Parus major*) and blue
tit (*Parus caeruleus*), the wood lark (*Lullula arborea*), the chaffinch (*Fringilla
coelebs*), and the yellowhammer (*Emberiza citrinella*) have a prolonged
molt that extends through the migration season. Some of these birds
engage in random movements during the time of greatest intensity of
molt and then direct their flight south as the molt activity wanes. When
the latter time comes, fat deposition begins. North American passerines
that engage in extensive migratory movements show the same tendency
to complete the postnuptial molt early and accumulate fat before beginning their autumnal migration southward. This has been pointed out by
Tordoff and Mengel on the basis of examination of large numbers of
migrants killed by a television tower while flying at night.[7] Extensive
studies made by Dr. Ned K. Johnson on New World flycatchers belonging to the genus *Empidonax* have also shown that migration and heavy
molt do not overlap in this group of birds. Molt may occur on either the
summering or the wintering ground, but an examination of migrating
flycatchers shows molt only in the very early or very late stages, if at all,
at this time.

[6]Dolnik, V. R., and T. I. Blyumental. 1967.
[7]Tordoff, H. B., and R. M. Mengel. 1956.

In Nearctic populations of the red-backed sandpiper, or dunlin (*Erolia alpina*), the postnuptial molt, according to Dr. Richard T. Holmes, begins in mid-June.[8] The first feathers to be replaced are the primaries, followed by the secondaries and rectrices. The molt of the body feathers begins between July 10 and 25 and is at least half completed by the time the birds begin their migration. The early part of the migration, however, is very leisurely, with the red-backs drifting about the arctic tundra and moving south only a few hundred miles in two to three months. During this time the body molt is completed without an excessive energy drain. When the birds are ready to leave Alaska and fly south to the California coast, most of them have new flight and body feathers. If the molt is not completed by then, it is suspended until the winter quarters are reached. This sometimes occurs when cold weather comes early in October and forces the birds south.

In the spring of the year, the prenuptial molt occurs largely while the birds are slowly drifting northward between mid-February and early May and is completed before the final long-distance flight to the arctic nesting grounds. This again eliminates any excessive energy drain.

The red-backed sandpiper is a north temperate wintering species, which probably accounts for its very late fall migration that permits the late summer and early autumn molt to take place in the Arctic. Southbound migrants reach California in peak numbers by late October and early November, which is long after most other migrant shorebirds have passed through. Certain other members of the genus winter in south temperate regions. This is true of the pectoral sandpiper (*Erolia melanotos*), the Baird sandpiper (*E. bairdii*), and the least sandpiper (*E. minutilla*). In each of these species southward migration from the Arctic begins in July, and most of the body molt as well as replacement of flight feathers takes place on the wintering grounds.

The molt of the wing feathers is more strictly determined by the migratory habits of the species than is that of the rest of the body plumage.[9] The Stresemanns have set up a series of categories for wing molt based upon its relationship to migration.

In group A, adult long-distance migrants, the wing molt begins in the breeding area. When the migratory urge develops, molt ceases, except for completion of the growth of new feathers. Molt continues again in the

[8]Holmes, R. T. 1966a, 1966b.
[9]Stresemann, E., and V. Stresemann. 1966.

Downy young Baird's sandpiper (*Calidris bairdii*) about to be released after being banded at Barrow, Alaska. *Photographed July 23, 1968, by Robert T. Orr.*

winter quarters. The distal primaries, which are most important to flight, are retained until migration has been completed. This situation is found in one race of the herring gull (*Larus argentatus heuglini*), in the turtle dove (*Streptopelia turtur*), northern populations of the peregrine falcon (*Falco peregrinus*), the red-footed falcon (*Falco vespertinus*), the honey buzzard (*Pernis apivorus*), the scops owl (*Otus scops*), and the alpine swift (*Apus melba melba*).

In group B, which includes a large number of long-distance migrants, particularly gulls, shorebirds, and Old World warblers, the wing molt does not start until wintering quarters have been reached. Some examples are the slender-billed shearwater (*Puffinus tenuirostris*), Sabine, gull (*Xema sabini*), the sanderling (*Crocethia alba*), the northern phalarope (*Lobipes lobatus*), the common cuckoo (*Cuculus canorus*), the barn swallow (*Hirundo rustica*), the spotted flycatcher (*Muscicapa striata*), the rosy pastor (*Pastor roseus*), and the common rosefinch (*Carpodacus erythrinus*).

Group C consists of birds that complete the wing molt before beginning migration. Some such species are the dunlin (*Erolia alpina*), the wryneck (*Jynx torquilla*), the sooty flycatcher (*Muscicapa siberica*), the snow bunting (*Plectrophenax nivalis*), and the Lapland longspur (*Calcarius lapponicus*).

Group D really represents a variant of group C, but the molt has been moved forward so that it takes place during the reproductive period. The Stresemanns here include Franklin's gull (*Larus pipixcan*) and Icelandic populations of the European golden plover (*Pluvialis apricaria*). The latter species may differ in this respect from the American golden plover (*Pluvialis dominica*). According to Sauer, who studied this species on St. Lawrence Island, Alaska, as well as in the laboratory, male American golden plovers go into "eclipse" plumage during the incubation period and assume a femalelike appearance, but some question exists as to when the annual molt is complete.[10] Many birds in their wintering quarters on Pacific islands have been observed still in process of molt. Some of Sauer's captive birds had completed neither their wing molt nor their body molt when the migration began. It is difficult to believe, however, that under natural conditions a bird like the American golden plover could undertake a migration of thousands of miles with the wing feathers in the process of molt.

In group E are included some birds that renew the wing plumage both on breeding grounds and in winter quarters so as to have fresh wing feathers for both autumn and spring migration. This is true of the willow

[10]Sauer, E. G. F. 1962.

warbler (*Phylloscopus trochilus*), which breeds in the Palearctic and winters in central and southern Africa; the bobolink (*Dolichonyx oryzivorus*), which nests in the northern United States and southern Canada and winters in Brazil and Argentina; and the Franklin's gull (*Larus pipixcan*), which nests in Canada and winters in Chile.

Group F consists of many Holarctic terns whose wing molt begins before fall migration but proceeds stepwise and is completed before the spring migration. In two species of terns the primaries are known to be renewed twice between breeding periods.

The Stresemanns also point out that the young of nearly all migratory birds go on their autumn migration with their first wing plumage. Some exceptions are the wryneck, the skylark (*Alauda arvensis*), and the arctic populations of the horned lark (*Eremophila alpestris*). In these birds the juvenal wing feathers are replaced by adult feathers before migration.

FAT DEPOSITION IN BIRDS

PASSERINES. *Zugunruhe* and fat deposition both occur in long-distance migrants in the spring and again in the autumn. For birds wintering on or near the equator in South America or Africa, there will be no change in the length of the photoperiod at the beginning of the northward movement. For transequatorial migrants that are spending the Northern Hemisphere winter below the equator in the Southern Hemisphere, there may even be a decrease in the daily photoperiod when they start north. After they cross the equator on their northward migration, the daily photoperiod again begins to increase.

Many Northern Hemisphere migrants, however, winter considerably north of the equator, and a number of avian physiologists believe that the accumulation of body fat in vernal migrants is a response to *Zugunruhe*, which in turn is the result of increased photoperiods. Thus the increase in bodily activity in migratory birds in the spring causes them to increase their food intake. In so doing they overcompensate, and the result is fat deposition. This theory has been defended by Kendeigh, West, and Cox on the basis of experimental studies on tree sparrows (*Spizella arborea*).[11] Other workers have demonstrated that in many species that do not migrate over very long distances, *Zugunruhe* and fat deposition are independent of one another, although both are dependent upon increased day length. Johnston found that white-throated sparrows

[11]Kendeigh, S. C., G. C. West, and G. W. Cox. 1960.

(*Zonotrichia albicollis*) initiated their northern migration from north central Florida before there was any noticeable fat deposition on the body.[12] They were in a lean condition. It is suggested that the early flights in this species are for short distances and that as the birds progress northward in subsequent days, their food intake increases, as does body fat. Only late migrants show premigratory fat deposition.

King and Farner's observations on white-crowned sparrows (*Zonotrichia leucophrys gambelii*) along the Pacific coast showed that most captive birds displayed fat deposition prior to the development of *Zugunruhe* in spring.[13] There were, however, some individuals that exhibited nocturnal restlessness before there was any fat deposition, proving that although one usually preceded the other, the former was not necessarily the cause of the latter.

Lengthening of the photoperiod and an increase in ambient temperature in spring both favor the reduction of caloric loss and provide greater opportunity for an increase in caloric intake. Nocturnal restlessness, therefore, could be merely a means of dissipating excess energy and must be interpreted carefully.[14]

In the fall there appears to be the same tendency toward premigratory fat deposition as seen in the spring in those species that engage in extensive migratory movements. An analysis of the lipid levels of samples of a number of species of migratory passerine birds that were killed at an airport ceilometer in Georgia on the night of October 7–8, 1954, was made by Odum and Connell.[15] The total lipids in percentage of net weight (g./100g.) for seven species of migrants that winter south of the United States in Central and South America (and may even fly nonstop five hundred miles or more across the Gulf of Mexico) averaged 29.8 percent, with extremes of 21.2 and 41.8. The fat was primarily subcutaneous and interperitoneal. The species involved and the number of individuals sampled were as follows: black-throated blue warbler (*Dendroica caerulescens*) sixteen, bay-breasted warbler (*Dendroica castanea*) four, ovenbird (*Seiurus aurocapillus*) sixteen, Philadelphia vireo (*Vireo philadelphicus*) six, red-eyed vireo (*Vireo olivaceus*) four, summer tanager (*Piranga rubra*) six, scarlet tanager (*Piranga olivacea*) three. By way of contrast, the lipids in thirteen yellowthroats (*Geothlypis trichas*) averaged only 22.2 percent, with extremes of 11.3 and 31.0. This species does not

[12]Johnston, D. W. 1966.
[13]King, J. R., and D. S. Farner. 1963.
[14]Farner, D. S. 1955.
[15]Odum, E. P., and C. E. Connell. 1956.

migrate as far as the others, wintering in southern United States, Mexico, and the West Indies. The longer migrants showed not only a higher lipid level but also a low coefficient of variability.

Another analysis of the lipid content of 308 birds representing ten species that were killed by striking a television tower while migrating at night along the Gulf coast of northwestern Florida in the autumn of 1956 was made by Odum.[16] White-throated sparrows (*Zonotrichia albicollis*), which do not migrate beyond the Gulf coast, had a lipid content amounting to less than 2 percent of the wet (undesiccated) weight. Bobolinks (*Dolichonyx oryzivorus*) and scarlet tanagers (*Piranga olivacea*), which winter at or south of the equator in South America, had a maximum lipid content amounting to 50 percent of the wet weight. Odum estimated that any small bird with a wet weight fat index of 27 percent could make a nonstop flight, under average conditions, of at least six hundred miles. This, as he points out, is the shortest possible route between the Gulf coast and the Yucatan Peninsula, and one which many migrants are presumed to follow. Since all the bobolinks and tanagers as well as most of the wood warblers (Parulidae) and rails and about half of the vireos that were killed had more than this necessary minimum, they could easily have traversed the Gulf. Some could have flown nonstop for at least fifteen hundred miles.

Nisbet added further to our knowledge of the energy requirements of trans-Gulf migrants and made some corrections.[17] He concluded that the fat reserves should be sufficient to ensure a sustained flight of fifty to sixty hours. His particular interest was in the blackpoll warbler (*Dendroica striata*), whose migration is discussed in Chapter 8. According to Nisbet, and this does not agree with the findings of Murray, birds of this species in their southward migration leave New England, pass over Bermuda without stopping in autumn, and fly at least as far as the Lesser Antilles and probably to Venezuela.[18] They are reported to have sufficient lipid reserve to enable them to fly nonstop for 105 to 120 hours in the usual weather in which they migrate.

A rather unusual opportunity to learn something about the bio-energetics of a passerine species making an extended migration over water was provided on October 24, 1965.[19] On that occasion a United States Coast Guard cutter was ten to twenty miles off the northeast

[16]Odum, E. P. 1960.
[17]Nisbet, I. C. T. 1963c.
[18]Murray, B. G., Jr., 1965, 1966a.
[19]Johnston, D. W. 1968.

coast of Cuba. During the afternoon, when there was a drizzly overcast, thirty-five small birds, including twenty-five palm warblers (*Dendroica p. palmarum*), flew aboard. They were preserved and later analyzed for fat content. This was found to be extremely low, with the mean weight of fat in the sample being 0.43 gram per bird. In some individuals it was down to 0.05 gram. By comparison, the average fat in a sample of thirty-four palm warblers taken in autumn in Tallahassee, Florida, prior to trans-Gulf migration was 2.66 grams per bird, and that of thirty taken at Jacksonville, Florida, at about the same time was 1.79 grams per bird. The water content of these three samples was not significantly different, which led to the conclusion that the nonfat dry body components were being catabolized. This utilization of nonfat dry body components by migrants after the fat index becomes very low has been suggested by others.[20] Some palm warblers are thought to migrate from Florida to the Yucatan Peninsula, a distance of about six hundred miles. Cuba would represent a refueling point in the route.

In northeastern England, warblers leave for the south in the autumn migration without accumulating much migratory fat.[21] Many of these species change from an insect diet to one of soft fruit at this time of year. This provides a food that is rich in soluble carbohydrates. Some stop in southern England to feed on fruit and accumulate fat. The sedge warbler (*Acrocephalus schoenobaenus*) is one of these. Others may stop in parts of Europe where soft fruits ripen early in the autumn. In Northumberland in northeastern England, blackcap (*Sylvia atricapilla*) and garden (*Sylvia borin*) warblers feed to a considerable extent on blackberries (*Rubus fruticosus*) and elderberries (*Sambucus niger*) in late September and October. This is also true of adult whitethroats (*Sylvia communis*). The juvenals of this species, however, as well as sedge (*Acrocephalus schoenobaenus*) and willow (*Phylloscopus trochilus*) warblers, leave for the south before these soft fruits are ripe. These early migrants may compensate for this by eating fruit in southern England, where it ripens several weeks earlier than in Northumberland. Since they are all long-distance migrants wintering in Africa, they must develop a fat reserve before beginning an extended flight around or across the Mediterranean as well as over North Africa.

Experimental work on the brambling (*Fringilla montifringilla*), which is a migratory European passerine, has shown that when the photo-

[20]Odum, E. P., *et al.* 1964.
[21]Evans, P. R. 1966.

period was suddenly increased from the eight hours to which the brambling would naturally be exposed in midwinter in England to 14.5 hours,
there was a rapid increase in fat deposition, gonadal recrudescence, and
manifestations of nocturnal restlessness within eight days. The longer
exposure would equal the length of daylight in mid-April. Lofts, Marshall, and Wolfson attempted to demonstrate that fat deposition in this
species was not essential to *Zugunruhe*.[22] They captured bramblings before
nocturnal migratory restlessness started. The captive birds were kept on
a strict diet. During the first few weeks they gradually lost weight but
finally arrived at a level that they maintained until the start of *Zugunruhe*.
This caused them once again to start losing weight because of the increased energy demands. After the termination of *Zugunruhe*, their
weight gradually increased again. Control birds showed an initial gain
in weight, probably as a result of easily available food and lack of exer-
cise. They then remained at a fixed level until April, when there was a
rapid increase in weight accompanied by nocturnal restlessness. After
they attained a peak on April 20, there was a rapid decline in weight,
correlated with a decrease in *Zugunruhe*.

Ward has gathered some interesting data on premigratory fat in
certain species of passerine birds in Nigeria.[23] Wheatears (*Oenanthe
oenanthe*) may put on up to 33 percent; the yellow wagtail (*Motacilla
flava*), up to 39 percent; and the subalpine warbler (*Sylvia cantillans*), up
to 40 percent. From their wintering grounds in Nigeria, they must cross
the Sahara en route to their nesting areas in northern Europe.

Body fat and proximity to the breeding area may have a marked influence on the number of migrant birds captured in traps and nets. This
has been pointed out by Lack and Lack in their analysis of nocturnal
migrants of the thrush family that have been captured at Skokholm,
Pembrokeshire, in western Britain.[24] Their records, covering the period
between 1947 and 1965, show that most species are more commonly
captured on the ground in spring than in autumn. The smaller number
taken in autumn is attributed to the fact that the birds are much closer
to the start of their migratory flight. They are therefore less likely to meet
unfavorable weather conditions and, even if they do, are less apt to be
grounded because their body reserves in the form of lipids are high. In
spring they are near the terminus of a long flight, and their body re-

[22]Lofts, B., A. J. Marshall, and A. Wolfson. 1963.
[23]Ward, P. 1963.
[24]Lack, D., and P. Lack. 1966.

serves are greatly depleted. Unfavorable weather at this time, when they are tired, more readily grounds them.

HUMMINGBIRDS. Hummingbirds, because of their small size, great activity, and the fact that they are warm-blooded, or homoiothermous, vertebrates, have a very high metabolic rate. Some of the smaller species of hummingbirds have a wing beat of fifty to seventy strokes per second. The speed of these birds in flight was once thought to be as much as fifty miles per hour. More recently Pearson has indicated that it is probably closer to twenty-five miles per hour.[25] The fuel they utilize to produce the necessary energy comes largely from the nectar of flowers and to some extent from small insects. Sugar is a quick source of energy and one that is available all year round in tropical and subtropical regions.

In the tropics the high ambient temperature and the year-round abundance of food provide a most satisfactory habitat for members of this group. Farther north and also probably farther south, and in the high mountains, daily as well as seasonal changes in temperature and the scarcity or absence of food in the winter season present problems for these birds. The problem of daily temperature change in regions where it becomes cold at night has been solved by the ability of hummingbirds to lower the body temperature at such times and become torpid. This reduction in energy outlay prevents them from succumbing to starvation from overnight fasting. Pearson (1953) mentions another method employed by hummingbirds in the Andes of Peru to circumvent the problem of temperature changes. In the altiplano, where the elevation of that high Andean plateau is rarely lower than 12,500 feet for over 150 miles, Estella's hummingbird (*Oreotrochilus estella*) resorts to caves at night and may nest in these caves. Even in summer the outside temperature often falls below freezing. This would be fatal to small birds that were in a torpid condition; within the caves, however, the temperatures are much higher and relatively constant.

Nocturnal torpidity provides hummingbirds in areas far north of the tropics with a means of solving the problem of lack of food at night, but it cannot tide them over the winter, when food is absent or very scarce in their breeding range. This necessitates a southward movement to areas where food is present, the temperature higher, and the days longer so that there is plenty of time for feeding.

[25]Pearson, O. P. 1961.

Several northern species of hummingbirds engage in migratory movements, but the most interesting and significant migration from the standpoint of bioenergetics is that of the ruby-throated hummingbird (*Archilochus colubris*). This is the only member of the family that occurs east of the Mississippi. Ruby-throated hummingbirds appear in southern United States by late March or early April, and the northernmost migrants arrive in Canada by May. After the nesting season is over, the southward migration begins. A few winter in extreme southern United States, but the vast majority go to Mexico and to Central America as far south as Panama. For many of these hummingbirds this entails a nonstop flight of over five hundred miles across the Gulf of Mexico. Odum and Connell found that this species had an average premigratory fat deposition of 2.0 grams.[26] The total lipids in percentage of wet weight ranged from 40.6 to 45.9. This is in contrast to 11.1 to 15.1 percent or 0.4 grams for ruby-throated hummingbirds during the nonmigratory period in June and July. These authors suggest that 2.1 grams of fat is sufficient fuel for a flight of eight hundred miles. Although some question has arisen on this point, the fact remains that the birds make a nonstop flight.[27] Earlier studies by Dr. Pearson on the metabolism of hummingbirds were made on captive individuals that were induced to hover in a jar where the carbon dioxide output as well as oxygen consumption could be measured.[28] It was shown that while their resting rate was between sixty-five and seventy calories per gram per hour for hummingbirds weighing about four grams, it increased to over four hundred calories per gram per hour when they were hovering. This figure is regarded as higher than the metabolic rate of a hummingbird in forward flight, as in migration; under these circumstances, lift is derived from the forward motion, which does not occur when a bird is hovering in still air.

WATER BIRDS. It has been pointed out by Moreau that many kinds of water birds winter in Africa far to the west of the longitude of their Palearctic nesting grounds.[29] To arrive there from northern Europe, it is necessary that they fly diagonally across the Sahara Desert. Nevertheless, observations at oases in the Sahara reveal that very few individuals are seen at these places. It is probable, therefore, that a nonstop flight of

[26]Odum, E. P., and C. E. Connell. 1956.
[27]Pearson, O. P. 1961.
[28]Pearson, O. P. 1950.
[29]Moreau, R. E. 1967.

some fifty to sixty hours may be involved in the passage from Europe to tropical West Africa. Little information is available on the percentage of fat deposition in these birds prior to migration, although it has been shown that the wood sandpiper (*Tringa glareola*) increases its weight, presumably by fat deposition, by as much as 32 percent prior to migration.

The Pacific race of the American golden plover (*Pluvialis dominica fulva*) is a shorebird with a remarkable migration that is equaled or excelled only by the nominate race of the species, *Pluvialis dominica dominica*, and by the arctic tern (*Sterna paradisaea*). Its breeding range extends from the Yamal Peninsula and the Yenisei River in Siberia east along the arctic coast to Cape Prince of Wales, Alaska. Pacific golden plovers winter in Hawaii, southern China, Taiwan, the Malay Archipelago, eastern India, Australia, Tasmania, New Zealand, and many of the Pacific islands. Some even winter along the coast of Africa from Somaliland to the Cape of Good Hope. Their migration is over water and includes great distances of nonstop flight. The distance from Alaska to Hawaii alone is about 2,400 miles.

Johnston and McFarlane made a study of these birds on Wake Island over a period of approximately two years and attempted to analyze their energy requirements for migration.[30] Northbound migrants were abundant on Wake Island in late April, and southbound individuals began appearing in late July or August. Some plovers winter on the island. Spring migrants were found to weigh more than fall migrants or wintering birds. In April the average weight was 153 grams and the maximum weight was 192.1 grams. The average August weight was 133 grams. The average weights of the body lipids for April and August were 26.8 grams and 22.8 grams, respectively. The average lipid weight in spring would allow for fifty-six hours of flight at a speed of sixty-five miles per hour, which would permit 3,640 miles of travel. The average lipid weight in autumn would permit fifty hours of flight at the same speed, or 3,250 miles of travel. The fattest April birds had an estimated flight range of 6,200 miles, whereas the fattest fall bird had an estimated flight range of 5,900 miles. The fact that the lipid content of golden plovers is proportionately less than that obtained for migratory passerines is thought to be compensated for by their greater speed in flight. Most passerines fly at less than thirty miles per hour, whereas it is estimated,

[30]Johnston, D. W., and R. W. McFarlane. 1967.

as indicated above, that the flight speed of plovers is in excess of sixty miles per hour.

FAT DEPOSITION IN OTHER VERTEBRATES

FISHES. The deposition of fat on the body prior to migration is not confined to birds. It appears to be characteristic of most adult organisms that engage in seasonal movements. Juvenile migrants of many species, on the other hand, often feed en route. Young eels must do this during their one- to three-year journey in the Atlantic. Young salmon feed as they move downstream to the sea. Young whales nurse from their mothers as they move away from the breeding grounds to colder waters.

Prior to the start of migration, adult salmon accumulate a large amount of body fat. The fat level, however, decreases with the expenditure of energy after migration commences. This is to be expected, since no food is taken during the long journey.

Analyses of migrating sockeye salmon (*Oncorhynchus nerka*) during their 715-mile trip up the Fraser River in British Columbia to spawn has revealed some interesting information.[31] The fish were sampled at three localities: before they entered the river, 250 miles up the river, and at the spawning ground. The head, skin, bones, and tail are the main source of fat and the flesh the major source of energy. As far as the internal organs are concerned, the alimentary tract is the major source of fat and protein, and the greater portion of this reserve is expended during the first 250 miles of the trip. It was determined that .47 percent of the total energy is expended in the formation of the testes and 8.1 percent in the development of the ovaries during the trip.

Herrings, like salmon, accumulate considerable body fat prior to spawning, and the spawning area may be several hundred miles from the feeding grounds. The body of these fishes has its lowest fat level right after reproductive activity is completed. In may other kinds of fishes there may be marked fat deposition prior to spawning even though there is little or no migrating.

MAMMALS. Bats that hibernate show a sharp increase in weight in the fall of the year as a result of fat deposition prior to entering winter torpidity. This increase may amount to from 25 to 30 percent of the total body weight.[32] Twente showed that the guano bat (*Tadarida brasi-*

[31]Idler, D. R., and I. Bitners. 1960.
[32]Orr, R. T. 1954.

liensis), which is known to migrate rather than hibernate, does not show this sharp increase.[33] Instead, it begins adding weight earlier in the fall. Likewise, on their return in the spring of the year, these migratory bats showed less weight loss than hibernating bats. Thirty-one banded males that returned to a cavern in Oklahoma in spring showed an average loss of 17.2 percent, whereas 183 banded females showed a loss of 21.2 percent. By comparison, the average weight loss during hibernation by *Myotis velifer* was 26.8 percent for males and 29.9 percent for females.

Some kinds of seals and sea lions have a well-developed social system whereby the dominant males establish territories on land and secure harems of females. In species such as the northern fur seal (*Callorhinus ursinus*), the Steller or northern sea lion (*Eumetopias jubata*), the California sea lion (*Zalophus californianus*), and both the northern and southern elephant seal (*Mirounga angustirostris* and *M. leonina*), the males may stay from several weeks to nearly two months on or about the defended territory without going to sea for food. In most of these species, the males or members of both sexes are migratory. On their arrival at the breeding colonies, these males have extensive fat deposition on the body and especially in the neck and thoracic region. This serves to provide the energy requirements for the extended period they will undergo without food and water, during which time they will engage in defensive battles and breeding activities. Likewise, it probably provides much of the energy needed for their migrations, although essentially nothing is known about their food intake during such times.

Cetaceans have developed a thick layer of blubber beneath the dermis, which serves several purposes. It is composed of connective tissue and fat. Furthermore, the lipid content of cetacean blubber shows some variation on different parts of the body. It is highest on the dorsal surface and lowest on the flanks.[34] Some figures are available on the percentage of blubber to body weight in certain cetaceans. It may amount to 27 percent in the blue whale (*Balaenoptera musculus*), 23 percent in the finback (*Balaenoptera physalus*), and 21 percent in the sei whale (*Balaenoptera borealis*). In the right whale (*Eubalaena glacialis*) blubber constitutes 30 to 45 percent of the total weight. It is correspondingly high in porpoises and dolphins and amounts to 32 percent in the sperm whale (*Physeter catodon*).

Blubber, because of its reduced vascularity, serves as an insulating mechanism and assists in thermoregulation for cetaceans, especially in

[33]Twente, J. W., Jr. 1956.
[34]Slijper, E. J. 1962.

species that live in colder ocean waters. Furthermore, in metabolizing fat, considerable water is produced, which is utilized by these marine mammals to compensate for water loss resulting from high salt intake. Another very important function of blubber is to provide a source of fuel for the extensive migrations in which many species engage. The amount of blubber as well as of other forms of fat deposition increases during the summer months. Species of baleen whales living in arctic and antarctic waters feed extensively on krill (euphausiids), which are small crustaceans very rich in fat. As the cold season approaches, these whales move toward equatorial and subequatorial waters, where suitable food is scarce or lacking. Accumulated body fat provides the necessary energy for these journeys, and since this becomes considerably depleted, the amount of insulation is reduced by the time the whales arrive in the warmer waters. This reduces the danger from overheating in an animal that lacks sweat glands and does not depend on other standard mammalian means for cooling the body, such as respiration. In the females there is further depletion, after they give birth to young, as a result of lactation. On the return journey to the polar regions, the young develop a protective layer of blubber at the expense of the mother.

FAT DEPOSITION IN INVERTEBRATES

Relatively little is known about the physiological aspects of migration in invertebrates other than for a few species of insects. Fat, however, is assumed to be the basic fuel which most organisms must rely upon as the source of energy for extensive travel.

Both the monarch butterfly (*Danaus plexippus*) and desert locust (*Schistocerca gregaria*) are known to accumulate body fat prior to migration. Johnson has summarized such information as is available on the energy potential of these two insects.[35] The monarch is estimated to have sufficient accumulated fat at the beginning of migration to enable it to fly for about 117 hours. It is not known to what extent fat may be replenished en route, but since some butterflies travel as much as two thousand miles over a period of weeks, it seems likely that this occurs. The desert locust is estimated by some investigators to have sufficient fat at the start of migration to fly for thirty-five hours. In both species, fat is the basic fuel that provides energy except for the first few minutes of flight, when glycogen is used.

[35]Johnson, C. G. 1965.

OTHER CHANGES ASSOCIATED WITH MIGRATION

The migration of juvenile salmon from the freshwater streams in which they were hatched to a marine environment where they will grow to sexual maturity, and their subsequent return to fresh water to spawn and die, involves many biochemical changes in the body. Such changes in many respects are more involved than those related to the seasonal movements of higher vertebrates. Young salmon, after living in fresh water for varying periods of time, depending upon the species, exhibit migratory behavior. It is generally believed that this is controlled by the endocrine system. Studies by Baggerman and others have shown that increased thyroid activity may be an important factor inducing migratory disposition.[36] In yearling coho salmon (*Oncorhynchus kisutch*), which usually remain in fresh water for a year or longer before migrating to the sea as smolts, it has been found that thyroid activity increases before the young salmon show a change of preference from fresh to salt water. After they migrate to the sea, thyroid activity decreases. The change in salinity preference associated with migratory disposition (possibly induced, at least in part, by increased thyroid activity) appears to be correlated with the length of the daily photoperiod. In juvenile salmon a long photoperiod induces a salt water preference, whereas a short photoperiod postpones or inhibits this. Juvenile salmon normally move to the sea in the spring of the year when the days are increasing in length; hence there appears to be a significant relationship between day length and migration, with the pituitary-thyroid system playing an important part.

In connection with changes in the salinity of the water, experimental studies on chum salmon (*Oncorhynchus keta*) by Shelbourn have shown that salt water definitely increases schooling in the fry and has been suggested as advantageous to survival.[37] During the period of migration downstream, it would appear to be of little benefit to young salmon. However, when they enter the sea, schooling may have a distinct survival value as a means of escaping predators in addition to being more efficient biologically for a homing population.

The daily photoperiod also appears to control the movements of other fishes into a different type of water.[38] The three-spined stickleback (*Gasterosteus aculeatus*) shows a correlation between day length and

[36]Baggerman, B. 1960.
[37]Shelbourn, J. E. 1966.
[38]Baggerman, B. 1957.

salinity preference. This species, however, behaves in a reverse manner from salmon. In the spring an increase in the length of the photoperiod induces the stickleback to move from salt water to fresh water, where it spawns.

Very different physiological changes are involved in the return migration of Pacific salmon to spawn and die. Much yet remains to be learned about these changes. Once salmon enter fresh water, feeding ceases. The length of time between departure from the sea and death varies to some extent with the species, but in the sockeye salmon (*Oncorhynchus nerka*) it is about four to six weeks. At the time salmon leave the sea, the body is rich in fat. In the female the gonads undergo maturation during this journey. One marked change, believed to result from the cessation of food intake, was found by Wood et al.[39] This is the decrease in histidine. This amino acid decreased to just a small fraction of its initial value in the body muscle, alimentary tract, head, skin, bones, and tail in sockeyes shortly after the start of the spawning migration. The decrease has been attributed to the fact that the fish cease eating histidine-containing foods. It has also been found that the level of sodium increases and that that of potassium decreases in coho salmon as the spawning grounds are approached.[40]

It has been demonstrated in several species of birds that there is an increase in the glycogen content of the pectoralis muscles and the liver toward the beginning of the migration season.[41] This buildup in glycogen may assist in the utilization of fat, which is the chief fuel used by migrants.

There is a definite seasonal cycle in the function of the thyroid gland in many vertebrates. The role of this structure in avian migration, however, is still not clearly known, although it has been suggested that thyroid activity may release migratory behavior or that it may bring about the necessary metabolic condition for migration. It has even been proposed that migratory patterns may have evolved through selection in species whose thyroid was inadequate to bring about the increased metabolic activity needed in cold weather. Some years ago Höhn pointed out that the increased energy requirements for migration as well as the restlessness of migrants suggest increased thyroid activity at these times.[42] He warned, however, that "any relationship between

[39]Wood, J. D., et al. 1960.
[40]MacLeod, R. A., et al. 1960.
[41]Naik, D. V. 1963; John, T. M., and J. C. George. 1966.
[42]Höhn, E. O. 1950.

migration and thyroid function is still largely speculative" (p. 467). Since then a number of physiologists have tried to associate the thyroid with migration, but the role that this gland may play is still not clear. John and George have demonstrated in two species of migratory wagtails, *Motacilla alba* and *M. flava*, that there are four distinct phases in thyroidal activity between October and April as indicated by the histological structure of the glandular tissue.[43] In October and November there is moderate thyroidal activity. This reaches a low in December and January with only a small amount of colloid in the follicles, followed by a great increase in thyroid activity from February to April. Several days prior to migration in April there is a release of thyroxin. It is suggested that this increase in thyroxin in the blood at this time enhances oxidative metabolism and thereby promotes the utilization of accumulated fat during migration.

CONCLUSIONS

Dolnik and Blyumental have summarized migratory disposition by stating that it is characterized by the integration of several physiological and psychical processes that may be independent of each other at other times of the year.[44] They indicate their belief that, in birds, photoperiodic stimulation of the hypothalamus is the first step, although certain other external stimuli such as air temperature and humidity may also be factors. The activation of the hypothalamus stimulates the feeding centers and simultaneously changes the hormonal balance. The stimulation of the feeding centers results in fat deposition in the body, and the change in the hormonal balance changes the behavioral pattern, which had previously been associated with nesting and territoriality. Hyperphagia and the accumulation of fat provides the bodily energy necessary for migration, and the hormonal changes reduce the threshold for the behavior pattern of migration, which is a genetic character of migratory species. They further point out that in sedentary species, or populations or individuals, the hypothalamus lacks the proper integrating program, or the hormonal situation is different, or the genetic factor or factors for migratory flight are absent.

When a migratory bird comes to the end of the premigratory period, the innate releasing mechanism (I. R. M.) comes into action. If the internal stimulus is weak, strong external stimuli are needed. These may involve temperature, food, and perhaps social interactions.

[43]John, T. M., and J. C. George. 1967.
[44]Dolnik, V. R., and T. I. Blyumental. 1967.

6

THE MIGRATIONS OF INVERTEBRATES

AND COLD-BLOODED VERTEBRATES

In the preceding chapters the advantages of certain types of population movements, to individuals as well as to species, have been discussed. The effects of the external environment and of internal physiological factors have also been considered briefly. Before discussing either the mechanics of migration or the means by which various organisms maintain their proper orientation during these movements, we should look at some selected examples of migratory patterns. For convenience only, insects, fishes, amphibians, and reptiles are included in this chapter, and examples of the routes followed by certain species are given.

INSECTS

Cyclic or seasonal movements occur in a number of kinds of invertebrate organisms, including marine and freshwater plankton, certain polychaete worms, and some arthropods. The only extensive migrants among these nonvertebrate animals, however, are a few of the insects, notably some members of the orders Lepidoptera and Orthoptera. Population movements of various types have evolved in a number of kinds because of their ability to fly. These movements range from irruptions, postbreeding dispersal, and emigration to true migration along well-established routes.

The best-known and most extensive migrant in this group is the monarch butterfly (*Danaus plexippus*), which is a New World species ranging throughout many parts of the Americas. In recent times it has even been successful in becoming established on some of the Pacific islands, including the Philippines, Sumatra, Java, and Hawaii, as well as in Europe. This extension of range may in part have been the result of accidental introduction by man, but in other instances it appears that

The larvae of the monarch butterfly (*Danaus plexippus*) are conspicuously striped. *Photograph by Edward S. Ross.*

it was accomplished by flight. In any event, the food plant milkweed, a member of the genus *Asclepias*, or closely related types of dogbane are essential for the larvae.

The pale green eggs of the female are laid on the underside of a leaf of the host plant and may number several hundred. After four or five days, the eggs hatch and the larvae, which are rather brilliantly marked with yellow, black, and green, feed on the leaves of the milkweed. After molting a number of times, the larvae attain a maximum length of about two inches and prepare to pupate. This involves wandering some distance at first, then becoming attached to twigs by their tails. The attachment is made by means of silk that is produced by glands in the mouth. Then the larval skin is shed, leaving the chrysalis. Development takes place within, and, depending upon the environmental temperature, the adult butterfly emerges in a few days to several weeks. Three broods hatch during the summer.

After emergence as adults, monarchs may drift from area to area, feeding occasionally on nectar. The first two broods die after a month or two, but in autumn those that emerged last tend to gather into groups, and these aggregations begin to move southward. They are usually spread out rather loosely, although in years of abundance there are records of masses of monarchs almost darkening the sky. In Washington in 1928 a flock of monarchs estimated to be several miles wide and ten to fifteen miles long was observed in the Cascade Mountains. The number of individuals in this flock was believed to be in the billions.

There appear to be rather specific flyways in eastern North America, the Mississippi Valley, and along the Pacific coast that these insects follow.[1] In this respect their movement patterns are not unlike those of migratory birds inhabiting the same region. The autumn migration is a first for the individuals participating. How they are guided is not yet known, although the behavioral pattern seems obviously to be genetic. Smell may play a significant role in orientation. Each year the migra-

[1]Zahl, P. A. 1963; Roer, H. 1967.

A swarm of wintering monarch butterflies on a Monterey cypress tree. *Photographed at Stinson Beach, Marin County, California, January 1966 by Edward S. Ross.*

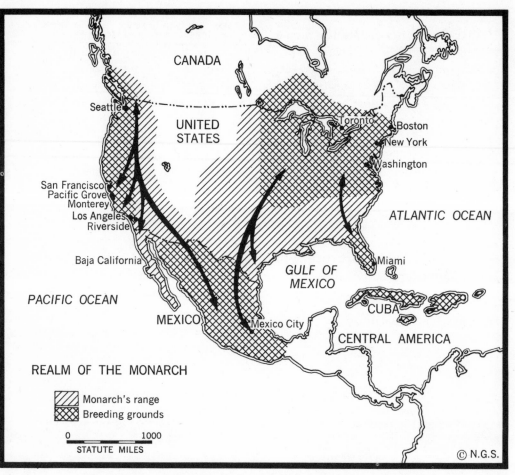

CANADA

UNITED STATES

Seattle

Toronto

Boston
New York

Washington

San Francisco
Pacific Grove
Monterey
Los Angeles
Riverside

ATLANTIC OCEAN

Baja California

Miami

GULF OF
MEXICO

PACIFIC OCEAN

CUBA

MEXICO

Mexico City

CENTRAL AMERICA

REALM OF THE MONARCH

Monarch's range
Breeding grounds

0   1000
STATUTE MILES

© N.G.S.

Realm of the Monarch. (After Zahl, P. A., 1963)

tory monarchs come to the same trees to winter and even seem to rest
on the same trees en route. The male monarch has scent pockets on the
hind wings. In southward migration the males take the lead and may
possibly leave a trail of odor to be followed by the females. This scent
may also be deposited on the butterfly trees and shrubs which are used
as resting spots en route and on those where large numbers congregate
in winter year after year. "Butterfly trees" are quite famous in some
places and a source of tourist attraction. The principal wintering areas
for the species are in Florida, western and southern Mexico, and coastal
California.

Obviously many monarch butterflies fail to survive the winter even
in more favorable southern areas. Nevertheless, a large number do, and
these start northward the following spring. Some are almost two thousand
miles from where they hatched as caterpillars late the previous summer.
This we know both from observation and from banding. There are

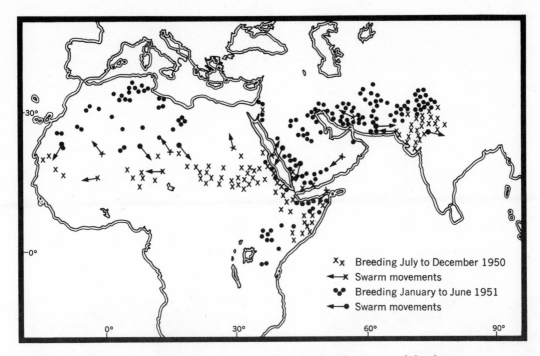

Xx Breeding July to December 1950
←—x Swarm movements
•ᵥ• Breeding January to June 1951
←—• Swarm movements

Map of northern Africa showing the summer and winter breeding areas of the desert locust (*S. gregaria*) with the southerly autumn and northerly spring migrations. (After Williams, C. B. 1958)

records of individuals banded in Ontario, Canada, by Dr. F. A. Urquhart of the Royal Ontario Museum that were subsequently taken 1,870 miles to the south in San Luis Potosi, Mexico.[2] The majority of the monarchs, however, do not travel great distances. Robert Brownlee of Stanford Research Institute placed white bands on the wings of seventeen thousand of these butterflies in the autumns of 1965 and 1966 near Santa Cruz in central California. Out of seventy recaptures, the most distant was at Santa Barbara, California, a distance of less than 250 miles.

The desert locusts (*Schistocerca gregaria*) of North Africa and southwestern Asia have fairly definite seasonal movements that are correlated with the rainfall. In North Africa desert locusts may produce two

[2]Urquhart, F. A. 1960.

broods a year, but each in a different region. They live in the northern area from January to June, which is the rainy season there. When the dry period comes in June, a southern movement takes place to areas where the seasons are reversed. Here the locusts remain from July to December. Breeding occurs in both regions.

The family Coccinellidae, containing the ladybird beetles, is known for the seasonal mass movements that are made by certain species in both the Old and the New World. These movements sometimes amount to several hundred miles and are principally between hibernating or estivating areas in the mountains and the lowland feeding areas. One

A swarm of convergent ladybirds (*Hippodamia convergens*). *Photograph by Edward S. Ross.*

of the best-known of these migrants is the convergent ladybird (*Hippo-damia convergens*) of North America. Studies in California have shown that these beetles feed principally on insects attacking cultivated crops and fruit along the coast in summer. Later they migrate to the mountains, where aggregations of thousands may hibernate during the winter at altitudes up to five thousand feet. In spring there is the return to the coast.

FISHES

Migratory patterns have developed in many kinds of fishes, both freshwater and marine, because of their mobility. These patterns are primarily associated with a periodic return to the spawning area. With most freshwater species, the movement is rather local and rarely involves more than a few miles of travel. Lake-inhabiting fishes may migrate at the breeding season to a specific locality near shore used year after year, or they may move into streams that are tributaries to the lake. The former type of behavior is well exemplified by the white bass (*Roccus chrysops*) in North America, whereas the latter pattern of movement is found among certain kinds of trout that move out of the lakes in which they spend most of the year and spawn in streams.

The movements of some of the larger marine fishes as well as those kinds that alternate between salt and fresh water may be exceeded only by the most extensive avian migrants.

The tunas are all pelagic species, and extensive banding has revealed some interesting facts pertaining to their distribution, particularly in the Pacific area. The albacore (*Thunnus alalunga*) is believed to breed in tropical water. The young, however, make extensive migrations to distant parts of the sea where food is abundant and do not return to the tropics until maturity. The same is probably true of the bluefin tuna (*Thunnus saliens*). Tuna tagged off the coast of southern California and northwestern Mexico in 1962 were taken two years later near Japan and Iwo Jima. The distances that some of these fishes traveled ranged from 4,500 to 5,100 miles. There is a record of a tuna tagged 1,300 miles north of Hawaii and captured 471 days later off the coast of Japan. The distance between these two localities is 2,370 miles.

Many smeltlike marine fishes migrate to specific spawning areas during the summer. The capelin (*Mallotus villosus*), which is circumpolar in distribution, occurring in arctic and subarctic waters, may go south as far as 40° N. latitude in the Atlantic. Most of the year the majority of the capelin are far out at sea. For a brief period in summer, however, the sexually mature adults, most of which are three years old, migrate to coastal areas in very large numbers and spawn. In Newfoundland the species spawns in June and July, principally in shallow water near beaches, where many are washed ashore by wave action.[3] Some are also known to spawn in deeper water as much as two hundred miles offshore, but these may represent a separate population. In the North Pacific along the coast of British Columbia the spawning of this species takes place in late September and October late at night near the water's edge at high tide. Temperature is probably an important factor controlling reproduction in this fish.

Pacific herring (*Clupea pallasi*) are widely distributed in coastal eastern Pacific waters from Alaska south to southern California. Schools of these fish move to inshore waters prior to the spawning period, usually from the middle of January to the middle of April. The later spawning occurs in more northern waters. The eggs are laid on marine vegetation in the intertidal zone or just below it. One of the longest migrations for herrings is engaged in by one of the southern British Columbia populations, whose members spawn along the eastern shores of Vancouver and other islands in the Strait of Georgia and spend the rest of the year in the feeding ground in the Pacific Ocean off the Strait of Juan de Fuca.

The best-known and most interesting of the anadromous fishes are the salmon, of which there are two genera, *Oncorhynchus* and *Salmo*. The various species of *Oncorhynchus* are confined to the North Pacific and the freshwater systems that flow into it. Five species reproduce in rivers, streams, and lakes of western North America. These are the sockeye (*O. nerka*), the coho or silver salmon (*O. kisutch*), the pink or humpback salmon (*O. gorbuscha*), the chum salmon (*O. keta*), and the chinook or king salmon (*O. tshawytscha*). With the exception of certain landlocked populations of the sockeye, the young of all these normally migrate to the sea to mature after a period ranging from a few weeks to two years in fresh water, depending on the species. This may be a trip of as much as two thousand miles down the Yukon River or one thousand miles down the Columbia River, or it may involve movement only from tidal estuaries into the nearby ocean.

The majority of the Pacific salmon spend most of their adult life in the Gulf of Alaska, which they may circle several times, traveling thou-

[3]Pitt, T. K. 1958.

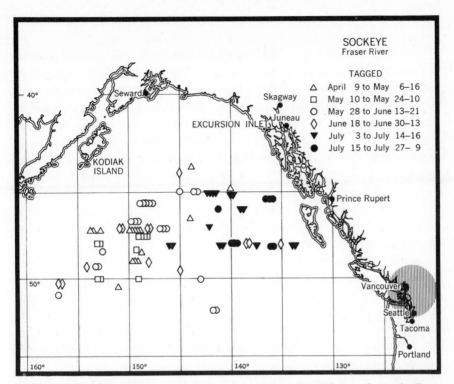

SOCKEYE
Fraser River

TAGGED

△ April 9 to May 6–16
□ May 10 to May 24–10
○ May 28 to June 13–21
◇ June 18 to June 30–13
▼ July 3 to July 14–16
● July 15 to July 27– 9

Recoveries of sockeye salmon, tagged at sea between April and July 1962, in the Fraser River area as reported by October 10, 1962. Identified according to tagging period and location. (From Neave *et al.*, 1962)

sands of miles while doing so. Some of the salmon that move up the Columbia River far to the south to spawn have previously been captured and tagged off the coast of southeastern Alaska. It has been estimated that the ultimate distance some salmon travel from the locality in which they were hatched may be as much as three thousand miles. The distance traveled depends upon the species. Some salmon do not spawn until they are four years old; however, the pink salmon completes its life cycle in but two years. Spawning occurs in the rivers of Asia from northern Korea to the Lena River in Siberia and in North America from central California to the Northwest Territories of Canada. In Washington and Oregon pink salmon spawn only in the odd years.

Despite the short life cycle, one-way journeys of up to seventeen hundred miles have been recorded by Neave *et al.* for this species.[4]

The Atlantic salmon (*Salmo salar*) spawns in the freshwater streams of eastern North America and northern Europe and then migrates to the sea. Unlike members of the various species of Pacific salmon, Atlantic salmon do not necessarily die after spawning. They may engage in another migration to the sea, like steelhead (*Salmo gairdnerii*) in the North Pacific Ocean, and return in a subsequent year to spawn again in the home stream. American Atlantic salmon have been taken on the west coast of Greenland, and those from Sweden have also been recorded there, a distance of almost three thousand miles from the home streams of both. The marking of salmon has shown that they are capable of returning to spawn in the very stream in which they were hatched after an absence of several years.

Freshwater eels of the genus *Anguilla* have a migration that is the reverse of that of salmon. They reproduce in the sea where the adults die, and then the young migrate to freshwater streams, where sexual maturity is attained after a number of years. Their migration routes are believed to be associated with oceanic currents. Two species of these eels are known, one of which occurs in the streams and lakes of western Europe and the other of which occurs in the streams of eastern North America. The European eels (*Anguilla anguilla*), occurring in the British Isles and in continental Europe from Scandinavia south to the Iberian Peninsula, require from five to twenty years to mature. They then move downstream to the ocean, where they follow the Canary Current and later the North Equatorial Current across the Atlantic Ocean to the Sargasso Sea. The sexually mature eels then spawn at considerable depths and die. The young, on hatching, are called leptocephali. They drift to the surface and move with the Gulf Stream, which takes them north and then northeast across the Atlantic to the shores of Europe. This journey requires three years. During this time they have a leaflike appearance and are sometimes referred to as leaf fish. As they approach the continental coast, they undergo a remarkable metamorphosis into elvers, which have a short, cylindrical body. Then they enter freshwater streams, to spend some years maturing into adult eels, after which they migrate back to where they were hatched, like their parents before them.

The American eels (*Anguilla rostrata*) also leave their home streams at maturity and drift, probably with the Labrador Current, to the Sargasso

[4]Neave, F., T. Ishida, and S. Murai. 1967.

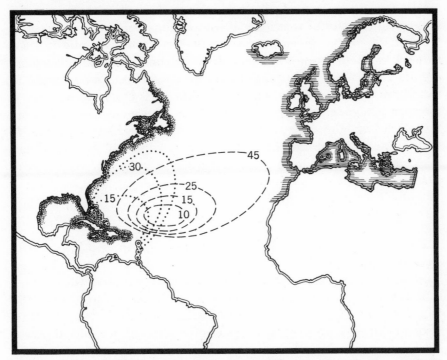

Migration of the eels. The European species (*A. anguilla*) occurs along the coasts outlined with lines, the American species (*A. rostrata*) where there are dots. The curved lines show where larvae of the lengths indicated (in millimeters) are taken. (After Norman, in Young, J.Z.: *The Life of Vertebrates*, Oxford, Clarendon Press, 1950)

Sea, where they spawn somewhat southwest of the European eels. The young of this species also drift with the Gulf Stream but mature into elvers within one year, at which time they are at the mouths of the rivers and streams of eastern North America. They ascend the home stream, where some years are required to attain maturity.

The striped bass (*Roccus saxatilus*) of the Atlantic coast of North America is a migratory fish that has been successfully introduced to the Pacific coast. The first introduction was in San Francisco Bay in 1879, with an additional planting in 1882. By 1889 the species was being taken commercially. These bass spawn in the spring in fresh water and then move into salt or brackish water in the summer. In California this introduced species set up a migratory pattern similar to that which the species fol- lows in eastern North America.[5] In winter the population is centered in the delta of the Sacramento-San Joaquin river systems, consisting of a network of about seven hundred miles of channels. Within this region, salinity varies, depending largely upon the winter and spring runoff. In spring this entire delta, as well as the lower parts of the main rivers, is used for spawning. In summer most of the bass move down into San Francisco Bay, and some enter the sea. They have been taken fifty to seventy-five miles up and down the coast. In the fall there is a mass migration back to the fresh water of the Sacramento-San Joaquin river systems.

AMPHIBIANS

The migrations of amphibians serve to bring individuals of both sexes of a species to suitable breeding areas. All members of this class must lay their eggs in water or at least in a moist situation where desic- cation will not take place. In a few tropical forms the eggs may even be maintained within parts of the adult female or male during the period prior to hatching. In most species, however, the eggs are laid in ponds, lakes, or slow-moving streams.

In temperate parts of the world the vocalization of frogs and toads in early spring is a familiar sound at night. The calling of males serves to bring females as well as other males to a specific location. The actual distance traveled in such migrations in all probability rarely ever ex- ceeds a mile, and the area of movement, according to Dr. James Oliver, never exceeds two miles in diameter.[6] Most frogs, toads, and salamanders move away from water after the breeding season. In some species, how- ever, the reproductive migrations involve movements within a lake or stream or from one pond to another.

In eastern North America green frogs (*Rana clamitans*) tend to live in fast-flowing streams. Such an environment is not suitable for the deposi- sion of eggs or for their subsequent fertilization. When the breeding season comes, adults migrate to lakes, ponds, or other situations where the water is quiet. Aquatic salamanders, such as the hellbender (*Crypto- branchus alleganiensis*) of eastern North America, likewise move from various parts of streams or lakes to other specific situations that are favor- able for the laying of eggs.

[5]Calhoun, A. J. 1952; Chadwick, H. K. 1967.
[6]Oliver, J. A. 1955.

In many kinds of amphibians the migration to the breeding site is overland. Salamanders appear to be guided largely by olfaction, whereas the toads and frogs depend to a considerable extent on sound. Visual clues provided by celestial bodies, however, seem also to be important for some species. The same migration routes seem to be followed each year, though they are relatively short as compared with those of more mobile types of animals. Even the daily movements are rather uniform in some species. Stille, in his study of Fowler's toads (*Bufo fowleri*) along the shores of Lake Michigan, found that these amphibians followed rather narrow lanes in their periodic movements to the lake shore from their daytime retreats.[7] These lanes averaged 26.7 feet in width, although they ranged up to 700 feet in length.

Some amphibian migrations are to winter hibernating locations. There is one report of the capture of 280 pounds of leopard frogs (*Rana pipiens*) by a frog hunter in Wisconsin who stayed in one place by a pool in autumn and captured the frogs as they came there to enter the water. The bottom of the pond was a hibernating site for these amphibians.

REPTILES

The principal reptilian migrants are sea turtles, but there are seasonal movements engaged in by some terrestrial species. These local migrations are mostly to breeding areas or to winter dens. Desert tortoises (*Gopherus agassizi*) in North America are known to move regularly each year between their winter quarters and their summer foraging grounds. The dens are tunnels in the ground that may accommodate a number of individuals. The summering grounds must provide a sufficient quantity of food plants.

In the Galapagos Islands there appears to be a periodic migration by the adult females of the giant land tortoises (*Testudo elephantopus*) from the highlands to the coastal lowlands to lay. Following the deposition of the eggs in the ground or sand, the tortoises are believed to travel back up the volcanic slopes to the cooler, moist uplands. Presumably, the young at some stage engage in the same altitudinal migration.

No significant migrations are known among lizards. There are a number of kinds of snakes that make limited seasonal movements. In western North America certain rattlesnakes (*Crotalus* spp.) move in the autumn to common dens, where they remain until spring, when the environmental

[7]Stille, W. T. 1952.

temperature becomes favorable for emergence. Extended studies have shown that some snakes return to the same den each year.

Sometimes winter snake dens are occupied by more than one species. Criddle has reported the occupation of an ant hill in Manitoba, Canada, by 257 snakes representing three species, as follows: 8 Great Plains garter snakes (*Thamnophis radix*), 101 red-bellied snakes (*Storeria occipitomaculata*), and 148 smooth green snakes (*Opheodrys vernalis*).[8] There are records of even greater numbers of species of snakes aggregated together in winter. Sometimes amphibians are also found with them.

The most famous reptilian migrants are the sea turtles, of which there are two families. One of these contains a single species, the leatherback turtle (*Dermochelys coriacea*). The other represents the true sea turtles (Cheloniidae), of which there are four genera: *Lepidochelys* (the ridley), *Caretta* (the loggerhead), *Eretmochelys* (the tortoise shell or hawksbill), and *Chelonia* (the green turtle). All the marine turtles are inhabitants of tropical or subtropical seas, and most have developed geographically distinct forms in the Atlantic, Pacific, and Indian oceans. All appear to engage in migratory movements, some of which are very extensive. Much of our knowledge of the movements of the marine reptiles has resulted from studies on the green turtle (*Chelonia mydas*) by Dr. Archie Carr and his students at the University of Florida.

The most spectacular migration made by green turtles in the Atlantic is between the Brazilian coast and Ascension Island. As a result of tagging female sea turtles when they came ashore on the sandy beaches of this tiny island in the center of the South Atlantic, investigators proved that some individuals came from along the coast of Brazil fourteen hundred miles to the west. The breeding season for this species on Ascension Island is from April to June. During much of the year the adults are to be found in the sea pastures off Brazil. The young move from their hatching place to the South American coast presumably by drifting with the current. Similar migrations by sea turtles to remote breeding islands occur in other parts of the world.

[8]Criddle, S. 1937.

7

AVIAN MIGRATION

RECENT HISTORY

A great deal of information has been obtained about avian migration. This is partly because birds constitute the largest group of migrants and partly because they are more easily studied than most other kinds of animals. Their relatively large size, their vocalizations, and the habitats they occupy make them easily seen. Written observations on bird migration go far back, and many books have been published on the subject.

One of the most important volumes on avian migration appeared in 1900 with the publication of *The Migration of Birds as Observed at Irish Lighthouses and Lightships Including the Original Reports from 1888–97, Now Published for the First Time, and an Analysis of These and of the Previously Published Reports from 1881–87 Together with an Appendix Giving the Measurements of about 1600 Wings.*[1] The author was Richard M. Barrington, a member of the British Association Committee for Obtaining Observations on the Migration of Birds at Lighthouses and Lightships. The book gives a very complete account of information known up to that time on coastal migration in Ireland.

A more comprehensive work entitled *Studies in Bird Migration*, by William Eagle Clarke, appeared in two volumes in 1912.[2] This was the most complete account published up to that time on the migratory movements of European birds. In addition to giving detailed accounts of many species, Clarke discussed theories of migration and the effect of environment, especially on bird movements.

The first book to present a modern approach to the study of bird migration was A. Landsborough Thomson's *Problems of Bird-migration*, published in 1926.[3] Dr. Thomson covered many aspects of avian migra-

[1]Barrington, R. M. 1900.
[2]Clarke, W. E. 1912.
[3]Thomson, A. L. 1926.

tion, including flyways, behavior of migrants, regular and irregular migrations, methods of studying migration, and the techniques involved in marking individuals for future recognition. He also provided an excellent bibliography for each chapter in his book.

This was followed in 1939 by Frederick C. Lincoln's excellent work on *The Migration of American Birds*.[4] Dr. Lincoln, who was on the staff of the United States Fish and Wildlife Service and an authority on migration, incorporated a vast amount of data obtained from Government records. He was also author of a brief edition of this work that appeared as U. S. Fish and Wildlife Circular 16 in 1950.[5] In this publication he mentioned that a file of over three million entries on banded birds was the basis of his work.

The information available on bird migration from all parts of the world was skillfully summarized in an outstanding book written by the French ornithologist Jean Dorst, entitled *Les Migrations des Oiseaux* and published in 1956.[6] An American translation appeared in 1962.[7] Dr. Dorst in his book presented not only the basic data on the migrations of birds over various parts of the world and the history of this subject, but also the most recent developments in methodology and new theories to account for the orientation of birds during migration.

KINDS OF MIGRANTS

In the Northern Hemisphere the majority of birds that migrate southward to winter are insectivorous passerines, water birds, and birds of prey. Exceptions include a few seedeaters that are migrants, and a few northern insectivorous types such as nuthatches, tits, and woodpeckers that are largely resident. The winter food of these insectivorous residents, for the most part, is secured by probing for larval or pupating insects, largely in the bark of trees. Water birds are forced to migrate because their food sources are sealed by ice. Birds of prey may correlate their southern movement with that of their prey, as in the case of the sharp-shinned hawk (*Accipiter striatus*) in North America, or with the onset of the dormant season in many kinds of northern rodents. In the Southern Hemisphere, as pointed out by Moreau, the majority of breeding species of birds that migrate northward are nonpasserines.[8]

[4]Lincoln, F. C. 1939.
[5]Lincoln, F. C. 1950.
[6]Dorst, J. 1956.
[7]Dorst, J. 1962.
[8]Moreau, R. E. 1966.

HOLARCTIC ROUTES

Though no two species of birds have the same migration pattern and probably very few individuals within a given population follow exactly the same route, there are certain broad flyways adhered to by large numbers of avian migrants in their spring and autumn movements. Names have been given to these routes, and they have been found to be convenient terms for game biologists, especially those concerned with waterfowl.

Dr. Frank C. Bellrose has proposed the use of the term *corridor* for the more precise passageway used by species or populations within the broader flyway.[9] As he points out, a corridor along which a species moves between its summering and wintering grounds is primarily biological in nature and must provide the elements necessary for the survival of the particular population. The use of such corridors has an evolutionary origin. The flyway is a geographical term, and while useful in a general way, it includes numerous corridors used by many species.

A knowledge of the specific corridor or corridors along which a species moves has proved essential in establishing proper management for game species and even in preventing extinction. For example, the whooping crane (*Grus americana*) had its population depleted to a minimum of fifteen birds in 1941. The nesting ground of this small group was found to be in the Wood Buffalo Park area of northern Alberta and in the adjacent Northwest Territories in Canada. Whooping cranes winter about 2,400 miles to the south in the Aransas Refuge in Texas. Protection was afforded the cranes in both areas, but it was necessary to work out the exact migration route and to inform people all along the way in the Dakotas, Montana, Nebraska, Oklahoma, and Texas that these birds must not be shot. The result was that by September, 1968, there were fifty whooping cranes counted in Texas.

NEARCTIC MIGRATION. In continental North America the migratory birds of Canada and the northern United States tend to move within one of four major flyways. Most species that nest in eastern Canada migrate along the eastern and western shores of Hudson Bay and the eastern continental coastline, converging during the southward movement in New England. Radar studies on the coast of Massachusetts have shown that the fall movement of most land birds is to the south-

[9]Bellrose, F. C. 1968.

west and that in the spring it is to the northeast or east-northeast. Some waterfowl, like the canvasback (*Aythya valisineria*), move southeastward from the central Canadian prairie provinces to come to this Atlantic Coast Flyway. Many of the passerine species continue south along the Atlantic coastal area to southeastern United States. Some winter there, but others take off from southern Florida to the Caribbean islands or South America.

The Mississippi Valley provides a broad natural north-south flyway for many birds that nest in the upper part of that valley as well as in central Canada and even eastern and central Alaska. This is a very important route for waterfowl, since many northern-nesting species winter in the Mississippi delta. Some passerine species, like Harris'

Principal migratory routes of the canvasback (*Aythya valisneria*). (From Stewart, R. E., Geis, A. D., and Evans, C. D.: *Journal of Wildlife Management*, 22:353, 1958)

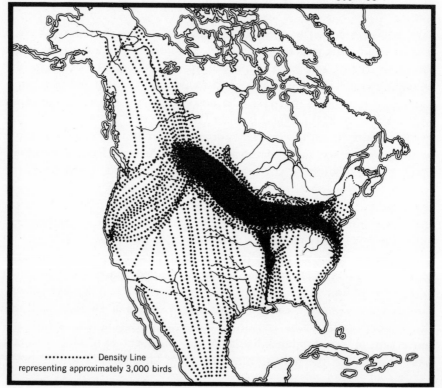

.... Density Line
representing approximately 3,000 birds

sparrow (*Zonotrichia querula*), move almost directly south from their nesting area in north central Canada and winter in the Mississippi Valley from Iowa and Nebraska south to eastern Texas. There are many other species, however, that continue on after reaching the Gulf coast. Some go east to Florida, then south with migrants from the Atlantic Coast Flyway, and then still farther south from the tip of that state to the West Indies, or even on to South America. Others turn west and then follow around the shores bordering the Gulf of Mexico to winter in Mexico, Central, and even South America. It has been rather clearly shown that others cross the Gulf in a nonstop flight, arriving at the Yucatan Peninsula or points in Central America.

A number of species of birds that have a relatively broad breeding range in eastern North America make use of both the Atlantic Coast Flyway and the Mississippi Flyway. This is true, for example, of the scarlet tanager (*Piranga olivacea*), which occurs in summer from the edge of the Great Plains east to New England. The eastern birds move southwest along the Atlantic coastal region to northern Florida, and from there they take off for South America. The western population may move straight down the western side of the Mississippi Valley to southern Texas and Louisiana and from there to South America. The migratory pattern of this species is shaped like a great fan that converges to a narrow strip on reaching Central America en route to Colombia, Ecuador, Peru, and western Brazil, where the scarlet tanager winters. The rose-breasted grosbeak (*Pheucticus ludovicianus*), whose breeding range is somewhat similar to that of the preceding species, comes down in a very similar manner to southern United States between northwestern Florida and eastern Texas, but its flight is in a broad band across the Gulf of Mexico, with some birds arriving as far north as the coast of Veracruz and others going directly to the Yucatan Peninsula. The species winters from Veracruz to northern South America.

To the west of the Mississippi Valley there is what is termed the Central Flyway, which originates in the north along the Arctic coast of Alaska. Birds moving south along this route pass through Alberta, Montana, Wyoming, and then through a broad area extending south to the Gulf coast of Texas and west to New Mexico. Many of them follow the east coast of Mexico if they are continuing south. A few go from New Mexico south over the plateau of Mexico. Some waterfowl moving south from Canada and Alaska leave this route in southern Alberta or in Montana and go diagonally southwest to enter the Pacific Flyway.

The Ross' goose (*Chen rossii*) as well as a number of canvasbacks does this.

An outstanding migratory bird refuge in North America is located in the state of Utah within the general range of the Central Flyway. This is the Bear River Migratory Bird Refuge, established in 1928 on the delta of the Bear River, which empties into the Great Salt Lake. Here sixty-five thousand acres are administered by the United States Fish and Wildlife Service. The refuge contains extensive marshlands where ducks and geese nest and winter and it is estimated to contain up to a million waterfowl at times in late August and early September. As many as 100,000 canvasbacks (*Aythya valisineria*) have been recorded at one time on the marshland. Up to half a million pintails (*Anas acuta*) may pass through in the fall. In addition to attracting waterfowl as a nesting and wintering site, the refuge also provides nesting sites for large numbers of shorebirds and several species of gulls.

The Pacific Flyway is used principally by birds that summer in coastal Alaska and western Canada. Most migrants follow north-south valleys after they get into the United States. Large numbers of waterfowl, especially Canada geese (*Branta canadensis*) and pintails (*Anas acuta*), winter in the Sacramento and San Joaquin valleys of California. Along the coastline white-winged (*Melanitta deglandi*) and surf scoters (*M. perspicillata*) move southward and winter in large numbers from southern Alaska to Baja California. Members of the Pacific population of black brants (*Branta nigricans*) nesting in western Alaska fly south also along the Pacific shoreline, feeding in the shallow bays where eel grass grows. Their principal wintering areas are bays along the western shore of Baja California and some of the bays on the west coast of the mainland of Mexico. Populations of white-crowned sparrows (*Zonotrichia leucophrys*) and golden-crowned sparrows (*Zonotrichia atricapilla*) that breed in Alaska and British Columbia move south along the Pacific Flyway, and many winter in central California. There are other species that continue south to the peninsula of Baja California, and a number go south along the west coast of the mainland of Mexico. The latter route is taken by many birds from the Great Basin region between the Rocky Mountains and the Cascade-Sierra Nevada axis.

On either side of the North American continent are routes taken by certain charadriiforms, particularly some shorebirds and terns. The Atlantic Ocean Route involves flight between Labrador, Nova Scotia, New England, and northern South America. For some species this may involve a nonstop flight of 2,400 miles over water. The most notable migrant to take this course is the Atlantic subspecies of the American golden plover (*Pluvialis dominica dominica*) on its southward migration. Nighttime radar observation made by Nisbet and Drury in spring along the Massachusetts coast showed bright, fast-moving echoes going in a northwesterly direction. At the same time the echoes of passerines were moving parallel to the coast in a northeasterly direction.[10] The north-west-moving echoes were attributed to shorebirds arriving from South America. Similarly, in the fall of the year fast-moving echoes going to the southeast are attributed to water birds leaving New England for South America.

The Pacific Ocean Route between Alaska and various Pacific islands is taken by but a few shorebirds. Notable among these are American golden plovers that nest in western Alaska. Like representatives of this species nesting in northeastern North America, some of the Pacific population migrate a long distance over water. Many plovers go to the Hawaiian Islands to winter. The nearest land is Alaska, which is over two thousand miles distant. Others travel to Oceania, Australia, and New Zealand. Other shorebirds taking the Pacific Ocean Route include the bristle-thighed curlew (*Numenius tahitiensis*), the wandering tattler (*Heteroscelus incanus*), the sanderling (*Crocethia alba*), and the ruddy turn-stone (*Arenaria interpres*).

Very few birds take the same migration route north in the spring that they follow southward in the fall. The spring migration in general is a more direct and rapid one. Furthermore, it is generally more wes-terly, at least in North America, so that a loop is formed. A striking example of this is displayed by the Atlantic golden plover population, whose southward migration from arctic North America to the pampas of Argentina is by way of the Atlantic Ocean Route. On the return north in the spring, however, these same plovers fly northwest to Central America, across the Gulf of Mexico, and up the Mississippi Valley. The loop for most migrants is far from the magnitude of that of the golden plover. Bellrose and Graber, in their studies on migration in the Mid-west, concluded that loop migration was normal for all species there.[11] One explanation of this is that it is an adaptation to prevailing winds.

Although there exists considerable difference in opinion whether each bird takes exactly the same migratory route each year, it is agreed that

[10]Nisbet, I. C. T., and W. H. Drury, Jr. 1967.
[11]Bellrose, F. C., and R. R. Graber. 1963.

the terminal points at each end of the migration are very specific. Banding has shown that for most species the individual returns to almost the same spot each year.

A careful study of this sort was made on mourning doves (*Zenaidura macroura*) in Missouri a few years ago by Tomlinson, Wight, and Baskett.[12] Over a period of five years 951 adult males, 652 adult females, and 411 juveniles of both sexes of this species were banded in the summer. The annual mortality rate for adult doves in Missouri has been found to be about 52 percent. With corrections for mortality and banding efficiency, it was found that all of the surviving males and 92 percent of the surviving females returned to nest where they had nested the previous summer. At least 90 percent of the recaptured doves were taken within a mile of the original point of capture. This indicates a very accurate homing for adult doves. Few of the juveniles, on the other hand, were recaptured in succeeding summers.

The duplication of the exact route in successive migrations by animals, however, has not been proved except for a very few species. Mueller and Berger recently concluded that the route taken by a bird is the combined result of the standard direction taken by the migrant, of wind drift, which varies, and of topography of the land, at least for diurnal migrants.[13] Mrs. Nice divided the song sparrows upon which she worked for many years at Columbus, Ohio, into four categories.[14] These were spring transients, summer visitants, fall transients, and winter visitants. Although there were returns of some banded summer and winter visitants, none of the approximately 150 banded transients was ever recaptured in subsequent seasons at Columbus.

PALEARCTIC MIGRATION. Because of climatic and alimental factors, many birds of northern Europe and northern Asia, like their North American counterparts, are forced to move southward in winter. Some go to southern Europe and survive well in the Mediterranean region. The majority of northern European species, however, move to the vast African continent, where favorable conditions for survival prevail. This involves flight over an extensive area of water, the Mediterranean Sea, or else the skirting of it by way of the Near East or via Gibraltar on the west. Some species take the longer routes, but others fly directly across the Mediterranean from southern Europe. Casement's studies show migration to be widespread over the Mediterranean except in the Ionian

[12]Tomlinson, R. E., H. M. Wight, and T. S. Baskett. 1960.
[13]Mueller, H. C., and D. D. Berger. 1967a.
[14]Nice, M. M. 1937.

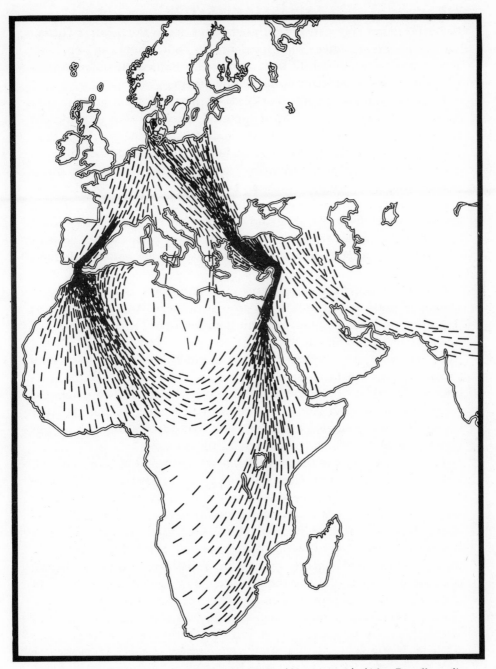

General directions taken by European white storks (*Ciconia ciconia*). (After Rupell, modified by Verheyen, 1950a.)

Sea.[15] He found no great concentrated flights across the Strait of Gibraltar. Simmons also gives some evidence to show that water-crossings may occur more frequently than suspected.[16] Somewhat different conclusions, however, have been reached by others.

D. R. Mackintosh asserts that birds of prey will go to great lengths to avoid a water-crossing.[17] Most raptorial species as well as storks depend for extended soaring flight on updrafts produced by rising thermals. These are lacking over large bodies of water; hence most birds of prey and white storks (*Ciconia ciconia*) migrating from Eurasia to Africa move southward through the Near East and Asia Minor or else cross the Mediterranean at Gibraltar. The European cranes (*Grus grus*), on the other hand, fly by flapping and can therefore engage in flock formation. Rising thermals are unnecessary; hence they make a direct crossing to North Africa, often across the widest part of the eastern Mediterranean.

Collman and Croxall have pointed out that many birds that nest in eastern Europe winter in Africa or southwestern Asia.[18] During the migrations a large number of them pass through Turkey. The Black Sea presents a formidable barrier to the north, but in the northwest there are two narrow stretches of water at either end of the Sea of Marmora, between the Black and Aegean seas. These are the Dardanelles and the Bosporus, which are 150 miles apart. At these two points the distance from land to land is as little as half a mile. Because of their dependence on thermals for soaring flight, most raptors and many storks converge at these points, particularly at the Bosporus.

At the western end of the Mediterranean, the Strait of Gibraltar provides a relatively narrow water-crossing from the Iberian Peninsula to Morocco. While most of the raptors from Europe cross to Africa east of the Mediterranean, a few cross at the west end. According to Lathbury, about 96 percent of these are honey buzzards (*Pernis apivorus*) and black kites (*Milvus migrans*).[19] Most of them approach the Rock of Gibraltar from the north and make use of the updrafts to gain altitude. Before continuing south or southwest to Morocco, they soar high over the crest of the Rock. This helps to sustain them in their water-crossing.

Radar observations on fall migration in England show that the ma-

[15]Casement, M. B. 1966.
[16]Simmons, K. E. L. 1951.
[17]Mackintosh, D. R. 1949.
[18]Collman, J. R., and J. P. Croxall. 1967.
[19]Lathbury, G. 1968.

jority of the warblers, chats, flycatchers, and other small nocturnal migrants move south-southeast.[20] In western continental Europe, on the other hand, banding has shown that nocturnal autumn migrants move south-southwest. Dr. David Lack suggests that the south-south-east direction taken by British birds serves to reduce the danger of west-ward drift into the Atlantic as a result of easterly winds. By the time the birds reach the south of France, it is presumed that they reorient in a south-southwest direction so as to join the great mass of continental birds moving into the Iberian Peninsula. These shifts in direction, there-fore, seem to have adaptive value. Lack further suggests that movement to the Iberian Peninsula before crossing to northern Africa is made not because the birds thus avoid a long flight across the Mediterranean but because the western Sahara provides more food for migrants. Farther south in Africa they again must shift to the east to arrive at the principal wintering grounds.

The problem of crossing the Mediterranean for migrating birds from Europe and western Asia is somewhat comparable to that presented by the Caribbean Sea and the Gulf of Mexico to some North American migrants. The latter, however, do not have to contend with inhospitable land after completing their overwater trip. They arrive in a tropical environment, although their voyage over water has been somewhat longer. North African arrivals must subsequently cross extensive desert areas where food and water are scarce or lacking and where climatic conditions may be rather extreme.

The red-backed shrike (*Lanius collurio*) of Europe and western Asia migrates to the eastern Mediterranean and then appears to fly over the sea, possibly making use of some of the islands of Greece to reach North Africa. From here it moves south to the Congo to winter. A somewhat similar migration is made by the golden oriole (*Oriolus oriolus*), which breeds in eastern Europe and winters in East Africa.

The movement of many northern Asiatic migrants is to the southwest. A number even winter in tropical Africa. One of the most remarkable migrations is made by the wheatear (*Oenanthe oenanthe*). There are four recognized subspecies, two of which are resident in Africa (*O. o. phillipsi* and *O. o. seebohmi*). The other two are either Palearctic or Nearctic. *O. o. leucorhoa* nests in northeastern Canada, Greenland, Iceland, Jan Mayen, and the Faeroes. In migration, most of this population moves through the British Isles and western Europe to western Africa. *O. o.*

[20]Lack, D. 1963.

oenanthe nests across northern Europe and Asia to Alaska. Practically the entire population of this subspecies, even those birds nesting in Alaska, moves southwest across Asia to the savanna country of Africa. Some winter as far south as Zambia and Nyasaland.

Many Palearctic birds from eastern Europe and extreme western Asia move south by way of the Middle East and pass through the Caspian Sea area. For some species the fertile south shores of this sea provide the first major refueling area on their journey to Africa.[21] Immediately to the south of the Caspian Sea, which is about 650 miles in extent from north to south, are the Elburz Mountains. This east-west range is about six hundred miles in length and rises to an average height of from ten thousand to twelve thousand feet. The highest peak is 18,550 feet. South of this is the arid desert of the Iranian plateau. Autumn migrants may fly directly over the Caspian Sea or use its east coast as a guideline. Some follow the south coast as a guideline on arrival there, even though this is at an angle to their migration direction. Swallows following east along the south coast arrive at more fertile feeding areas. Some species make a stopover before continuing, but many others continue directly south over the high Elburz range, probably flying at twelve thousand feet or more. This appears to be particularly true of night migrants unless the weather is very unfavorable and causes them to become grounded.

Most shorebirds moving southward tend to veer westward on reaching the south Caspian coast. This guides them in the direction of their wintering ground, west of south of the Caspian. The northern phalarope is an exception. It moves east because it winters in the Indian Ocean east of Africa. The fertile south Caspian region is not regarded as an essential refueling area for waders.

Recently Safriel, as a result of several years of observation at the head of the Gulf of Aqaba, pointed out that raptors, lesser black-backed gulls, and storks are far more abundant there in migration in spring than in fall.[22] He suggests that the fall migration is on a broad front that may include Arabia at its western fringes while in spring the core of the northward migration from Africa is shifted westward. Part of it is channeled up the Rift Valley, which extends from east central Africa north across the Gulf of Suez, then up the Gulf of Aqaba to the Dead Sea, Jordan Valley, and Anatolia.

[21]Feeny, P. P., *et al.* 1968.
[22]Safriel, U. 1968.

MIGRATION IN THE SOUTHERN HEMISPHERE

Much needs to be learned about the movements of land birds of the Southern Hemisphere, especially on the continent of South America. Moreau, in his excellent work on *The Bird Faunas of Africa and Its Islands*, lists three species that breed in southern Africa and migrate north across the equator to winter.[23] One of these is the nightjar (*Caprimulgus rufigena rufigena*), which nests during the summer rainy season as far north as Rhodesia and southern Angola and winters from northern Nigeria to Darfur. The pennant-winged nightjar (*Semeiophorus vexillarius*) nests in southern Africa north to Tanzania and the southern Congo and winters north of the equator. A similar migratory pattern is shown by the amethyst starling (*Cinnyricinclus leucogaster*), which breeds north to Kenya and Tanzania and winters in Ethiopia and the southern Sudan. Some individuals of these last two species are found on the equator all year round.

A reversal of this type of migration from a breeding range south of the equator to a wintering ground to the north is seen in Abdim's stork (*Ciconia abdimii*). This species breeds just south of the Sahara Desert in the woodland and steppe country from Senegal and Guinea on the Atlantic to Ethiopia. The nesting season commences with the start of the summer rains. After the rainy season ends, these storks move to southern Africa to winter between 10° and 35° S. latitude. A maximum migration of two thousand miles may be involved.

There are also birds of southern Africa that move north after the nesting season but do not quite cross the equator. Their migration is truly confined to the Southern Hemisphere. This is especially true of certain swallows and cuckoos and of a number of species on the island of Madagascar. The blue swallow (*Hirundo atrocaerulea*) breeds in Malawi and Rhodesia during the wet season and spends the rest of the year in Uganda. The ploceid *Quelea quelea*, which causes so much damage in certain agricultural areas, shows some migratory patterns in certain regions. Some of these birds that nest in the Republic of South Africa, especially the province of Transvaal, move north by the end of March as much as four hundred miles and winter in Malawi and Zambia, where they remain until October. The Madagascar little cuckoo (*Cuculus poliocephalus*) breeds in Madagascar and is found there between late

[23]Moreau, R. E. 1966.

September and April. During the rest of the year it is found in eastern
Africa from Kenya and the eastern Congo south to Mozambique.
Somewhat similar patterns of movement are shown by certain other
Madagascar birds.

As pointed out by Moreau, there is a difference between migrants
that come to winter in Africa from the Northern Hemisphere and those
that come from the Southern Hemisphere. Most of the Palearctic migrants, apart from birds of prey and water birds, are passerines, whereas,
apart from swallows, the majority of the Ethiopian migrants are nonpasserines such as swifts, cuckoos, and caprimulgids.

Broeckhuysen divides the migrants in the Cape region of South Africa
into three categories.[24] First there are the Palearctic migrants that come
south from Europe and Asia to winter. Forty-eight species fall into this
category. More than half of these are members of the order Charadriiformes, principally waders, and nearly one-fifth are passerines. The
second group comprises the African migrants that breed in the Cape
region but leave for the winter. The ten species in this group are limited
to the cuckoo (*Cuculidae*), swift (*Apodidae*), and swallow (*Hirundinidae*)
families. The third group consists of eight species of swifts, swallows,
and flycatchers (*Muscicapidae*) that are resident farther north in Africa
but appear to be migratory in the southern Cape region, as their numbers become greatly reduced in winter. They are regarded as locally
migratory.

Broeckhuysen points out some interesting breeding biology relative to
certain of the Palearctic migrants that winter in the Cape region of
South Africa. Most of them spend twice as much time in the wintering
grounds as they do on their northern breeding areas in Europe or Asia.
Some even breed in the wintering territory. The European bee-eater
(*Merops apiaster*), which nests in southern Europe and Asia, arrives in
the Cape region in late September and early October. A number of
these birds, which may or may not be from Europe or Asia, establish
nesting colonies and rear young during November and December. By
late January, adults and young leave the Cape region and are believed
to move north and join nonbreeding bee-eaters in other parts of southern
Africa. In Rhodesia the species leaves in late March and early April.

Two possible explanations are presented to account for this strange
behavior. Either the bee-eaters breeding in the Cape are true Palearctic
migrants that may also nest in Europe and Asia, or they represent a

[24]Broekhuysen, G. 1967.

different population that moves farther south in Africa during the Southern Hemisphere summer and does not go as far north as the birds that breed in Europe and Asia. Furthermore, the Cape population has reversed its time of breeding. This last explanation seems to be the most plausible.

A somewhat similar type of behavior is seen in the white stork (*Ciconia ciconia*), the whiskered tern (*Chlidonias hybrida*), and the black-necked grebe (*Podiceps caspicus*). All of these are Palearctic breeding birds that occur in the Cape region of South Africa during the Southern Hemisphere summer, and some of each of these species breed there.

VERTICAL MIGRATION

On virtually all major mountain ranges in temperate parts of the world, local seasonal movements of an essentially vertical nature are made by many species of birds. Such migrations involve a movement to higher elevations to nest during climatically favorable seasons of the year, and a reverse trend after the reproduction period. Relatively short distances are traveled to obtain suitable summering and wintering habitats.

Such movements are characteristic of a number of species of accentors, especially those nesting fairly high in the Himalayas, such as the rufous-breasted accentor (*Prunella strophiata*), the robin accentor (*P. rubeculoides*), the brown accentor (*P. fulvescens*), and the maroon-backed accentor (*P. immaculata*). Other accentors inhabiting the various mountain ranges of Eurasia have similar seasonal vertical movements.

While many Old World warblers nesting in the Palearctic winter in southern Asia and Africa, there are a number of species with very limited altitudinal migrations. Pallas' warbler (*Phylloscopus proregulus*), the dusky warbler (*P. fuscatus*), and the orange-barred willow warbler (*P. pulcher*), all of whom nest above the seven-thousand-foot level in the Himalayas, move down into the foothills to winter.

Most interesting vertical migrations occur among certain gallinaceous birds because these, for the most part, are made on foot. Some of the mountain quail (*Oreortyx pictus*) in the Pacific coastal parts of the United States move to the higher parts of the Cascades and the Sierra Nevada to nest and spend the summer. Individuals are known to occur up to 9,500 feet in Yosemite National Park. By late August or early September, while food is still plentiful, the downward movement of these birds of the high country starts. This no doubt is the result of natural selection. On rare occasions winter snows come at an early date. It seems logical to assume that those quail that tended to have a late migration would suffer high mortality, whereas the chances of survival of those that moved to the lowlands early in the autumn would be much greater. Most of the quail winter below the snow line. In the spring they work their way up the slopes as the snow recedes and food becomes available.

A reverse vertical migration occurs among blue grouse (*Dendragapus obscurus*) in the same general area occupied by the mountain quail. Although this species ranges down to essentially sea level in places, it also occurs in the Sierra Nevada, the Cascades, the coastal ranges, and the Rocky Mountains of western North America. In the higher mountainous regions such as the Sierra Nevada of California, blue grouse nest at middle to moderately high elevations in open pine and fir forests. In late summer, when the young have attained sufficient size, the family groups begin to migrate, but their movement is upward, not down. Sometimes the females precede the juvenals to the wintering areas. As they progress, they feed on berries and other available food, and finally, by the time the heavy snows come, they may be close to the timberline. Many coveys winter in dense clumps of conifers, especially red fir (*Abies magnifica*), and feed almost entirely on the buds of these trees until they start to move downward in the spring. It has been shown recently that grouse may travel as much as thirty miles from the breeding area to the winter range.[25]

Vertical migrations occur not only in the Northern Hemisphere but also in the Southern Hemisphere. In Rhodesia there is a downward movement of a number of kinds of birds of the montane forests for the winter season.[26]

[25]Zwickel, F. C., I. O. Buss, and J. H. Brigham. 1968.
[26]Irwin, M. P. S. 1957.

8

MIGRATIONS OF LAND BIRDS

With many kinds of land birds, especially small passerine species, migration presents few spectacular aspects and is of interest only to the ornithologist. One's attention is called to the arrival of summer visitants by their song. The fall exodus is quiet. This is in marked contrast to the conspicuous mass movements of most migratory waterfowl, whose appearance is eagerly awaited by sportsmen, or to the passage of flocks of shorebirds. Nevertheless, the majority of avian migrants are land birds. The distinction made here between land and water birds is purely artificial and solely for expediency. Only a few of the so-called land migrants are considered, so as to illustrate the general pattern of movement in certain orders and families. Dorst gives an excellent account of this subject in his work on avian migration.[1]

HAWKS AND VULTURES

Many hawks of the Northern Hemisphere move southward in autumn. Their migrations are made during daylight hours when they are able to make use of thermals and updrafts. The thermals serve to give them altitude from which to glide to the next thermal. Updrafts are most often found along the crests of ridges, which are favored migration lanes. In eastern North America, hawks follow fairly definite migration routes along the major north-south ridges, such as those bordering the Connecticut Valley and the Hudson. There are places where these birds funnel in and at times appear in large concentrations. One of these localities is Hawk Mountain on the Kittatinny Ridge in eastern Pennsylvania.

The concentration of diurnal birds of prey at Hawk Mountain left

[1]Dorst, J. 1962.

them very vulnerable to being shot by well-meaning but uninformed persons, and it was estimated that for many years from 3,000 to 5,000 hawks were killed annually at this one locality. In 1934, through the energy of Mrs. Charles N. Edge, a vigorous conservationist, the vantage areas on Hawk Mountain were acquired and a sanctuary established. In that year alone, 10,776 hawks and vultures, representing seventeen different kinds of birds, were counted passing by in migration. By 1936 the annual number recorded was 16,734. The fame of Hawk Mountain Sanctuary spread rapidly, and now it attracts large numbers of visitors and provides an ideal site for the study of the flight of various falconiform birds.

From observations there it has been found that raptor migration begins early in September, led by broad-winged hawks (*Buteo platypterus*), with ospreys (*Pandion haliaetus*), bald eagles (*Haliaeetus leucocephalus*), red-shouldered hawks (*Buteo lineatus*), and sharp-shinned hawks (*Accipiter striatus*) following. The red-shouldered and sharp-shinned hawks are largely immature birds. By early October, the broad-winged hawks, whose numbers in passing Hawk Mountain generally exceed those of all other species of hawks, are gone. This early migrant travels farther south than any of the other species, wintering in Central and northern South America. Sharp-shinned hawks reach their peak numbers in the third week in October; red-tailed hawks (*Buteo jamaicensis*) and goshawks (*Accipiter gentilis*), in late October and November. Small falcons pass principally in October.

It has been pointed out that there are interesting correlations among the factors of time of migration, distance traveled, and food availability.[2] The early migrants travel the farthest south, whereas most of the late-arriving species do not winter very far south of their summer range. The broad-winged hawk lives largely on reptiles and amphibians, which go into hibernation early in the north—hence its early movement southward to the tropics. Sharp-shinned hawks time their migration so it coincides with that of the small passerine birds upon which they prey.

In the Great Lakes region of North America there is a tendency for hawks to concentrate along shorelines, which they follow. Overwater flights are avoided as much as possible because of the absence of thermals or updrafts over such bodies and the necessity of expending much more energy in labored, flapping flight. Similarly, some species tend to follow the eastern continental coast of North America in migration.

[2]Broun, M. 1937.

Long Island Sound and Cape May are famous places to observe the flight of birds of prey. This route is used particularly by ospreys and turkey vultures (*Cathartes aura*).

The migration of the turkey vulture, whose breeding range includes much of the Western Hemisphere from Canada south to Patagonia, is rather ill-defined. During some winters these birds are seen over most of their breeding range, but in general there is a definite southerly movement in the autumn. Migrations have frequently been noted in the vicinity of Washington, D. C., with flocks of up to thirty or more individuals observed moving south in October and November.[3] Recently an observer thirty miles south of Tecolutla, Veracruz, Mexico, noted a very large aggregation of turkey vultures moving north on March 27.[4] Several thousand individuals were estimated to be in the flock, which was about three miles in length. Additional flocks of smaller size were seen along the coast of Veracruz the following day.

Just as extensive migrations of hawks and vultures take place in Europe and Asia, with many species moving south to Africa or southern Asia to winter. The movement from Europe and Asia Minor is largely around the eastern end of the Mediterranean Sea for many species, although not for all. The osprey (*Pandion haliaetus*) of Europe may move south to Africa via the Dardanelles, from the Iberian Peninsula, or even directly across the widest part of the Mediterranean. Such a water-crossing is not surprising for this species, since its food comes either from the sea or from freshwater lakes and rivers. Common buzzards (*Buteo buteo*) of northern Europe may winter in France or Spain, and some cross to North Africa at Gibraltar. Populations of this species from Russia and Asia Minor are rarely found at the Bosporus, but they are abundant during migration in southern Turkey and even on the island of Cyprus, en route to Africa in spite of their dislike for water-crossings.

The honey buzzard (*Pernis apivorus*) is one of the earliest as well as most common European migrants to pass over the Bosporus en route to Africa in autumn.[5] This species appears in early August, followed at about the end of the third week of that month by black kites (*Milvus migrans*). Both of these species are also common migrants across the Strait of Gibraltar. Lathbury records the autumn migration of raptors in the Gibraltar region as extending from the first week in August to the third week in September.[6] Sparrow hawks (*Accipiter nisus*) are abun-

[3]Bent, A. C. 1937.
[4]Bussjaeger, L. J., *et al.* 1967.
[5]Ballance, D. K., and S. L. B. Lee. 1961.
[6]Lathbury, G. 1968.

dant migrants at the Bosporus in the last half of September. After leaving Europe by the Bosporus, most of these birds cross Asia Minor to the Taurus, according to Cameron *et al.*, and then turn south along the Levant coast to Suez.[7] At the Gulf of Iskenderun they are joined by migrants from Russia and Turkey. Short-toed eagles (*Circaetus gallicus*) and Egyptian vultures (*Neophron percnopterus*) are among the more common migrants from Asia Minor, with the last-mentioned species appearing very early in autumn. Among the late migrants passing the Bosporus and Suez are the spotted eagle (*Aquila clanga*) and the lesser spotted eagle (*Aquila pomarina*). Their migration starts late in September and continues until November.

Some Old World vultures participate in definite migrations, whereas others are sedentary. Species such as the griffon vulture (*Gyps fulvus*) and lammergeier (*Gypaetus barbatus*) that are found nesting as far north as the desert areas of central Asia move southward in the fall of the year and fly across the Himalayas to winter in India. The Egyptian vulture (*Neophron percnopterus*) in the Mediterranean region moves south of the Sahara Desert for the winter. Other species, particularly those inhabiting central Africa, are relatively sedentary. This is true also of the cinereous vulture (*Aegypius monachus*), which lives on the central Asiatic steppes and at altitudes up to ten thousand feet in the Himalayas. A few of the birds from higher elevations in the Himalayas may move down to central China to winter.[8]

One of the more fascinating and, until recently, relatively little-known migrants is Eleonora's falcon (*Falco eleonorae*), a species somewhat resembling the peregrine but with dimorphic plumage and considerably longer wings, tail, and tarsi. Dr. David A. Bannerman in his *Birds of the Atlantic Islands* gives an excellent summary of all that was known of this species up to the early 1960's.[9] Most of the observations were those of Captain Polatzek, who studied this species in the Canary Islands between the years 1902 and 1905, and subsequently those of Richard Vaughan, who observed these falcons on Mogador Island off Morocco and also in the Mediterranean. Quite recently a young German ornithologist, Hartmut Walter, spent two years working on this species in the eastern Mediterranean so as to provide a rather complete picture of its life history, its migratory pattern, and, more especially, its remarkable relationship to the migration of passerines.[10]

[7]Cameron, R. A. D., *et al.* 1967.
[8]Grossman, M. L., and J. Hamlet. 1964.
[9]Bannerman, D. A. 1963.
[10]Walter, H. 1968a, 1968b.

The majority of Eleonora's falcons nest on a few islands in the eastern Mediterranean where there are estimated to be no more than three thousand pairs. Small numbers have been recorded from the Canary archipelago and a few other islands off the northwest coast of Africa. The earliest that these birds are seen around the nesting islands is May, and most of them do not arrive until August. Unlike most falconiforms, this species is semicolonial, with many pairs sometimes nesting on a small rocky islet close to one another. Their peculiar nesting season, when most other Northern Hemisphere species are finished with reproductive activity, is correlated with their food habits. One of the first clues to this came with the discovery of large numbers of bodies and feathers of small land birds around these falcons' nests on a rocky island where land birds are essentially absent.

Dr. Walter's studies have now shown that Eleonora's falcons secure their food by capturing passerine migrants several thousand feet in the air over the sea. The small birds have nowhere to escape to, and as they pass by in large numbers in migration in August and September, they provide the food for the falcons. It has been estimated that these falcons capture close to one million passerines during the migratory period. This, however, is a small percentage of the estimated one billion migrants that move over the Mediterranean area in passage between Europe and Africa.

The completion of the nesting season in early October by Eleonora's falcons is followed by their departure from their nesting islands by the end of that month. This also is the end of the migration season for most small land birds. From the end of October until the following summer, these falcons are known only from the island of Madagascar, which seems to be their major wintering ground. It is possible that the birds from the islands off northwest Africa may winter somewhere in southwest Africa, but to date there are no records of this.

CUCKOOS

Cuckoos are related to the plantain-eaters or touracos of Africa. The two families to which they belong, consisting of 127 species and 19 species, respectively, constitute the order Cuculiformes. The touracos are sedentary birds of the forest and lack the ability to carry on extended flight. Some members of the cuckoo family, such as the American roadrunners, are poor flyers and travel largely on foot. Typical cuckoos, however, are arboreal and many of them are capable of flying long distances. This is particularly true of species in temperate zones, where most cuckoos are migratory. The yellow-billed cuckoo (*Coccyzus americanus*) and black-billed cuckoo (*Coccyzus erythropthalmus*) of North America both winter in South America. The common cuckoo (*Cuculus canorus*) of Europe migrates to central Africa, while the same species farther east in Asia winters in the islands of southeastern Asia.

One of the more remarkable migrations is made by the shining cuckoo (*Chalcites lucidus*), which breeds in New Zealand and Australia. The New Zealand birds make a transequatorial flight over water of more than two thousand miles to the Solomon Islands, where they winter. Lesser migrations are made by cuckoos in South Africa and Madagascar.

NIGHTJARS

The largest family of the order Caprimulgiformes, the Caprimulgidae, consists of a group of essentially nocturnal birds whose cryptic coloration resembles that of owls. Nearly seventy species of so-called nightjars are found in various parts of the Americas, Africa, and the Eurasian continent. All are insect eaters, and those that live away from the warm equatorial regions of the world are migratory. The most extensive migration is made by the common nighthawk (*Chordeiles minor*) of North America, which may be found as far north as Alaska and Newfoundland in summer. Common nighthawks winter from Colombia and Venezuela to Argentina. The European nightjar (*Caprimulgus europaeus*) moves southward to central Africa. The pennant-winged nightjar (*Semeiophorus vexillarius*) breeds during the rainy season in southern Africa. Toward the end of summer in February and March, when the dry season comes and insects get scarce, members of this species move north to the savanna areas of central Africa, where they remain until spring.

HUMMINGBIRDS

The smallest avian migrants are some species of hummingbirds. These are members of the New World family Trochilidae, which is largely confined to tropical and subtropical zones. Over two-thirds of the more than three hundred species are found in the northern half of South America. A single species reaches Alaska, and only one species occurs in eastern North America. Nearly sixty species occur in Mexico and Central America.

The most extensive migrant in the family is the rufous hummingbird (*Selasphorus rufus*), which ranges farther north than any other member. Its breeding range extends from about latitude 61° N. in Alaska and in the Yukon Territory south to extreme northern California. The farthest inland that it has been recorded nesting is western Montana. Adult males arrive in the southern part of the breeding range in Oregon and Washington by early March and are followed by the females several weeks later. The males also precede the females on the southward migration, which begins very early. Males moving southward may be seen in the central Sierra Nevada·of California by the middle or latter part of June. Since the females do the nest building, incubating, and caring for the young, it is not surprising that they stay behind. The rufous hummingbird winters in west central Mexico, principally in the states of Zacatecas, Jalisco, Michoacan, and Mexico.

Closely related to the rufous hummingbird, and migratory within most of its range, is the Allen's hummingbird (*Selasphorus sasin*). The ranges of the two species overlap very slightly in southwestern Oregon and northwestern California. The Allen's hummingbird is restricted to a narrow coastal strip from southern Oregon to Ventura County in southern California during the spring and summer months. A resident population of this species occurs on some of the islands of the Santa Barbara group and is known to breed on San Clemente and Santa Barbara islands. It has been accorded separate subspecific status and is known as *Selasphorus sasin sedentarius*. The mainland population is migratory.

Allen's hummingbirds winter in the coastal areas of extreme southern California, the northern half of the peninsula of Baja California, and possibly on the mainland of northwestern Mexico. They are the first summer visitants to appear in northern California. By mid-February the buzzy noise of the males may be heard in the San Francisco Bay region, and the females appear soon after. Nesting begins early, and as in other hummingbirds, the female is the sole guardian of her two white eggs and the young that emerge from them. The males are kept away from the nesting territory by the females. Two broods and occasionally even three are produced in a single season.[11] The southward movement begins in July, and by late August or September only an occasional straggler is seen.

[11]Lilly, D. F., and R. T. Orr. 1959.

A third member of this genus, the broad-tailed hummingbird (*Selasphorus platycercus*), is also migratory. It breeds in the mountains of the Great Basin region of western North America and winters in west central Mexico, principally in the states of Zacatecas, Jalisco, Mexico, and Guerrero. The northward movement of this hummingbird is in late March and April. This is later than that of the other two species of *Selasphorus* previously mentioned. The breeding range of the broad-tailed hummingbird, however, is subject to intense cold and long winters and therefore is not suitable for early nesting, which, however, is possible in the coastal regions frequented by the Allen's and rufous hummingbirds.

Very extensive migrations are made by the tiny calliope hummingbird (*Stellula calliope*), which is the smallest species of bird in North America. The average weight for this species is three grams, yet it is capable of migrating from northern British Columbia south to Mexico City, a distance of over three thousand miles. The calliope hummingbird is a species of the mountains of western North America, where it nests from Alberta and British Columbia south to the Sierra San Pedro Martir in northern Baja California. It may nest as high as the timberline, at elevations of over eleven thousand feet. In the southern part of the breeding range, spring arrivals may appear early in March, but in the north they are generally not seen until May. As with most other migrant species of hummingbirds, the males are first to leave. In the central Sierra Nevada, Grinnell and Storer reported that no males were seen after the end of June.[12] The females and the young of the year depart later. The winter range is principally in the Mexican states of Michoacan, Guerrero, and Mexico.

PASSERINE MIGRANTS

In the Eurasian continental area most of the smaller birds move southward to tropical Africa and to a lesser extent to India and Malaysia. In winter, Central America is teeming with passerine birds that nest throughout Canada and the United States. A few examples of some of the major groups of passerine migrants follow.

TYRANT FLYCATCHERS. The Tyrannidae is a large New World family of insect-eating birds containing over 360 species. Representatives may be found from Canada to southern South America, but the

[12]Grinnell, J., and T. I. Storer. 1924.

great metropolis for this group lies in the tropical lowlands of Mexico, Central, and northern South America.

With very few exceptions, flycatchers outside of tropical and sub-tropical regions are migratory and move to more favorable areas nearer the equator when flying insects become scarce in autumn. Most tyrant flycatchers migrate at night like the majority of other insectivorous passerines. There are, nevertheless, some exceptions seen among king-birds of the genus *Tyrannus*. These birds are diurnal migrants, traveling in loose flocks. The eastern kingbird (*T. tyrannus*), which nests as far north as southern Canada, moves southward in this manner to Central and northern South America. Those who have observed these birds in migration say that they travel mostly in the early morning and late afternoon. In certain wide-ranging species like the western flycatcher (*Empidonax difficilis*), which breeds from Alaska south to southern Mexico, the northern part of the population moves south to winter with resident members of the same species. Other species of the genus *Empidonax* are entirely migratory. The Acadian flycatcher (*E. virescens*) of eastern United States and southern Ontario winters in eastern Colombia and eastern Ecuador.

SWALLOWS. Swallows are essentially worldwide in distribution, being found nearly everywhere there are flying insects. Those that inhabit more northern regions engage in marked migratory movements. The bank swallow (*Riparia riparia*) is a circumpolar species, breeding in Europe, northern and central Asia, and in North America from Alaska and northern Canada south to southern United States. The Eurasian populations winter in central and southern Africa and southern India, and the North American birds move southward to Brazil, Bolivia, and Peru.

The barn swallow (*Hirundo rustica*) occurs in summer throughout Europe, northwestern Africa, northern Asia, and most of North America from Alaska to south central Mexico. The Eurasian swallows winter in tropical and southern Africa, India, and islands in the Indian Ocean. The North American barn swallows winter in South America from Colombia south to Brazil, Argentina, and Chile.

Medway and Nisbet have summarized the movements of barn swal-lows in eastern Asia on the basis of returns from tens of thousands of wintering individuals banded in northern Malaya.[13] Some of these banded swallows were found nesting at high latitudes in Siberia from

[13]Medway, Lord, and I. C. T. Nisbet. 1968.

the vicinity of Lake Baikal east and south to North Korea. The distance between the wintering and nesting areas for some was 2,500 miles.

An extensive migration is made by the cliff swallow (*Petrochelidon pyrrhonota*) of North America, which breeds from Alaska south to southern Mexico. The winter range extends from Brazil to central Argentina. A very similar migratory pattern is shown by the purple martin (*Progne subis*), whose summer range extends from southern Canada to central Mexico. This species winters in the Amazon Valley of Brazil.

The summer and winter ranges of some swallows overlap. For example, the violet-green swallow (*Tachycineta thalassina*) and the tree swallow (*Iridoprocne bicolor*) both summer as far north as Alaska. The southern end of the breeding area for the violet-green is southern Mexico, while the tree swallow nests as far south as southern United States. Both winter from southern California to Central America. The rough-winged swallow (*Stelgidopteryx ruficollis*) breeds from Canada south to Brazil. The Central and South American rough-winged swallows are nonmigratory, but those in Canada and the United States move south of the Mexican border to winter.

Swallows are diurnal migrants that fly in loose groups. These groups, however, may be composed of large numbers of birds. Swallows forage in flight and therefore, like swifts, are able to secure their food while migrating. Most North American swallows begin their southward migration by mid- or late August, but in northern Europe this movement appears to start earlier. Some individuals begin leaving in July.

Dorst has pointed out that banding records show that swallows nesting in the British Isles tend to winter in southern Africa, those that breed in northern and central Europe go to western and central Africa, and swallows from western Europe go southeast through Egypt and Arabia to eastern Africa.[14]

THRUSHES. The family Turdidae is large and cosmopolitan. Its members are so closely related to Old World warblers and Old World flycatchers that some taxonomists regard all of these as belonging to the same family. All are essentially insectivorous. The thrushes, however, are much more widespread than the other two groups. While many species are found in tropical parts of the world, there are a number of thrushes that breed in the northern coniferous and deciduous forests and even on the tundra of North America, Europe, and Asia. One of the

[14]Dorst, J. 1962.

latter species is the wheatear (*Oenanthe oenanthe*), which is Holarctic in distribution. In North America wheatears nest from northern Alaska east to Labrador. In winter these birds, like those from the Palearctic, migrate principally to tropical Africa, with smaller numbers in southern Asia east to the Philippines.

The common thrushes of northern North America belonging to the genus *Hylocichla* (*Catharus* according to some authors) all move southward in winter. Most widespread is the hermit thrush (*H. guttata*), which ranges from Alaska east to Labrador and south in the mountains of the Pacific coast to southern California. Hermit thrushes winter as far south as Guatemala, although some of the more northern birds of this species may winter in southern Canada.

OLD WORLD WARBLERS. Most of the Old World warblers (family Sylviidae) that breed in the Palearctic are migratory. Many species found in summer in Europe or western Asia winter in Africa. Savi's warbler (*Locustella luscinioides*) breeds locally from central Europe south to northern Africa and east to western Siberia. The winter range of this species is thought to be tropical and northeastern Africa. The river warbler (*Locustella fluviatilis*) has a very similar summer and winter range. Pallas' grasshopper warbler (*Locustella certhiola*) breeds from western Siberia east to Kamchatka, Manchuria, Korea, and Japan and winters in India and Malaysia. Similar migratory movements are followed by the several species of reed warblers of the genus *Acrocephalus* that breed in northern Asia.

There are a number of warblers of the genus *Sylvia* that breed in northern and central Europe. Included are the barred warbler (*S. nisoria*), the garden warbler (*S. borin*), the blackcap (*S. atricapilla*), and the lesser whitethroat (*S. curruca*). All of these species winter principally in Africa. Farther east in Asia other members of the same genus, such as the desert lesser whitethroat (*S. minula*) and Hume's lesser whitethroat (*S. althaea*), move to warmer parts of southern Asia in winter.

Some of the more migratory of Old World warblers are members of the genus *Phylloscopus*. The willow warbler (*P. trochilus*), which is so widespread over northern Eurasia in summer, migrates to tropical and southern Africa. Even willow warblers from eastern Siberia are believed to make this extensive migration. The wood warbler (*P. sibilatrix*), which breeds in northern European latitudes and western Siberia as well as in some of the higher mountains farther south, winters in tropical Africa as far south as the equator. Some other members of this genus breeding in central and eastern Asia move farther south on that continent in autumn.

OLD WORLD FLYCATCHERS. There are about ten recognized species of flycatchers belonging to the genus *Ficedula* that breed in various parts of Europe and Asia. All those populations inhabiting northern areas where temperatures drop markedly in the winter season migrate southward. A good example is the pied flycatcher (*F. hypoleuca*), which ranges from western Europe to western Siberia and from as far north as 70° N. latitude south to northern Africa. With the exception of the northern Africa population, most pied flycatchers winter in the equatorial grasslands of tropical Africa, some reaching the lower Congo. Eastern Palearctic species such as the Mugimaki flycatcher (*F. mugimaki*) of eastern Siberia and Manchuria and the Korean flycatcher (*F. zanthopygia*) winter as far south as Malaysia, Sumatra, and Java.

The spotted flycatcher (*Muscicapa striata*) is the most widely distributed species of this family, ranging from western Europe east to Mongolia and from 70° N. latitude south to northern Africa, Asia Minor, and the western Himalayas. The northern migratory populations of the spotted flycatcher from Europe and western Asia winter as far south as tropical and southern Africa. More easterly populations winter in Arabia and northwestern India. Those inhabiting extreme southern Europe and northern Africa are largely resident.

PIPITS AND WAGTAILS. The family Motacillidae is worldwide and contains fifty-four species. Some kinds are resident, particularly those found in Africa. Being largely insectivorous, all of the arctic and north temperate species migrate southward in winter. The water pipit (*Anthus spinoletta*) nests on the tundra and at alpine heights on mountains around the Northern Hemisphere. North American water pipits winter southward as far as Mexico and Central America. Northern Europe water pipits winter in central and southern Europe, with a few reaching northern Africa. Those from northern Asia winter principally in China and the plains of northern India west to the Near East and Egypt. There are a number of other species of pipits with much more restricted summer ranges in the Palearctic, and there is one, Sprague's pipit (*Anthus spragueii*), with a summer range in western North America. Wintering pipits aggregate in flocks, usually in grasslands.

The yellow wagtail (*Motacilla flava*) is another Holarctic species that nests on the northern tundra and moors. In winter this species is found in southern Africa, India, Malaysia, and occasionally New Guinea. It is interesting to note that the yellow wagtails breeding in northwestern Alaska do not migrate south in North America but cross over to Asia, from where they probably came after the end of the late Pleistocene. They are presumed to winter in Malaysia and the Philippines along with stock from eastern Asia.

VIREOS. These are members of a New World family of insectivorous birds whose distribution is centered in the tropics from southern Mexico to northern South America. There are, however, some species that occur in the temperate parts of both North and South America, and nearly all these migrate toward the equator at the end of the breeding season. The red-eyed vireo (*Vireo olivaceus*) merits special comment because of its very extensive range, stretching from Canada to Brazil and Argentina. Red-eyed vireos breeding in northern North America move south to winter, and those breeding in southern South America move northward for the winter season. These vireos from either end of the range of the species, therefore, winter in areas where other members of the same species are resident the year round.

WOOD WARBLERS. The Parulidae is a New World family of birds consisting of the wood warblers and bananaquits. It is estimated to contain about 119 species, of which 109 are warblers. These warblers are distributed throughout North and South America, and all are insectivorous. The 59 species that breed in North America, north of Mexico, are almost all migratory to some degree. In this respect, as well as ecologically and geographically, they are the counterpart of the Old World warblers belonging to the widespread family Sylviidae.

Some species have a very extensive range. The yellow warbler (*Dendroica petechia*) breeds from north central Alaska to northern South America. By way of contrast, Kirtland's warbler (*Dendroica kirtlandii*) nests in an area no more than eighty miles in diameter in the pine woods of north central Michigan. Its limited range, however, in no way inhibits migratory movements. By the end of August or, at the latest, early September, the entire population of this species has left Michigan for the Bahamas, where individuals begin arriving in mid-September. By late April they are on their way via Florida, Georgia, and South Carolina to the jack-pine country of north central Michigan, where they arrive in May.

The great majority of warblers that have fairly extensive ranges in the United States or Canada during the summer season spend the winter in Mexico and Central America. A few go as far south as Panama, Colombia, Venezuela, and Ecuador. Anyone from the United States visiting southern Mexico in winter will feel right at home with the many species of warblers he knows as summer residents farther north. A few species, particularly those that nest in southeastern United States, winter in the islands of the Caribbean. Bachman's warbler (*Vermivora bachmanii*), which formerly nested from Arkansas south to Louisiana and east to South Carolina and Georgia, wintered in Cuba.

The cerulean warbler (*Dendroica cerulea*), a bird of the hardwood forests of the eastern half of the United States, probably winters farther south than any of the other northern species of wood warblers. It has been taken in Bolivia and regularly winters in the valleys of the Andes from central Colombia through Ecuador to southern Peru.

The distance traveled by wood warblers in migration may vary considerably within species. The pine warbler (*Dendroica pinus*) breeds from western Canada in Alberta south to Florida and east to the Atlantic coast in suitable deciduous and coniferous forests. The Florida population (*D. p. florida*) is resident, whereas the northern population (*D. p. pinus*) winters in the southern Mississippi Valley, the Gulf coast, and southeastern United States.

The blackpoll warbler (*Dendroica striata*), which breeds from Alaska east across Canada to Labrador and New England, has one of the longest migrations of any member of this family. It winters in northern South America south to northern Brazil. In migrating to its winter range, however, this bird does not make a direct flight but rather follows a zigzag course. According to Murray, who has obtained considerable evidence, warblers from western North America fly southeast toward the Atlantic coastal plain, then turn to the southwest and fly to Georgia and Florida.[15] From here these birds fly southeast, island-hopping along the Antilles to South America.

ICTERIDS. The Icteridae is another New World family. Its ninety-four species include the grackles, blackbirds, orioles, meadowlarks, bobolinks, cowbirds, troupials, oropendolas, and caciques. Although mostly tropical, the family is represented from Alaska south to Patagonia and the Falkland Islands. Most species of the temperate and north temperate parts of North America migrate southward for varying dis-

[15]Murray, B. G., Jr. 1965, 1966a.

The migration routes of a North American songbird, the bobolink (*Dolichonyx oryzivorus*). (After Hamilton, 1962)

tances to spend the winter in tropical or subtropical zones. The bobolink (*Dolichonyx oryzivorus*) makes a most remarkable transequatorial migration. Bobolinks nest in southern Canada, from British Columbia east to Nova Scotia, and south into northern United States, from northeastern California east to Pennsylvania. The species winters in eastern Bolivia, western Brazil, Paraguay, and northern Argentina. The maximum distance between the northernmost breeding area and the southernmost wintering ground is approximately six thousand miles.

Little is known about the early part of the northward migration of bobolinks except that they reach the northern shores of South America in April. The main northward flight is directly across the Caribbean to Jamaica, a distance of about five hundred miles, then ninety miles to Cuba, and another 150 miles to Florida. Some make a trans-Gulf migration from Yucatan to Louisiana. Most bobolinks arrive in the United States by late April or early May.

The birds nesting farthest north begin their fall migration in late July. The direction of flight is eastward to the Atlantic and then south to Florida for the majority of the migrants. A few fly to Guyana by way of the Antilles. The majority, however, go by way of Cuba, Jamaica, across the Gulf of Mexico to Yucatan, and down through Central America. A small number may go down the west coast of South America, as the species has been reported in Ecuador, the Galapagos Islands, and Peru.

TANAGERS. These are members of the Thraupidae, which, like the Icteridae, is confined to the New World; 218 of the 222 known species of tanagers inhabit tropical or subtropical regions and are essentially nonmigratory. Four species, however, have invaded temperate to north temperate parts of North America, and some have extended migrations. The western tanager (*Piranga ludoviciana*) breeds in the mountains of western North America from Alaska south to Arizona and Texas. The winter range extends from northwestern Mexico south to Costa Rica. The distance between summer and winter ranges of the scarlet tanager (*Piranga olivacea*) is much greater. This species nests from southeastern Canada south to the Carolinas, Alabama, and northern Texas. The winter range extends from Colombia to Peru and Bolivia. The summer tanager (*Piranga rubra*) and hepatic tanager (*Piranga flava*) of southern United States and northern Mexico both winter farther south in Mexico. These four species appear to have originated in tropical America, hence their movements southward in autumn bring them close to their ancestral home.

9

MIGRATIONS OF WATER BIRDS

Included in this chapter are selected examples of migratory patterns shown by certain species of marine birds, waterfowl, and shorebirds. Many of these breed in the far northern or southern latitudes and after their breeding season is over move rapidly toward the opposite end of the globe. A considerable number, therefore, are transequatorial migrants.

PENGUINS

Few birds are found in Antarctica in winter with the exception of the emperor penguin (*Aptenodytes forsteri*). This is the largest of the penguins, with a standing height of more than three feet and a weight of up to ninety pounds. It is also the only bird that is strictly antarctic at all seasons of the year, rarely venturing north of the Antarctic Circle. Its southern limits are said to be around the front of the Ross Ice Shelf, which is approximately 78° S. latitude, and its northern limits are determined by the limits of the pack ice except for its occurrence in the South Orkneys. Its occurrence there is attributed to the northward extension of the Palmer Peninsula (Graham Land) and the archipelago that curves northeast to the South Orkneys.

The breeding conditions of the emperor penguin are said to involve the worst climate endured by any living species of bird. The eggs are laid in late June, which is the middle of the antarctic winter, when the temperature may get as low as -80° Fahrenheit. The eggs are incubated on the feet of the adults of both sexes and even by nonbreeding birds if they have the opportunity. Emperor penguins are reported to be high in prolactin, a pituitary hormone that stimulates brooding, during the

135

Emperor penguins (*Aptenodytes forsteri*) in juvenal plumage, Bay of Whales, Ross Sea, Antarctica. *Photographed on 2nd Byrd Antarctic Expedition by Thomas C. Poulter.*

reproductive season. The incubation period ranges from sixty-two to sixty-eight days, and the young develop slowly and are brooded during the early weeks of life. By October or November the emperor penguins start a rather limited migration to the north, mainly on rafts of ice that break free. By January or very early February the young birds are able to care for themselves and go into the water. After a period of gorging on euphausiids, fish, and squid, and after having gone through the molt, they move southward by swimming to the breeding grounds, where they arrive by May.

Adélie penguins (*Pygoscelis adeliae*), unlike the emperor penguins, engage in fairly extensive migrations.[1] During the southern winter they stay in open water north of the pack ice, where they feed on krill (*Euphausia*), the small crustacean that is so important a food for baleen whales. In October, as spring approaches, they swim southward, sometimes as

[1]Emlen, J. T., and R. L. Penney. 1964.

much as four hundred miles, to their traditional nesting colonies on the antarctic continent. In the Cape Hallett region these colonies are on the ice about ten to twenty kilometers from the sea, according to Dr. Dietland Müller-Schwarze.[2]

PETRELS, FULMARS, SHEARWATERS,

AND THEIR ALLIES

There are a few antarctic birds that winter around the edge of the pack ice. The snow petrel (*Pagodroma nivea*) is one of these. It is circumpolar and breeds on South Georgia, the South Orkneys, the South Shetlands, the Antarctic Archipelago, and at a number of localities along the shore as well as inland on the antarctic continent. It winters principally along the edge of the pack ice and rarely ranges north of 50°

[2]Müller-Schwarze, D. 1967.

Adélie penguins (*Pygoscelis adeliae*) coming back from sea to the colony during the early part of the breeding season. They are probably females returning to take their turn at incubating. *Photograph taken at Hallett Station, Antarctica, during the 1964–65 season by Dietland Müller-Schwartze.*

S. latitude or outside the limits of the antarctic life zone. A somewhat similar movement that is merely associated with seasonal extension of the pack ice is made by the antarctic petrel (*Thalassoica antarctica*). Several kinds of penguins behave in a similar manner. In contrast, the giant fulmar (*Macronectes giganteus*) and the silver-gray fulmar (*Fulmarus glacialis*) nest around the shores and islands of Antarctica but regularly migrate north to 30° S. latitude, and along the west coast of South America the species move northward with the cool Humboldt Current in winter to within six degrees of the equator off Peru.

The Atlantic subspecies of Wilson's petrel (*Oceanites oceanicus oceanicus*) is a transequatorial migrant that nests in the Antarctic. Its breeding range extends along the mainland of the antarctic continent at South Victoria Land, King George V Land, Kaiser Wilhelm II Land, and Enderby Land, as well as on the Palmer Peninsula (Graham Land), South Georgia, the South Orkneys, and the South Shetlands. After the nesting season is over, some of these petrels move north and winter off the west coast of Africa and Europe as far as the British Isles. The majority winter in the western Atlantic off the east coast of South America, in the Gulf of Mexico, and off the east coast of North America almost to Baffin Land.

The Pacific population (*Oceanites oceanicus chilensis*), which breeds on islands near Cape Horn, does not engage in such an extensive migration. These petrels winter in the eastern Pacific along the coast of Chile and Peru.

The Atlantic population of the common or Manx shearwater (*Puffinus puffinus puffinus*) is another transequatorial marine migrant. These birds breed principally on islands along the coasts of England, Ireland, Scotland, Iceland, in the Faeroes, and along the west coast of Europe from northwestern France to Madeira and the Azores. Formerly the species also bred on the Isle of Man, from which the vernacular name of this shearwater is derived, and in Bermuda. A Pacific coast population (*P. p. opisthomelas*), commonly called the black-vented shearwater, nests on islands off the coast of Baja California, Mexico.

In the Atlantic the Manx shearwaters move south after the breeding season, adults leaving in August and young by early September. By mid- or late September most of the population is south of the equator. The wintering grounds are off the coasts of Brazil, Uruguay, and Argentina between 4° and 38° S. latitude, most of the birds occurring in the more southern latitudes. Few Manx shearwaters have been seen in this

region in the months of January and February, and it has been speculated that they may move even farther south to better feeding grounds in
the area of the Falkland Current, which flows northeast from the tip of
South America. The area is remote, and the direction of both the current
and the westerly winds would prevent the drifting of any casualties toward shore, where they might be picked up. By March they begin to
appear in numbers in the breeding areas of the North Atlantic.

A. Landsborough Thomson, in his excellent account of the movements
of Manx shearwaters in the Atlantic, based on very extensive banding
operations, suggested several benefits to be derived from such extensive
transequatorial migrations.[3] These are (p. 136) "(a) more abundant food
of the kind to which the birds are adapted in higher northern latitudes;
(b) better climatic conditions for obtaining food and for life generally;
and (c) longer hours of daylight for obtaining food."

The young of this species do not return to the European breeding
grounds at the end of the first year. A few of these first-year birds have
been found summering off the coast of eastern North America.[4] In the
second year a few of the young return to the breeding grounds, but not
until June or July. They return somewhat earlier the third year and are
present from the beginning of the nesting season in the fourth year. It is
thought that the majority of Manx shearwaters do not breed until their
fifth year.

There are no extensive transequatorial migrations by land birds of the
Southern Hemisphere that are comparable to those of many species of
the Northern Hemisphere. This has been attributed to the relatively
small land masses available in the Southern Hemisphere and the correspondingly small avian breeding population. This does not apply to
marine species, however. One of the most remarkable migrations is that
of the slender-billed shearwater (*Puffinus tenuirostris*).

The slender-billed shearwater is one of several species of the genus
Puffinus that are referred to as mutton birds in Australia and New Zealand. It breeds in huge colonies along the south Australian and Tasmanian coasts as well as on islands between these two areas in Bass Strait.
The adults arrive at the breeding areas in October, and laying commences in November. Banding studies have shown that females do not
breed until they are five years old and that males do not breed until the
age of seven. The single white egg is laid in a burrow, and both parents

[3]Thomson, A. L. 1965.
[4]Post, P. W. 1967.

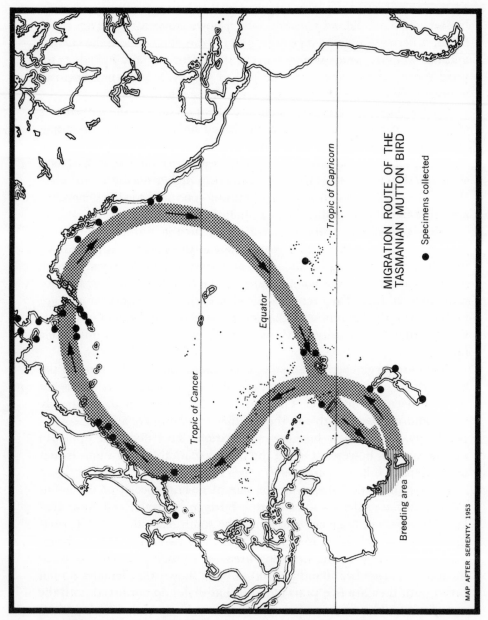

Migration route of the Tasmanian mutton bird. (After Serventy, 1953)

assist in the incubation, which takes fifty-two to fifty-five days. Each incubates, without food or water, for two weeks at a time.

The young are fed regurgitated food and become very fat. They leave the nest burrow at night when they are about fourteen weeks old and follow the same migration route as their parents. Their flight first takes them east and then northeast to pass northwest of New Zealand after which they continue up to the New Hebrides. From here they veer to the northwest, pass over the equator, and then north to the east coast of Japan. The route then is past the coast of Korea and across the North Pacific Ocean to Alaska. By late summer they move down the Pacific coast of North America and then they take a course diagonally across the Pacific to the east coast of Australia and arrive back at the nesting area. The young do not return to the place where they hatched until they are several years of age.

This migration is an enormous one that looks like a great figure eight, with the upper circle of the figure much larger than the lower one. It appears that food is an important factor. Shrimplike crustaceans, squid, and small fish are necessary in large quantity to maintain such vast numbers of birds.

The sooty shearwater (*Puffinus griseus*) also nests in the Southern Hemisphere but winters in the North Atlantic and North Pacific. In August it occurs in large numbers along the Pacific coast of North America.

Not all shearwaters are migratory. Those that nest in tropical or subtropical waters are not known to leave the general vicinity of the nesting area. This appears to be true of the various forms of Audubon's shearwater (*Puffinus lherminieri*), which breeds in Bermuda, islands of the Caribbean, the Cape Verde Islands, certain equatorial islands of the Pacific, including the Galapagos, and in the Indian Ocean. Even the Pacific coastal population of the Manx shearwater (*Puffinus puffinus opisthomelas*) spreads out only a few hundred miles to the north and south of its breeding islands along the northwest coast of Mexico after the nesting period is over.

Most albatrosses nest on oceanic islands, principally in the Southern Hemisphere. Outside of the nesting season they wander very widely over the ocean, usually following trade winds to areas where food for such pelagic species is abundant. They are the world's greatest gliders and can cover long distances by making use of air currents. The extent that young black-footed albatrosses (*Diomedea nigripes*) wander during their first year is seen in the recovery of an individual off the northwest coast of

Baja California, Mexico, on December 11, 1966, that was banded as a chick at Midway Island in the Hawaiian archipelago on March 2, 1966.[5] In slightly more than nine months between the time of banding and subsequent recovery, it had traveled at least 4,700 miles from west to east.

STORKS AND HERONS

Storks belong to the order Ciconiiformes, which also includes the various kinds of herons, egrets, bitterns, ibises, and their relatives. The great majority are associated with water, and some species in the Northern Hemisphere engage in fairly extensive migrations, although with many, the movements are more wandering in nature.

The white storks (*Ciconia ciconia*) of Europe have a migratory pattern that in many respects resembles that of European raptors. This is attributable to their manner of flight. Most members of the family Ciconiidae fly by means of regular flapping of the wings. The white stork soars and depends largely on thermals and updrafts to attain altitude, much like a hawk or vulture. Because of this, members of the species tend to avoid water-crossings, where thermals are lacking and where considerably more energy entailed in flapping would be required. Consequently, the movement of white storks from northern and eastern Europe in the fall migration is to the semiarid southeast, where there are thermals. Most of the migration is across the Bosporus to Asia Minor, then down the Jordan Valley past the Dead Sea and Gulf of Aden, and across the Gulf of Suez to the valley of the Nile. From there storks spread out as far as South Africa. This route entails a minimum of water-crossings. The spring migration to the north is the reverse of that of autumn. A smaller number of storks from western Europe migrate southwest in fall to the Iberian Peninsula and cross the Strait of Gibraltar to Morocco. From there they move south and east in Africa.

WATERFOWL

Arctic and subarctic marshlands as well as prairie potholes are the principal breeding grounds for waterfowl in the Northern Hemisphere. Since these wetlands freeze in winter, there is a vast southward movement of ducks and geese to a more favorable environment for this season.

In Europe the principal breeding grounds of migratory waterfowl are

[5]Hubbs, C. L. 1968a.

found in the Scandinavian and Baltic countries as well as in northern Russia. In migration most species fly to the southwest so as to arrive in western and southwestern Europe. Some continue south as far as central Africa. Birds from Iceland migrate southeast to reach wintering grounds in the British Isles and continental Europe.

In North America, waterfowl employ the four major continental flyways, although the Mississippi Flyway is most heavily utilized by dabbling ducks. Diving ducks show much less restriction to the central continental flyways and move south in large numbers along the Pacific and Atlantic flyways as well.

The most abundant North American duck is the mallard (*Anas platyrhynchos*). Dr. Frank Bellrose has estimated that of the approximately 17,500,000 ducks that migrate southward each year east of the Rocky Mountains, about 40 percent are of this species.[6] Mallards, principally from the northern Great Plains, winter from the northern boundary of the United States south to the extensive Gulf coast marshes.

The pintail (*Anas acuta*) is a more extensive migrant. A part of the Alaskan population in North America migrates to Hawaii to winter. This involves an overseas flight of a minimum of two thousand miles. Other pintails from farther east in arctic Canada move south as far as Central America, although many winter farther north in western United States and the southern Mississippi Valley. Blue-winged teal (*Anas discors*) are also extensive migrants. Birds nesting in central Canada have been taken in winter in Colombia and Venezuela.

A number of interesting migrations are to be seen among North American geese. Ross' goose (*Chen rossii*) has an unusual migratory pattern whose details have been discovered only in recent years. It was first reported by Samuel Hearne in his expedition in search of the Coppermine River northwest of Hudson Bay in 1770, although the species was not described until 1861, when John Cassin named it after Bernard Rogan Ross of the Hudson's Bay Company. Subsequently it became well known for its restricted winter range, which is in the Central Valley of California. The nesting area, however, was unknown until 1938, when Angus Gavin, the first white man to penetrate the Perry River of the Northwest Territories, found its summer range. Even now its breeding grounds are not completely known, although it is believed that all the Ross' geese in existence nest in the Perry River drainage, which flows into Queen Maud Gulf. The total population, based on counts made in the

[6]Bellrose, F. C. 1968.

wintering ground, is between thirty-five and forty thousand individuals, according to Ryder, who has published the most complete account of the breeding biology of this species.[7]

Ross' geese arrive on the nesting grounds in the arctic tundra between the last week in May and the first week in June, depending on weather conditions. Their route from central California, according to Ryder, based on 12,531 sightings in 1964, takes them through Oregon in March, Montana in April, and Alberta in May. Egg laying takes place in June, the young hatch in early July, and within several weeks large postnuptial flocks are formed and the molt takes place. By the end of August, all are capable of flight and ready for the southward migration to central California.

The white-fronted goose (*Anser albifrons*) is another species whose geographic races show some interesting migratory patterns. Four sub-species are currently recognized. *Anser a. albifrons* breeds in the arctic of northern Europe and northern Asia and winters from England south to southern Europe, in central and southern Asia and in Egypt. *Anser a. frontalis* nests along the arctic coast of Alaska, northwestern Canada, and northeastern Asia. It winters on the Gulf coast of Louisiana and Texas, along the Pacific coast of western North America, and in China and Japan. The probable breeding range of what is commonly called the tule white-fronted goose (*Anser a. gambelli*) is Victoria Island in arctic Canada, according to Delacour.[8] This population is known in winter only in the Central Valley of California. *Anser a. flavirostris*, the fourth subspecies, nests in western Greenland. A part winters in Ireland, with a few birds reaching England. The remainder migrate to the southeast coast of the United States.

The blue goose (*Chen caerulescens*) is now believed by many to be con-specific with the snow goose (*Chen hyperborea*). It nests in Baffin Land, Southampton Island, on the west coast of Hudson Bay, and in the Perry River region. The wintering ground is along the coast of Louisiana, three thousand miles to the south. In autumn the migration routes take these birds along the east side of Hudson Bay, then directly southwest to Louisiana. In the spring the northern route is west of the Mississippi to southern Manitoba, from where, after a stopover, the direction of flight is east to James Bay, then northward once again to the nesting grounds.

[7]Ryder, J. P. 1967.
[8]Delacour, J. 1954.

PLATE 1. Wintering monarch butterflies *(Danaus plexippus)* clustering on a conifer along the central California coast. *Edward S. Ross.*

PLATE 2. Ladybird beetles *(Hippodamia convergens)* aggregated in a summer cluster. *Edward S. Ross.*

PLATE 3. Young grunion *(Leuresthes tenuis)* hatch with the first series of high tides following the laying of the eggs. *Anthony Mercieca.*

PLATE *4.* The giant toad *(Bufo marinus)* of the American tropics seems to depend on visual clues for orientation upon being displaced. *Edward S. Ross.*

PLATE 5. Amphibians of the genus *Taricha,* including the rough-skinned newt *(T. granulosa),* have been found to possess remarkable homing abilities. *Nathan W. Cohen.*

PLATE 6. The emperor penguin *(Aptenodytes fosteri)* is one of the few birds to winter in Antarctica *John H. Tashjian.*

PLATE 7. The cattle egret *(Bulbulcus ibis)*, native to Africa and Eurasia, invaded the Western Hemisphere in the late nineteenth or early twentieth century. The group shown here is on an acacia at Chunga, Zambia. *Walter A. Sheppe.*

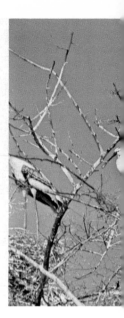

PLATE 8. A nesting pair of Abdim's storks *(Ciconia abdimii)* near Koro in southeastern Mali. This species breeds in equatorial Africa, then migrates south to winter. *Edward S. Ross.*

PLATE 11. Most of the Heermann gulls *(Larus heermanni)* of the world nest on Isla Raza in the north central part of the Gulf of California, Mexico. After the nesting season they make extensive movements north and south along the Pacific coast. *Robert T. Orr.*

PLATE 9. The spoonbills of Europe and Asia *(Platalea leucorodia)* winter in Africa and southern Asia. Photographed at Bharatpur. India. *Edward S. Ross.*

PLATE 10. A wintering male canvasback duck *(Aythya valisineria)* in central California. This species nests from Alaska south to northern United States but is most abundant in summer in the prairie marshes of Canada. *Rex Burress.*

PLATE 12. Isla Raza in the Gulf of California, Mexico, is the principal nesting ground for the elegant tern *(Thalasseus elegans),* which winters as far south as the coast of Chile. *Robert T. Orr.*

PLATE 13. The brown noddy tern *(Anoüs stolidus)* nests on tropical islands but outside of the breeding season it wanders widely over the ocean. *Cornelius G. Willis.*

PLATE 14. The parakeet auklet *(Cyclorrhynchus psittacula)* breeds on islands and along the mainland of Siberia and Alaska. In winter it migrates southward as far as Japan and central California. Photographed on St. Paul Island, Alaska. *Robert T. Orr.*

PLATE 15. A male ruby-throated hummingbird (*Archilochus colubris*). Many members of this species make a 500-mile nonstop flight across the Gulf of Mexico during migration. *Don Bleitz.*

PLATE 16. A female black-chinned hummingbird (*Archilochus alexandri*) settling on her nest to incubate. This species breeds locally in western North America from eastern Washington and northwestern Montana south to northwestern Mexico. It winters from extreme southern California to Guerrero and the Federal District of Mexico. *Don Bleitz.*

PLATE 17. The Steller sea lion (*Eumetopias jubata*) has definite seasonal movements along parts of the Pacific coast of North America. Shown here is a bull that has just been defeated by a harem master in a battle for territory on Año Nuevo Island, California. *Robert T. Orr.*

PLATE 18. The downward migration of the Canadian elk (*Cervus canadensis*) to lower elevations in autumn appears to be stimulated by snowfall. Two bulls are seen here in their summer habitat in Yellowstone National Park. *Clark Ross.*

PLATE 19. In East Africa the wildebeest (*Gorgon taurinus*) may engage in movements of as much as 200 miles to find favorable calving grounds where food and water are available. Photographed at Ngorongoro Crater in East Africa. *Lewis S. Rose.*

SHOREBIRDS, TERNS, AND GULLS

The birds considered in this group are all members of that very diversified avian order, the Charadriiformes. Some are resident, while others engage in the most extensive migrations known. For a number of kinds, such as many types of gulls, auks, and auklets, winter movements are more a sort of dispersal, with individuals, especially among some gulls, engaging in nomadic wanderings in search of food. Others have very specific migratory patterns.

One of the longest and most involved avian migrations is made by the American golden plover (*Pluvialis dominica*). There are two subspecific populations of this species. One of these, *P. d. dominica*, nests in the Canadian tundra from northern Baffin Land west to the vicinity of Point Barrow, Alaska. The other, *P. d. fulva*, occurs in summer in western Alaska and eastern Siberia. The golden plovers of northern Alaska and northern Canada fly east to Nova Scotia and Newfoundland, then move south over the Atlantic Ocean for about two thousand miles to the South American continent. They winter in Argentina, Uruguay, and southern Brazil. In the spring they move northwest to Central America, then to the Mississippi Valley and over the Great Plains and the Peace and Mackenzie river valleys to the arctic coast, from where they spread east and west to arrive at their nesting grounds. The major north-south axis of this elliptical round trip is about eight thousand miles, and the east-west axis, about two thousand miles. The annual round trip, therefore, may involve distances of sixteen thousand miles or more.

The western Alaskan population has quite a different migratory pattern. These birds appear to make a nonstop flight over the ocean to Hawaii; from there they move to various Pacific islands, some going as far south as New Zealand for the winter. Golden plovers from eastern Siberia move south to Malaya, India, Australia, Oceania, and even reach Africa.

The Eurasian golden plover (*P. apricaria*) does not have such an extensive migration. The species is resident in the British Isles, western Denmark, and northern Germany, but the birds from elsewhere in northern Europe and northern Asia winter chiefly in the areas surrounding the Mediterranean Sea. Unlike most of the American golden plovers, it does not cross the equator in migration.

The American golden plover makes the most spectacular trans-equatorial migrations of any wader, but there are other members of the order to which it belongs that also engage in some remarkable movements.

The white-rumped sandpiper (*Erolia fuscicollis*) is one such member. This species breeds from northern Alaska east across the Canadian Arctic to Baffin Land. The first southward movement begins in July but progresses slowly, with males in the lead. White-rumped sandpipers pass through the interior of Canada and the United States and go south to southern South America, where they occur from Paraguay to Tierra del Fuego as well as the Falkland Islands. There is even a record for South Georgia Island. The distance between the nesting area and the wintering grounds is nine thousand miles. The sandpipers leave the wintering area early in March, arrive in the United States in May, pass north through the plains states and Canada's Prairie Provinces, and arrive on the tundra to nest in June.

The migration of Baird's sandpiper (*Erolia bairdii*) is nearly as extensive as that of the white-rumped sandpiper. This species nests in Siberia, northern Alaska, arctic Canada, and northwestern Greenland. In migration it moves southward mainly through inland routes in August and September to South America, where it winters from the high Andes of Ecuador south to Tierra del Fuego at sea level. The northward migration through North America in April and May follows essentially the same route, though in reverse, as the autumn migration.

A somewhat different sort of migration is made by the sanderling (*Crocethia alba*), which is Holarctic in its breeding distribution. Sanderlings nest on some of the islands of arctic Canada, in Greenland, Spitsbergen, Franz Josef Land, and in parts of arctic Siberia. The southward migration is primarily along continental coastlines, although a few birds do go inland. The winter range includes southern Africa, Australia, South America as far as Argentina, and many of the islands of the Pacific. The northward migration in spring is principally coastal like the autumn migration.

The now extinct, or nearly extinct, Eskimo curlew (*Numenius borealis*) had a very extensive transequatorial migration, which contributed to its demise. This species bred from northern Alaska east to arctic Canada and wintered in southern South America east of the Andes from Brazil and Paraguay to southern Argentina. Its spring and fall migration routes were quite different. In the northward trip the curlews moved to northwestern South America, then made an overwater flight from Ecuador to Central America. From here they moved north as far as southern Mexico and then flew across the Gulf to the Mississippi Valley and north to the Arctic through the Canadian Prairie Provinces. In autumn the southward movement led them to eastern Canada, the Maritime Provinces, and New England. From there they made a nonstop flight over the Atlantic to the Lesser Antilles and then to South America. They were shot for sport (and subsequently marketed) during their passage south in eastern Canada and New England, on their wintering grounds in South America, and during their northward migration in Texas, the Mississippi Valley, and the Prairie Provinces. Their numbers at one time were said nearly to equal those of the passenger pigeon. Their fate has been nearly the same, although an occasional bird has been seen in recent years.

There are many other shorebirds that have migrations as extensive as the examples given, and in some of these species the wintering area may encompass a long distance on either side of the equator. For example, the surfbird (*Aphriza virgata*) is known to breed in the Alaska Range. The winter range extends nearly the entire length of the west coasts of North and South America from southeastern Alaska to the Strait of Magellan. The ruddy turnstone (*Arenaria interpres*), unlike the surfbird, has a broad circumpolar breeding range including parts of arctic Canada, Alaska, Siberia, Scandinavia, and Greenland. In North America it winters as far north as New Jersey and California, but many turnstones winter in South Africa, Australia, New Zealand, and Peru. The species is common in winter in the Galapagos Archipelago on the equator.

The wood sandpiper (*Tringa glareola*) breeds in parts of northern Europe and Siberia from the arctic tundra south to the tree belt, occasionally summering as far south as Holland and Belgium. In migration it passes through central Europe and parts of Asia. The European birds are believed to winter from tropical to southern Africa, where the species occurs extensively at this season. Asiatic migrants move as far south as Australia to winter.

The family Phalaropodidae is represented by only three species. They all nest in the Northern Hemisphere and migrate mostly south of the equator to winter. The Wilson's phalarope (*Steganopis tricolor*) is a species of the Prairie Provinces of southern Canada and the central plains and northern Great Basin of the United States. It nests in small potholes, sloughs, and marshes. As in the other two species of this family, the male does the nest building, incubates the eggs, and cares for the young. His plumage is duller than that of his mate. The food of the Wilson's phalarope consists principally of insect larvae, aquatic insects, and small crustaceans. It may be secured on shore or in the water. The breeding area must be left before winter; the ponds and marshes will then be frozen, and starvation would be inevitable. By August the southward migration by adults of both sexes and the young of the year is under way. There are movements to both the Atlantic and the Pacific coasts and then south to South America, where this species winters, principally in Argentina, Chile, and Patagonia. Some Wilson's phalaropes have even been noted in the Falkland Islands.

The northern phalarope (*Lobipes lobatus*) and the red phalarope (*Phalaropus fulicarius*) are Holarctic in distribution. They both nest in northern Alaska, northern Canada, Greenland, Iceland, Spitsbergen, Scandinavia, northern Russia, and Siberia. Their nests are along the margins of small freshwater ponds, and their habits are rather similar to those of the Wilson's phalarope except that food is obtained principally in the water, both fresh and salt. All three species, when swimming, usually move rapidly in small circles. This is believed to stir up small organisms that are used for food.

In late summer, shortened hours of daylight and lowering temperatures are associated with the departure of both the northern and red phalaropes from their summer ranges. In the Pacific area, northern phalaropes winter in the ocean from southern California and the Gulf of California south to southern South America. The species is exceedingly abundant in the vicinity of the Galapagos Islands. The European and Asiatic populations go south to southern Japan, the New Guinea region, and the northern Indian Ocean. The red phalarope winters off South Africa, the southern coast of Arabia, Mexico south to Chile, and in the South Atlantic near the Falkland Islands.

The most extensive avian migrant is the arctic tern (*Sterna paradisaea*). This species has a circumpolar breeding range, nesting along the coasts and on islands of northern Asia, Europe, and North America. The southernmost nesting area is Cape Cod in eastern United States, and the northernmost is the coast of northeastern Greenland within a few degrees of the North Pole. Nesting begins in May when the birds aggregate in colonies and begin to pair off. The female usually lays two or three eggs in a shallow depression on the ground, and the young hatch in three to four weeks. The chicks are fed fish by the parents and leave the colonies when they are about a month old. They are dependent on food from the adults for several more weeks. Those that survive the various problems that young terns have to contend with, which include predators, climate, and disease, are ready to make the most extensive journey made by any bird.

Arctic terns from northern Europe and eastern North America converge along the west coast of Europe by late summer or early autumn and fly southward to the west coast of Africa. From there some continue southward to the Antarctic or turn east after rounding Cape Hope and spread out over the sea between there and New Zealand. Others leave the west coast of Africa and cross the Atlantic diagonally to the east coast of South America. Some continue southward as far as the limits of the antarctic pack ice. This sort of migration entails great distances and nearly continuous movement throughout two-thirds of the year. Oliver L. Austin, Jr., mentions one downy young arctic tern he banded on July 22, 1927, at Turnevik Bay, Labrador, that was recovered October 1, 1927, along the coast of France.[9] Another, banded July 23, 1928, in New Brunswick, was recovered in South Africa on November 14 of the same year. This is a distance of about nine thousand miles and was probably covered in no more than ninety days. The Atlantic flight north in the spring is principally along the east coast of South and North America.

Arctic terns nesting in northwestern North America and northeastern Asia appear to migrate down the west coast of North and South America. Some continue south to the edge of the pack ice.

The south polar skua (*Catharacta skua maccormicki*), which breeds on the shores of the Ross and Weddell seas, usually winters in the general vicinity of the edge of the pack ice and is regularly noted in the North Pacific as far as the coast of British Columbia and frequently recorded off Japan, according to Voous.[10] A small percentage of the population, therefore, may be regarded as composed of transequatorial migrants.

For most birds in the Northern Hemisphere the general migratory direction is northward in the spring and southward in the autumn. The reverse is true for migratory species in the Southern Hemisphere. There are, however, many exceptions to this even among birds. This is especially true of those species whose migrations are influenced basically by gametic and alimental rather than climatic factors.

In the spring of 1966 and again in 1968 I visited Isla Raza in the Gulf

[9]Austin, O. L., Jr. 1961.
[10]Voous, K. H. 1965.

A Heermann's gull (*Larus heermanni*) on its nest at Isla Raza, Baja California, Mexico. *Photographed April 27, 1968, by Robert T. Orr.*

of California, Mexico. This tiny island is less than a mile in length and rises to an elevation of no more than one hundred feet, yet it is the nesting site for nearly all the Heermann's gulls (*Larus heermanni*) and elegant terns (*Thalasseus elegans*) of the world. A very few small colonies of these two species are found on several other islands in northwestern Mexico, but their numbers are insignificant compared with the Raza population, which was estimated to number about one million breeding birds around 1940.[11] After years of commercial egging, the population became greatly reduced. Presently the island is a wildlife refuge as a result of a decree by former president of Mexico Adolpho López Mateos on May 30, 1964. This was made possible through the concerted effort of many persons and several organizations, especially the Belvedere Scientific Fund of San Francisco, the National Audubon Society, Dr. Enrique Beltran, who was then subsecretary of forestry and game, and Dr. Rodolfo Hernandez Corzo, director general of wildlife for Mexico.

Today several hundred thousand elegant terns and Heermann's gulls as well as a few royal terns (*Thalasseus maximus*) nest here, and their numbers, it is hoped, will continue to increase with protection. From

[11]Walker, L. W. 1965.

midsummer until midwinter some of the terns move north about one thousand miles, as far as the central California coast, while others go thousands of miles to the south to winter along the coast of Peru and Chile. The postbreeding movements of the Heermann's gulls, likewise, take them northward along the Pacific coast of North America to southern British Columbia, although most of them winter from Oregon south to the coast of Guatemala. Some of each species have to move south while others move north to arrive at the nesting island.

The Heermann's gulls are the first to arrive on Isla Raza, reaching there by the end of March, following which the pairs space themselves out over the valleys of the island. The terns come early in April, and after large aggregations are present along the shore, groups settle in circular

A large aggregation of nesting elegant terns (*Thalasseus elegans*) with nesting Heermann's gulls on the periphery. Note the difference between the two species in the spacing of individuals. *Photographed at Isla Raza, Baja California, Mexico, April 27, 1968, by Robert T. Orr.*

masses in the center of the gull colonies. The gulls are usually several feet apart but the terns no more than one foot. A tern colony on its first night of establishment on the nesting grounds, according to Walker, may be no more than twenty feet in diameter and composed of several hundred birds, whose sheer numbers force the gulls to the outside of the circle.[12] Eggs are laid almost immediately, but the next day there is rapid loss of those on the periphery by the predatory gulls, and the number of tern eggs in the colony may be reduced by half before nightfall. The following night, however, the tern colony increases to a greater size than that of the previous night as a result of an influx of other pairs whose females are ready to lay. Thus the tern colonies, which are scattered over the island amid the gull colonies, increase by night but are reduced somewhat by day. The increase is greater than the effect of gull predation, and these masses of shimmering gray-white birds with red bills and black on their heads soon reach amazing proportions.

[12]*Ibid.*, 1965.

As the first eggs hatch in the center of the colony, the young move toward the side, leaving an unoccupied space in the center that continually enlarges as the season progresses. This allows gulls to come into this area and effect predation from the center as well as the outside. Despite this, many young terns survive, and they, like the young gulls, leave with the adults by summer, following the same pattern with some going north while others go south.

Brown pelicans (*Pelecanus occidentalis*) nesting amongst cardon (*Pachycereus pringlei*) on a desert island, Isla Granite, Baja California, Mexico. *Photographed April 1967 by Robert T. Orr.*

Elegant and royal terns (*Thalasseus maximus*) often nest together. The royal terns are distinguished with difficulty but tend to have white foreheads. *Photographed at Isla Raza, Baja California, Mexico, April 28, 1967, by George E. Lindsay.*

PELICANS

Another species whose migration in part of its range bears a resemblance to that of the Heermann's gull and the elegant tern is the brown pelican (*Pelecanus occidentalis*). This species occurs on the southeast coast of the United States and around the Caribbean as well as along the Pacific coast of North America south to the Galapagos Islands and Peru. Along the west coast of North America brown pelicans breed on moderately small offshore islands in the spring. The northernmost breeding record is Bird Rock along the Monterey County coast in central California, where a few individuals have been known to nest. In midsummer a part of the Pacific coast population spreads out and moves northward as far as the British Columbia coast. By late the following winter the movement is southward to the warmer offshore islands of southern California and western Mexico, especially Baja California, where many breeding colonies are known to occur.

10

MIGRATIONS OF MAMMALS

True migration among mammals is almost entirely confined to four major categories—bats, cetaceans, pinnipeds, and large hoofed herbivores. Within these groups there is extreme diversity in size, from pipistrelle bats weighing several grams to blue whales, whose weight may exceed one hundred tons. All possess great mobility, which is essential for extensive travel.

BATS

Banding experiments have demonstrated that many kinds of bats make seasonal movements. This sort of behavior is not restricted to the solitary or tree-dwelling species such as the hoary bat (*Lasiurus cinereus*), the red bat (*L. borealis*), and the silver-haired bat (*Lasionycteris noctivagans*) of North America, although their migrations are best known. Other kinds, including a number of hibernators, also travel considerable distances from their summering localities to winter caves.

The exact routes followed by migratory bats still remain largely unknown, although data are accumulating. Hoary, red, and silver-haired bats in eastern North America occur in summer in boreal forests from New York State north to Canada. In winter they are found from South Carolina southward as well as to the west. In western North America the hoary bats move from their summer range in the northern coniferous forests to winter from central California southward through parts of Mexico. Red bats migrate in autumn from the interior valleys of California, where members of this species summer, to adjacent coastal areas to spend the winter. They are found in the San Francisco Bay region from October to May. During the day they hang on the undersides of broad-leafed trees and shrubs. In summer they are common in fruit orchards of the Sacramento and San Joaquin valleys.[1]

Griffin's banding work on cave bats in New England indicates that some species of the genera *Myotis* and *Eptesicus* make fairly extensive movements between their summer and winter quarters.[2] Of a total of more than 13,000 bats banded, about 8,500 were marked in winter in caves and the remainder in the summer colonies. The summer colonies are widespread over New England, but the caves are almost entirely in western Massachusetts, Connecticut, and Vermont. While not all of the vespertilionid bats in that area go to caves to hibernate, it is likely that a very high percentage of the population does. The greatest distance any of these bats was found to move between a summer colony and a winter roost was 168 miles. Movements of the same magnitude and of a similar nature have been found in bats of the genus *Myotis* in Europe. Studies on wintering populations of these bats at Brandenburg by Eisentraut have shown that the average distance between the summer and winter quarters is between 20 and 50 miles, with the minimum distance one-half mile and the maximum 160 miles.[3] Most bats that are recovered show close adherence to the same cave and even the same part of the same cave each winter, and they return to the same summer colony. In the Indiana bat (*Myotis sodalis*) in the central United States there is a tendency for individuals to return to the same cave to hibernate each winter, yet Hall found that a number of banded bats of this species that he studied would move to different caves in successive winters.[4] The distances moved varied from 2 to 320 miles.

Considerably greater migrations were found by Eisentraut to occur in the noctule (*Nyctalus noctula*) in Europe. He banded 1,464 individuals and recovered 19. The return was low, but it was discovered that the distances traveled were much greater than in *Myotis*. Out of 600 noctules banded in winter in Dresden, Germany, 5 were recovered. The greatest distance for a summer recovery was 470 miles at Kampiai, Lithuania. Two others were taken in Poland and another in western Germany. There is a record of a pipistrelle (*Pipistrellus pipistrellus*) that was banded in June in the province of Dnepropetrovsk, U.S.S.R., and recovered the following September near Plovdiv, Bulgaria, 720 miles away.

[1]Orr, R. T. 1950.
[2]Griffin, D. R. 1940, 1945.
[3]Eisentraut, M. 1934, 1943.
[4]Hall, J. S. 1962.

A very extensive study, referred to above, was made on the Indiana bat (*Myotis sodalis*) by John S. Hall that involved the banding of about twelve thousand individuals.[5] This was done mainly in wintering caves, but some were banded in summer and others in movement from the summering areas to the wintering caves. The results showed that although there is little difference between the summer and winter range of this species, individuals and populations within the species may migrate up to 320 miles. Furthermore, the caves that are inhabited, either in summer or winter, are all fairly close to watercourses. The suggestion therefore is made that the major rivers are navigation routes for bats of this species. When a bat learns a few river systems, it can travel considerable distances using these as a means of orientation.

Recently, Villa-R. and Cockrum summarized most of the available information on the movements of the guano bat (*Tadarida brasiliensis mexicana*), a member of the family Molossidae.[6] This species ranges from western United States south to South America. It is colonial and may occur in aggregations numbering in the thousands or even millions in western United States. In winter few or none of these bats are seen in this northern part of their summer range.

Because this species is regarded as one of the vectors of rabies, extensive banding operations have been carried on in recent years, especially at Carlsbad Caverns, New Mexico, where several million free-tailed bats occur in summer. Some thought that these guano bats hibernated deep in recesses in rocks; others speculated that they might migrate southward. The returns to date indicate that at least a substantial part of the population of the guano bat in the northern part of its range migrates southward to central Mexico, where large wintering colonies composed of both sexes may be found from December through February. A bat banded on September 18, 1952, at Carlsbad, New Mexico, was recaptured 810 miles to the south on November 25, 1952, at Las Barrochas, Jalisco. Another, banded at El Rincon, Nuevo Leon, on January 27, 1956, was taken 790 miles to the north at Selman Cave, Oklahoma, on June 4, 1956, and one banded January 27, 1956, at El Rincon, Nuevo Leon, was recaptured 510 miles to the north on August 27, 1956, at Carlsbad, New Mexico. Several guano bats banded October 6, 1957, at Tucson, Arizona, were recovered November 14, 1957, at Monte Largo, Sonora, about 540 miles to the south.

[5]Hall, J. S. 1962.
[6]Villa-R., B., and E. L. Cockrum. 1962.

Migratory movements have been recorded in some of the Old World fruit bats of the family Pteropidae. *Epomophorus wahlbergi*, one of the epauleted bats of Africa, is said to engage in seasonal migrations, and *Pteropus poliocephalus* of Australia is reported to make periodic movements between Queensland and New South Wales. Whether these are regular migratory movements along regular routes is not known.

CETACEANS

Whales, because of their great size and capability of traveling long distances, have been able to establish migratory patterns that take them to areas rich in food outside of their own reproductive season. These regions are principally the arctic and antarctic waters. It is in these cold parts of the ocean that the organisms upon which they depend occur in enormous numbers. The food consists primarily of small shrimplike crustaceans called krill. Polar seas, however, that are rich in food are too cold for newborn young. Consequently, most whales move to tropical or subtropical seas for a part of the year. Here the females bear their young. The latter grow rapidly on the rich milk they are fed, and as soon as they have developed a layer of protective insulation against the cold in the form of fat or blubber, the population migrates back to the feeding areas.

Because of the need to feed and reproduce in water of different temperatures, whales have established interesting migratory patterns. We know more about these than about the migrations of many other marine organisms for two reasons. Whales are large and easily seen in the sea, since they must come to the surface to breathe, and they have been hunted for generations because of their commercial value. Any seasonal change in status would quickly be noted.

Since the antarctic and arctic pack ice expands greatly in the winter season in each of the polar regions and establishes an impenetrable barrier for some months in the areas where krill is abundant, this is the time of year when whales move into equatorial or subequatorial waters to have their young and mate. However, nothing is known of intermingling of Northern and Southern hemisphere populations. Although a number of species are represented in both the north and the south, they breed at opposite times of the year, and each would normally be in cold summer waters at high latitudes when the other is near the equator. It is possible that some late migrants from one hemisphere might still be in the breeding area when early migrants from the opposite hemisphere arrive.

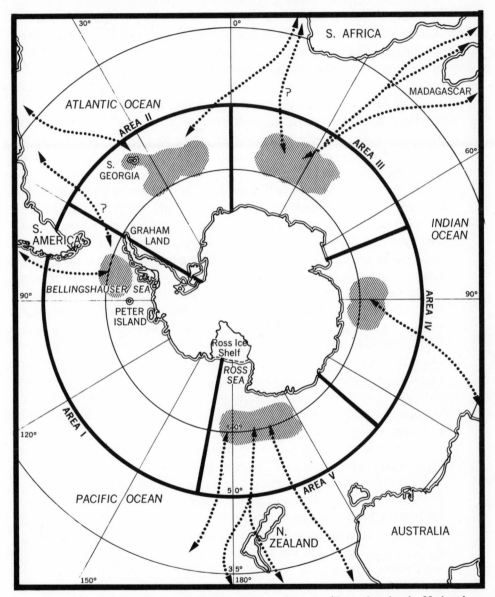

Distribution and migration of humpbacks in the Antarctic. (From data by the National Institute of Oceanography, England)

The migratory pattern of the humpback whale (*Megaptera novaeangliae*) in the Southern Hemisphere is fairly well known as a result of marking. It has been found that there are five distinct populations around the Antarctic.[7] For convenience in handling whaling statistics, the antarctic whaling grounds are divided into six areas marked by the following lines of longitude: Area I, in the eastern Pacific, extends from 120° W. to 60° W.; Area II, in the Atlantic, extends from 60° W. to 0° W.; Area III, south of Africa, extends from Greenwich meridian to 70° E.; Area IV, the West Australian Area, extends from 70° E. to 130° E.; Area V, the East Australian Area, extends from 130° E. to 170° W.; Area VI, the Western Pacific Area, which is really a subdivision of Area I, extends from 170° W. to 120° W.

Those humpbacks in Area I summer in or near the Bellingshausen Sea and migrate north along the west coast of South America to the equator as well as along the southeast coast. Area II humpbacks summer south and east from the vicinity of South Georgia. They winter off the east coast of South America, but north of those from Area I, and off the west coast of Africa north to the equator. Area III humpbacks summer north of Queen Maud Land. A part of the population winters off the south-west African coast, where there may be some intermingling with those from Area II and even some interchange. The other part of the population winters along the east coast of Africa north to equatorial waters and along the Madagascar coast. The humpbacks of Area IV spend the summer off northwestern Wilkes Land and then migrate north to winter off the west coast of Australia almost to the Timor Sea. The Areas V and VI populations summer north of Victoria Land and the Ross Sea. Those to the west winter north along the west coast of Australia, around New Zealand, and north almost to the Solomon Islands and the New Hebrides. Those from farther to the east, in the western sector of Area VI, move north to the central Pacific as far as Hawaii to winter. Extensive studies on the Australian humpback whale populations have been made by R. G. Chittleborough of Perth, Australia.[8]

There are also humpback whale populations that summer in the North Atlantic and the North Pacific. The North Atlantic population may be subdivided into one that moves down the coasts of Norway and the British Isles in autumn to breeding areas off northwest Africa, and an-

[7]Slijper, E. J. 1962.
[8]Chittleborough, R. G. 1953, 1959.

other that comes south from Newfoundland past the east coast of North America to the Caribbean Sea. The eastern North Atlantic humpbacks avoid the North Sea and the Channel in their migration and move north and south to the west of the British Isles. The northeastern Pacific population migrates south as far as the Gulf of California, Mexico, to breed, while the western Pacific population migrates to the Sea of Japan and occurs off the Ryukyu Islands and, formerly, the Marianas during the calving season.

The summer and winter distribution of blue whales (*Balaenoptera musculus*) and finback whales (*Balaenoptera physalus*) is somewhat different from that of the humpback in the Southern Hemisphere. The wintering grounds of humpbacks are mostly coastal, but this is not necessarily true of blue or fin whales. These large rorquals migrate mostly away from continental land masses and winter in areas where food is present in sufficient quantity. According to Slijper, the largest numbers are to be found in summer in the Antarctic in Areas I and II from longitude 20° to 70° W., in the South Atlantic; in Area III between 20° and 40° E., south of Africa; in Area IV between 80° and 110° E., southwest of Australia; in Area V between 150° and 170° E., which is southeast of Australia; and in Area I between 110° and 70° W., to the southwest of South America. This corresponds to the distribution of krill. Not too much is known of the rorquals' wintering grounds, since these whales tend to scatter rather than stay in schools. There are some winter concentrations off the northwest coast of Africa, in the Bay of Bengal, and the Gulf of Aden. Blue whales are also present in the central South Atlantic near Tristan da Cunha in winter. The spring migration of the blue whale back to antarctic waters precedes that of the fin whale.

The blue whale and fin whale are also represented by populations in the North Atlantic and North Pacific. In summer the blue whale of the North Pacific does not go north of the Aleutian Islands or the Kamchatka Peninsula, while the fin whale moves into the Bering Sea and even up into the Arctic Ocean. Both species move far south in winter. They are observed along both the Asiatic and American coasts during migration. In this respect they tend to differ from their Southern Hemisphere counterparts. Some of these northern rorquals move south along the Asiatic coast to the Indian Ocean, which is also a wintering area for antarctic whales but at the opposite time of year.

The North Atlantic blue whale population is divided, with part of it summering in Baffin Bay west of Greenland and the remainder in the region between northeastern Greenland and the Barents Sea. In southward migration the western Atlantic population moves through Davis Strait and down the east coast of North America past Newfoundland. Some of the eastern Atlantic blue whales move south on either side of Iceland as well as along the west coast of the British Isles and cross to the American coast. Others move down the coast of Europe to warmer waters near the equator. The reverse route is followed in spring migration. The Atlantic fin whales summer east of Spitsbergen. In their north-south migrations they pass on both sides of the British Isles.

The distribution of most of the other baleen whales is somewhat similar to that of the species already described, although some, like the sei whale (*Balaenoptera borealis*), do not go as far north in the Arctic or as far south in the Antarctic as most of the others. The interesting migration of the gray whale (*Eschrichtius gibbosus*), whose principal survivors summer in the Arctic Ocean, Bering Sea, Sea of Okhotsk, and the North Pacific and winter in the shallow lagoons along the northwest coast of Mexico, has already been considered in Chapter 2.

The sperm whale (*Physeter catodon*), a toothed cetacean with very different food habits from the baleen whales, shows a different sort of migratory pattern. The species is cosmopolitan, but its food consists primarily of fairly large cephalopods. Sperm whales, therefore, are found where there are cuttlefish. These invertebrates occur in greatest numbers where there is a mingling of cold and equatorial waters. Such conditions prevail along the west coast of South America, where the cold Humboldt Current contacts equatorial waters, turns west past the Galapagos Islands, and merges with the South Equatorial Current of the Pacific. A similar situation prevails off the west coast of Africa, where the cold Benguela Current likewise contacts equatorial waters and, for the most part, turns westward to become the South Equatorial Current of the Atlantic. Females and young males move in groups, usually dominated by an older male, between 40° N. and 40° S. latitude. They rarely venture into cold water. Most of the bulls, however, summer much farther to the north and south. In the North Pacific they move into the Bering Sea in summer. The extent of their movement toward arctic or antarctic waters is dependent on the presence of cephalopods. In the autumn they move to warmer waters to join the females for the winter.

Many of the smaller cetaceans appear to engage in seasonal migrations, but for the most part relatively little is known about these movements. With some of the porpoises and dolphins these migrations are fairly local and seem to be correlated with the movements of the fish upon which they feed. This has been found to be true of the Pacific white-sided dolphin (*Lagenorhynchus obliquidens*) and the Dall porpoise (*Phocoenoides dalli*).[9]

Studies made in the Bay of Fundy in northeastern North America by Neave and Wright indicate that harbor porpoises (*Phocoena phocoena*) migrate into this body of water in search of herring (*Clupea harengus*) in late May, June, and July.[10] More than 70 percent of the early arrivals stay within eight miles of shore and are considered to be females. The males arrive in July and stay farther from shore. In September both sexes move out of the bay. Somewhat similar seasonal movements to the Bay of Fundy in early summer and out of this area in autumn are engaged in by certain other cetaceans, including the finback whale, the blue whale, and the pilot whale (*Globicephala melaena*).

PINNIPEDS

Next to whales the most extensive mammalian migrants are some of the pinnipeds. Certain species engage in seasonal population movements that involve hundreds of miles. There are, of course, some pinnipeds that are sedentary. The hair or harbor seal (*Phoca vitullina*) is one of these, at least throughout most of its range. There are also both arctic and antarctic species that remain in the polar environment throughout the year. The Weddell seal (*Leptonychotes weddelli*) of the Southern Hemisphere, which does not live on the pack ice, is a nonmigratory species. The same appears to be true of the ringed seal (*Phoca hispida*) of the Arctic, which is an animal of open water in the fast ice.

The maximum distance between the rookeries and the southernmost wintering area for the northern fur seal (*Callorhinus ursinus*) is close to three thousand miles. This species breeds principally on St. Paul and St. George islands of the Pribilof group in the Bering Sea. Small colonies also occur on Robben Island near Sakhalin, on the Commander Islands east of Kamchatka, and on several small islands in the Kurile chain. The breeding rookeries of this seal were discovered about half a century after Vitus Bering discovered Alaska. In 1786 Gerassim Pribilof came across a group of small, barren, rocky islands in the Bering Sea. These

---

[9]Brown, D. H., and K. S. Norris. 1956.
[10]Neave, D. J., and B. S. Wright. 1968.

A northern fur seal (*Callorhinus ursinus*) rookery. A bull is seen in the foreground and another in the center of the picture, each with a harem of cows and pups. *Photographed on St. Paul Island, Bering Sea, July 18, 1968, by Robert T. Orr.*

islands, which now collectively bear his name, contained vast aggregations of fur seals in the summer months.

The discovery of the breeding site of this valuable fur seal resulted in its wholesale slaughter. This continued even after the United States purchased Alaska from Russia in 1867. In 1911 a treaty was signed by the United States, Japan, Russia, and Great Britain affording protection to the northern fur seal. In 1912, when the first complete census was taken, it was estimated that there were 215,000 seals. Proper management was provided, and pelagic sealing, except by aborigines, was prohibited. By 1958, as a result of this, the fur seal population on the Pribilof Islands was estimated to be between 1½ and 2 million. In addition, there were 40,000 to 60,000 fur seals on the Commander Islands east of Kamchatka and about the same number on Robben Island off Sakhalin, U.S.S.R.

After the breeding season, the Pribilof population moves south, usually within ten to ninety miles of the shore. The males winter mainly in the

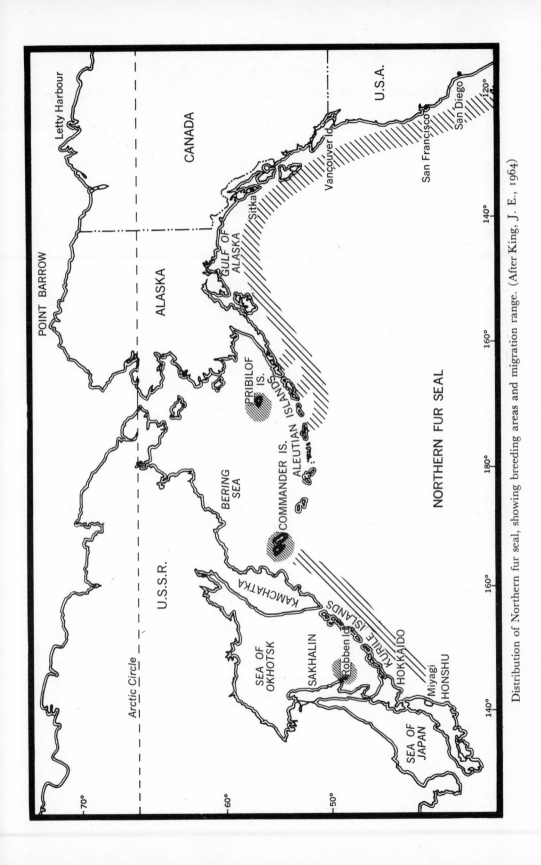

Distribution of Northern fur seal, showing breeding areas and migration range. (After King, J. E., 1964)

Gulf of Alaska, and the females and young go far to the south, with some to be found off the coast of southern California. Along the Japanese coast a somewhat similar situation prevails among members of the Asiatic population, although fur seals are not abundant there until late March or April. Prior to that they are believed to be widely scattered at sea. In the spring of the year the males move north once again to the rookeries, where they set up territories some weeks before the arrival of the females from much farther south (see Chapter 4).

A somewhat different migratory pattern is seen in parts of the range of the California sea lion (*Zalophus californianus*). This species presently has a discontinuous distribution. A small population, which may now be extinct, occurred in the Sea of Japan before World War II. Another population is found in the Galapagos Archipelago, about six hundred miles west of Ecuador. The largest population occurs along the west coast of North America with a breeding range known to extend from the Channel Islands off the coast of southern California south to the San Benito Islands off the west coast of Baja California and from islands in the Gulf of California probably south to Mazatlan, Mexico. In times past what may have been a southern extension of this population occurred on the Tres Marias Islands along the coast of Nayarit. Little is known about the California sea lions in the Sea of Japan. To the best of our knowledge the Galapagos sea lions are resident.[11] The California sea lion population of western North America, however, shows an interesting migratory pattern.

The young are born in June and July. The dominant bulls, as in other pinnipeds with a well-developed social structure, each dominate a harem of females. Unlike the male northern fur seal, the male California sea lion spends part of his time patrolling his harem area by swimming back and forth in front of it, while the females and young spend most of their time on the adjacent shore. There is no evidence of any significant migration occurring among members of this species living in the Gulf of California or along the mainland coast of Mexico. Those breeding on islands off the west coast of Baja California and southern California are partly migratory. After the breeding season, there appears to be a mass movement of the males to the north. Large numbers appear along the central California coast, and some are found as far north

[11]Orr, R. T. 1967.

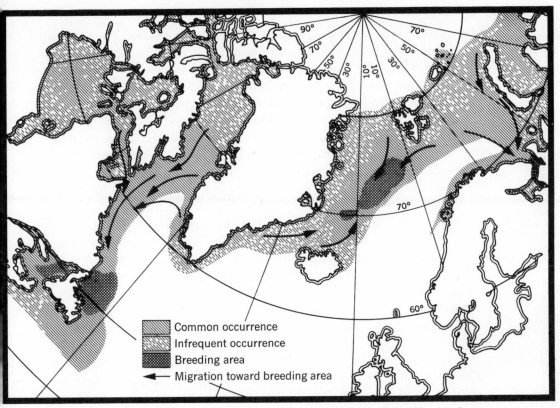

Occurrence and migrations of the harp seal, according to Nansen. (After Nansen, from Sivertsen, E., 1941)

as the waters off British Columbia.[12] As far as is known, the females remain around or near the rookery islands.

A somewhat similar migratory pattern is seen in the Steller sea lion (*Eumetopias jubata*) in the southern part of its range. This species has a breeding range that extends from Alaska south to central California. One of the largest rookeries outside of Alaska occurs on a small island called Año Nuevo along the central California coast. Here the breeding

[12]Orr, R. T., and T. C. Poulter. 1965.

population may number some two thousand individuals. The seasonal cycle begins with the first appearance of the bulls in late April or early May.[13] Unlike the California sea lion bulls, the males haul out on reefs and establish territories, thereby behaving somewhat like northern fur seal males. These territories are believed to be maintained by dominant bulls for anywhere from several weeks to two months. Although a few females remain about the island the year round, there is a great influx by the end of May, and maximum numbers are present by the end of June or early July. The bulls acquire harems of females, and the pups are born between the first week of June and the middle of July. Non-breeding males or bachelors are also present but restricted to less favorable parts of the island area. The harems break up by the latter part of July, and by the end of August all the bulls and bachelors have left. It appears that they move northward, as none can be found to the south of this region. The females remain in large numbers until around January, when many leave, not to return to the island until the following breeding season.

The harp seal (*Phoca groenlandica*), an arctic species of the North Atlantic region, also has a fairly extensive migration pattern, which has been summarized by Sivertsen.[14] It breeds in the vicinity of Newfoundland in the western North Atlantic, in the White Sea in the northwestern U.S.S.R., and around Jan Mayen in the Norwegian Sea. The adults migrate to the breeding areas in the autumn, and the young are born between January and April. Following this there is a migration northward to higher latitudes for the summer. Because of the restricted pupping range and the commercial hunting for the newborn young by planes and helicopters, the future of this species is in danger.

In the Antarctic there are several species of migratory seals. The crabeater seal (*Lobodon carcinophagus*) is common in the southern part of the Ross Sea and west of the Palmer Peninsula (Graham Land) in summer from January to March but moves north with the pack ice in winter and may occasionally be found along the coasts of New Zealand, Australia, and even South America. The leopard seal (*Hydrurga leptonyx*), which is also common in summer in the Ross Sea and in McMurdo Sound, moves north to antarctic islands such as South Georgia, Kerguelen, and Macquarie in winter and may even be found along the coasts of New Zealand and Australia.

[13]*Ibid.*
[14]Sivertsen, E. 1941.

HERBIVORES

Many kinds of antelope in Africa may move from one area to another in search of food or water, but these movements for the most part are determined by climatic conditions prevailing at the time. They may not occur each year if favorable conditions prevail in the home regions. When they do occur, the direction of movement and its extent may depend in large part on the availability of food and water in neighboring areas.

True seasonal migration in herbivores is largely restricted to certain northern species of artiodactyls such as caribou, moose, and wapiti. Even in these animals seasonal conditions play an important part. In years when unfavorable weather conditions come suddenly, the migrations may be rapid and the number of animals participating may be concentrated. In mild years, migration may take place slowly and be almost unnoticed at times.

The seasonal movements of the Alaskan barren-ground caribou (*Rangifer tarandus*) have been the subject of intensive studies.[15] Herds summering in the Rampart region may move all the way to Whitehorse to winter, although some individuals remain all year in the summer range. The largest herds in Alaska are in the area between Rampart on the Yukon and the White Mountain district. Most of these animals move southeast in the fall to the upper tributaries of the Yukon and Tanana rivers in the Yukon Territory. They may travel as much as three hundred miles.

Those herds in northern Alaska spend late June and early July in the foothills as well as higher parts of the Brooks Range.[16] Following this there is a dispersal to the coastal tundra when food becomes abundant there. By late August and early September the movement is once again south to the wintering range on the north edge of the taiga, although a few small bands remain all winter in the summer range. The maximum distance traveled, as with the herds described above, is about three hundred miles. Food, in the form of lichens and grasses in winter and sedges, willows, birch, and forbs (herbs other than grass) in summer, seems to be an important factor. In Mount McKinley National Park in

[15]Murie, O. J. 1935.
[16]Lent, P. C. 1966.

Alaska caribou move from the high country to the lower hills in early September.

Equally thorough studies have been made by the Canadian Wildlife Service on seasonal movements of the major herds of caribou in Canada.[17] The population of this species on the Canadian mainland in 1967 was estimated to be 357,500, with the principal regions inhabited being the Mackenzie District, Keewatin, northern Manitoba, and northern Saskatchewan. The number of separate populations is variously described as ranging from four to seven, but some exchange occurs from year to year between certain of the herds. In general the Canadian caribou spend the summer on the tundra and winter in the northern forests, principally within one hundred miles of the tree line. Some differences occur in times of migration of the various herds. Those in the more northern latitudes winter closer to the tundra and migrate to the summer ranges earlier. In northwestern Mackenzie in 1967 it was estimated that half of the herd reached the tundra by April 10. This contrasts with the arrival of half of the herds of southeastern Mackenzie and northeastern Saskatchewan on summer range a month later that year.

In parts of Canada there are definite migrations of moose (*Alces alces*) between summer and winter range. A six-year study in Wells Gray Park, British Columbia, by Edwards and Ritcey showed that the moose in that region summer largely in subalpine forests of alpine fir (*Abies lasiocarpa*) and Engelmann spruce (*Picea engelmanni*) at elevations of from 5,000 to 7,000 feet.[18] Here they show preference for seepage areas where small meadows are scattered among the trees. The movement to winter range may begin as early as October. Early snow stimulates an early downward movement. The winter range consists principally of lowland burned areas between 2,500 and 5,000 feet where there is an abundance of deciduous browse species of plants. The descent may be a slow one. While most of the moose are at the upper level of the burned areas by December, the downward movement may continue until March. The maximum distance traveled between summer and winter range may be as much as 40 miles, but, as the authors point out, this vertical movement is ecologically equivalent to a movement of 350 miles from the tree line in the Northwest Territories to the edge of the taiga in central Saskatchewan. In spring the upward movement to

[17]Banfield, A. W. F. 1954; Kelsall, J. P. 1968.
[18]Edwards, R. Y., and R. W. Ritcey. 1956.

summer range begins in April and is completed by May. While climate may play a part in this sort of migration, the basic reason for migration is the availability of food.

Certain herds of elk (*Cervus canadensis*) in North America, particularly those in the Jackson Hole region of Wyoming, engage in very definite migrations that are of a vertical nature. The summer range of the Jackson Hole herd is confined largely to the higher parkland and mountain meadows, where food is abundant at this season.[19] Rutting also takes place there in the autumn as a rule. When the heavy snows come around November and cover the forage, the animals migrate to lower levels, where they remain for the winter. In spring the reverse occurs, and the elk leave the valley floors and move back into the mountains. One of the interesting things about this spring movement is that food is usually abundant in the wintering grounds when the elk leave and is still sparse in the summering area when they arrive there.

Vertical migration of a similar nature occurs in deer in certain parts of the Pacific coast of North America. In the Cascade-Sierra Nevada axis of Oregon and California the so-called black-tailed deer migrates down the western slopes of these mountains in the autumn, and the typical mule deer form goes down on the east side to lower levels. This in general tends to segregate the two kinds during the late fall breeding season. However, Cowan found that there were certain areas where breaks in the mountain chain failed to produce a complete segregation as a result of migration, and interbreeding occurred.[20] Such areas were found in southern British Columbia and northern California. Cowan therefore decided that these two populations of deer represented but one species, *Odocoileus hemionus*.

[19]Murie, O. J. 1951.
[20]Cowan, I. McT. 1936.

11

MECHANICS OF MIGRATION

No two kinds of organisms migrate in exactly the same way. It has been shown that some species require a lifetime, which may consist of many years, to complete their migratory patterns. With other animals the migration may be seasonal, or it may occur more often, as in the case of organisms whose behavior is influenced by lunar periodicity. In the process of carrying out these population movements, whether they be once in a lifetime or once every lunar month, certain specific patterns of behavior are followed. Some species are gregarious, others are solitary. Some make a nonstop trip, while others travel leisurely. Some travel at night, others by day. Among aerial migrants some fly near the ground, while others fly at great heights. Some soar and glide, others do not. These are but some of the so-called mechanics of migration that will be touched on briefly in this chapter.

Since representatives of marine, aquatic, terrestrial, and aerial animals all engage in migratory movements, a number of methods of travel are employed. The movements of marine migrants such as salmon, herrings, tunas, sea turtles, pinnipeds, and cetaceans are accomplished by swimming, but there are other marine organisms that accomplish equally extensive movements without this great expenditure of energy. These are the commensal organisms associated with the more spectacular migrants. Under this category would come such animals as the barnacles that attach themselves to whales, sailfish, marlin, or even ships. Whale lice, which are parasitic crustaceans, also come under this category, as do remoras, or suckerfish, that may "hitchhike" with any of the larger marine fishes or cetaceans. Some aquatic animals migrate by swimming, but others may travel considerable distances overland.

Land mammals, apart from bats, depend upon walking to move between their summer and winter quarters, but most insects, birds, and all bats depend upon flight. There are exceptions, especially among gallinaceous birds. The seasonal vertical movements of certain quails and grouse to or from higher mountainous areas are accomplished to a large extent through walking. The pace is leisurely and feeding is accomplished en route.

SOLITARY VERSUS GREGARIOUS MOVEMENTS

In some kinds of insects great masses of individuals move together. This is the **pattern** exhibited by the migratory locust (*Locusta migratoria*)

Adélie penguins (*Pygoscelis adeliae*) migrating northward with the current on ice floes after leaving the breeding area. *Photographed near Cape Hallett Station, Antarctica, in January 1965 by Dietland Müller-Schwartze.*

of Africa. The sky may be partly darkened at times as they pass over-head. The monarch butterfly (*Danaus plexippus*) almost drifts during its migration, with individuals generally well spaced, although there are records of large masses of these insects moving more or less together. Most migratory fishes are schooling species, and the individuals tend to keep together. This is particularly true of marine forms. It has been suggested, as mentioned earlier, that there are advantages to moving in groups rather than singly, especially for smaller prey species. Numbers often tend to confuse enemies and thereby reduce the losses from pre-dation. Group movement, however, is not characteristic of the migratory patterns of most amphibians or reptiles.

Among birds we find both solitary and flock movement, depending upon the species. A number of diurnal migrants as well as others that may migrate either by day or by night move in flocks of various types. Waxwings and blackbirds fly in very compact groups but do not seem to have a definite formation. Swallows fly in loose groups and probably engage in feeding during flight. Ducks and geese have very definite formations that are typically V-shaped. Somewhat similar are the flights of pelicans, although the formation more often takes the form of a diag-onal line. Loons often fly in lines, with the individuals well spaced apart.

Diurnal birds of prey fly in loose groups that are often mixed as re-gards species. Their lines of flight also are generally narrow and tend to follow from one thermal to another. There has been considerable question as to whether the migrants move as individuals that follow the same line only because of the presence of thermals, or whether there is a tendency for these birds to travel in loose heterogeneous flocks irrespec-tive of this. Goodwin (1949), referring to observations made on birds of prey migrating around the head of the Gulf of Suez, expressed the opin-ion that the migrants moved as individuals rather than as members of a flock.[1] His conclusions were based on records made during seven days in the first two weeks of October. The total number of birds of prey counted each day ranged from below 1,000 to over 4,500. Most of the migrants were seen between 10 A.M. and 4 P.M., which is the time that thermals occur. Goodwin did admit that the sight of some birds rising with thermals seemed, on several occasions, to influence other birds to leave their course and join the "circus."

A somewhat different point of view has been taken by other observers of migrating birds of prey in the region of the Gulf of Suez. Simmons

[1]Goodwin, D. 1949.

expressed doubt that these migrants are drawn together only because they make use of the same thermal currents.[2] Tennent noted that birds that abandoned thermals to take an east-northeast course between the head of the Gulf and the Bitter Lakes, thereby avoiding a water-crossing, still remained in heterogeneous flocks even though they were forced to progress by flapping.[3] The fact remains that flock formation is accomplished with greater difficulty in species that progress by gliding after gaining elevation from thermals than it is in those that progress by other means. Storks depend upon thermals and do not fly in formation, while cranes fly by flapping and move in flocks.

Some nocturnal migrants fly in definite, compact flocks. These include many kinds of waterfowl and shorebirds, and certain herons. There has been some difference of opinion as to whether passerine birds migrating at night fly singly or in flocks. Lowery, as a result of observing migrants through a telescope as they passed across the face of the moon, concluded that there is a rather uniform dispersion, at least on a horizontal plane.[4] Lowery and Newman, however, commented on the spotty distribution of birds crossing the moon.[5] Observers found that there were periods when no birds were seen, followed by many sightings in close succession. Nisbet, as a result of radar studies of nocturnal migrants that incorporated measurements of the height of flight, has expressed the opinion that many small passerines, including members of the families Parulidae, Turdidae, and Emberizidae, migrate in small groups in which the individuals are well spaced.[6] Because of this, one would rarely see more than a single member of a flock crossing the face of the moon. So-called "angels" observed on the radar screen consisted of from two to twelve birds.

Dr. William J. Hamilton III has suggested that flocking may improve the accuracy of orientation in birds.[7] He points out that shorebirds, certain songbirds, notably the bobolink (*Dolichonyx oryzivorus*) of North America, and some sea birds that make very extensive migrations have a greater requirement for accuracy in navigation than short-distance migrants. For an individual flying singly, the chances of success on the initial flight would seem to be much more a matter of chance than for a

[2]Simmons, K. E. L. 1951.
[3]Tennent, J. R. M. 1967.
[4]Lowery, G. H., Jr. 1951.
[5]Lowery, G. H., Jr., and R. J. Newman. 1966.
[6]Nisbet, I. C. T. 1963b.
[7]Hamilton, W. J. III. 1967b.

member of a flocking species, where the experience of those that have previously made the flight is advantageous. Dr. Hamilton also cites the long-tailed cuckoo (*Eudynamis taitensis*) which nests in New Zealand and winters to the north in islands of the Pacific. The flight from summer to winter quarters involves a nonstop trip over the sea of from one thousand to three thousand kilometers, and pinpoint accuracy is essential. This species, unlike other migratory cuckoos on continental land masses, migrates in flocks.

Hamilton also suggests that the V-formation used by certain flocking birds, particularly pelicans, waterfowl, storks, gulls, cranes, cormorants, and herons, is a form of orientation communication enabling the individuals constituting a particular flock to take the greatest advantage of the collective orientation experience of all concerned. This is an interesting theory in view of the fact that V-formation has usually been given an aerodynamic explanation and has been regarded as the result of each individual taking advantage of favorable air currents formed by the bird ahead. To further substantiate his theory, Hamilton comments on the habit of many birds that fly in V-formation of keeping the same formation after alighting on the water. This is especially noticeable among certain species of geese and pelicans. Here there is no question of aerodynamics involved.

It has long been known that nocturnal avian migrants utter call notes while in flight at night and that each species has its own characteristic calls. The significance of these call notes, however, has been subject to considerable speculation. It seems logical, as suggested by Hamilton, that they provide a communicatory means of keeping members of a flock together.[8] In some species the nocturnal calls are the same as those given in the daytime, but in others they are very different. Small passerines seem to migrate at night in groups in which the individuals are widely spaced. Frequently a flock is composed of more than one species. Vision is not likely to play a significant role in maintaining such a flock formation in the air after dark, but vocal communication could possibly do so.

In some of Hamilton's experiments he played back tapes of the nocturnal migratory calls of bobolinks to captive members of the same species. Those individuals that were in physiological migratory condition responded actively and often flew up and hit the top of the containing apparatus. He suggested that the calls of nocturnal migrants passing

[8]Hamilton, W. J. III. 1962b.

overhead may serve to induce grounded birds to fly up and join those flocks.

Other possible explanations for the utterance of calls by nocturnal migrants have been proposed, including their use for echo ranging and as an expression of fear or of hunger while flying at night.

TIMES OF MIGRATION

Locusts and butterflies in general migrate during the daylight hours, with sunlight and consequent rising temperatures seemingly serving as a stimulus to flight. In the butterfly *Ascia*, migratory flight, according to Johnson, is confined to the period between 9 A.M. and 4 P.M.[9] There are a number of instances of nocturnal migration in butterflies. Painted lady (*Vanessa cardui*) and monarch butterflies have both been observed flying at night, although this is probably not a regular occurrence. Night flights of butterflies are most often noted over the sea, where rest is impossible.

Moths generally migrate at night, but there are a number of kinds that have been seen migrating during the daytime. These include the silver Y moth (*Plusia gamma*) and the hummingbird hawk-moth (*Macroglossa stellatarum*), which have been observed making diurnal flights in England. The hummingbird hawk-moth goes to Britain each year from southern Europe and northern Africa. Williams records observations of these moths arriving along the south coast of England near Hastings that were made by a Mr. A. D. Wilkinson.[10] The moths came in from the sea in the late afternoon between 5 and 6 P.M., presumably after crossing from the Continent.

The smolts of sockeye salmon (*Oncorhynchus nerka*) in their movement through Lake Babine in central British Columbia were found in studies by Groot, and by Groot and Wiley, to migrate most actively in the evening and early morning hours.[11] Greatest movement occurred between 9:30 P.M. and 11:30 P.M. and between 3:00 A.M. and 5:00 A.M. Pacific Standard Time during the last week in May. Sunset was around 8:20 P.M., and sunrise, about 3:35 A.M. Thus the greatest movement began seventy minutes after sunset and thirty-five minutes before sunrise.

The time of entrance of mature kokanee salmon to their spawning stream appears also to be governed by light intensity. Lorz and North-

[9]Johnson, C. G. 1965.
[10]Williams, C. B. 1958.
[11]Groot, C. 1965; Groot, C., and W. L. Wiley. 1965.

cote made a study of this species at Nicola Lake in south central British Columbia between 1958 and 1963.[12] Here spawning takes place in the latter part of August and September. The salmon moved inshore in the late afternoon and entered the spawning stream in the evening when the light intensity fell below one hundred luxes. As the season progressed, the migrations occurred earlier each evening. This was correlated with the earlier onset of dusk. The movements of the fish upstream took place in darkness.

Other salmonid fishes are known to move into the spawning streams only under the cover of darkness. This is true of brown trout and lake trout. Loftus found that river-spawning lake trout in eastern Lake Superior began entering the Montreal River a short time after dusk.[13] This movement reached its peak before midnight.

In the kokanee salmon, once the spawning stream has been entered after dusk, migration may continue for well over twelve hours until the following morning.

In autumn in England, Lack, using radar, found small movements of shorebirds over land occuring two hours before sunset.[14] In late August and early September the first movement of small passerines was noted at about 7:30 P.M. The movement reached its peak between 9 P.M. and 10 P.M. and remained strong until 5 A.M., when a marked decline began. This was shortly before sunrise. Shorebirds were recorded coming in from the direction of Holland after dark. All movement seemed to cease around sunrise, but later in the morning there was an influx of diurnal shorebird migrants from Holland, Scandinavia, and Scotland. The source of these flights was deduced by the direction from which the birds came.

As a result of extensive radar studies made on nocturnal migrants in Illinois, Dr. Frank Bellrose was able to show that spring migration began around 6 P.M. and reached its peak shortly after 10 P.M.[15] Migration ceased between 5:30 A.M. and 6:30 A.M. No significant difference was seen between clear and overcast skies in this regard. In autumn, migration began shortly before 6 P.M. and terminated at about 6:30 A.M. On clear nights a peak was reached just before 9 P.M., whereas on overcast nights the peak in 1962 was at about 3 A.M. and in 1963 was at nearly 4 A.M.

[12]Lorz, H. W., and T. G. Northcote. 1965.
[13]Loftus, K. H. 1958.
[14]Lack, D. 1963.
[15]Bellrose, F. C. 1967.

Dr. Richard R. Graber, in his studies on nocturnal migrants in Illinois, likewise found that the radar peak occurred shortly before midnight.[16] However, aural records indicated a peak after midnight and usually just before dawn. Graber attributed the increased aural recordings in the latter part of the night not to an increase in the number of birds passing overhead but to an increase in the call rate. The latter is related to a postmidnight decrease in the altitude of flight. A reduction in altitude is believed to increase the flight density as a result of compressing the migrant swarms. This in turn produces a situation of potential peril, and the increase in call rate may therefore be for the protection of the migrants against collision.

Probably, therefore, neither radar observations that indicate a peak in number of nocturnal avian migrants prior to midnight, nor aural records showing a greater number of individuals calling after midnight are accurate indices. It would appear, according to Graber, that after midnight the reduction in altitude of flight to below fifteen hundred feet not only induces an increase in the number of call notes but brings most of the migrants below the effective range of the radar. The fact that migrants are not recorded below this level is recognized on nights when all radar observations are above fifteen hundred feet yet there are high kills at TV towers. In all likelihood it appears that most nocturnal migrants continue flight until nearly dawn.

In studying the migration of hawks, vultures, and storks from Europe and Asia Minor as they passed through southern Turkey in autumn, Cameron *et al.* found that there were two distinct peaks in numbers of raptors passing each day.[17] Very few birds were noted at dawn, but the number built up as the temperature increased. One of the peaks occurred around 10 A.M., and the other, in late afternoon. Very little movement was noted at midday, and in the evening there was a sudden drop in numbers, probably as a result of the decrease in thermals. The peak of the stork migration was always found to occur between 9 A.M. and noon.

SPEED OF MIGRATION

Little is known of the speed of travel of insects. Migratory locusts are said to travel at a maximum of ten miles per hour. The yellow African butterfly (*Catopsilia florella*) has been timed at twelve to sixteen miles

[16]Graber, R. R. 1968.
[17]Cameron, R. A. D., *et al.* 1967.

per hour. Most butterfly migration flight speeds are slower.

Migrating monarch butterflies have been found to travel more than a thousand miles a month. One individual banded at Highland Creek, Ontario, on September 12 was taken on the ninth of the following month at Liberty, Mississippi, a distance of 1,060 miles.[18] Another, banded at the same locality on September 13, was captured on the twenty-fifth of the following month at Brownwood, Texas, a distance of 1,345 miles. The fastest flight for the species was established by an individual that was banded at Highland Creek, Ontario, on September 18 and taken seventeen days later at Roxie, Mississippi. The distance between these two localities is 1,060 miles, representing a minimum flight of over 62 miles a day.

Allen followed the movement of fin-marked coho salmon (*Oncorhynchus kisutch*) along the coast of Washington in autumn to determine their rate of migration.[19] Large numbers of marked salmon that had been hatchery raised in Puget Sound were recovered off the coast of central Washington in early September, 1953. During the first two weeks of the following month, peak numbers were netted in the Seattle area, 150 nautical miles away. The elapsed time was three to four weeks, making the average distance traveled per day from five to seven nautical miles. This does not represent the actual swimming velocity of salmon in the sea, since they usually have to contend with strong currents. A Canadian survey concluded that sockeye salmon (*Oncorhynchus nerka*) travel an average of thirty miles per day at sea, pink salmon (*O. gorbuscha*) twenty-four miles per day, and chum salmon (*O. keta*) sixteen miles per day.[20] Since salmon actively swim during only about one-third of the twenty-four-hour daily cycle, it has been concluded that their speed at such times must exceed three to three and one-half miles per hour.[21]

Groot and Wiley, using time-lapse photography combined with sonar, found that young sockeye salmon smolts migrating in Lake Babine, British Columbia, moved most rapidly in the early evening.[22] On May 23, 1963, the speed of eighteen schools of smolts averaged 1.05 ft./sec. between 10:00 and 10:15 P.M. This was early evening in this latitude. The speed between 1:00 and 1:15 A.M. averaged 0.81 ft./sec. In early

[18]Urquhart, F. A. 1960.
[19]Allen, G. H. 1966.
[20]Neave, F., *et al.*, 1962.
[21]Neave, F. 1964.
[22]Groot, C., and W. L. Wiley. 1965.

morning between 6:00 and 6:15 A.M., nine schools had an average speed of 0.82 ft./sec.

Meinertzhagen provides some interesting data on the comparative flight speeds of migrant and nonmigrant birds of the same species and concludes that birds attain higher speeds in migration than they do in ordinary cruising.[23] The ground speed of most small birds is less than thirty miles per hour. Most ducks and geese migrate at speeds of between forty and fifty miles per hour, although some species have been questionably recorded at seventy miles per hour.

By measuring the speed of progress of migrating hawks between two points at Hawk Mountain Sanctuary in eastern Pennsylvania, investigators have been able to obtain fairly accurate estimates of the speed of flight of certain species. The red-tailed hawk (*Buteo jamaicensis*) moves by the ridges there in migration at approximately forty-five miles per hour. Bald eagles (*Haliaeetus leucocephalus*) and golden eagles (*Aquila chrysaëtos*) have each been timed at about fifty miles per hour.

A check on the speed of small nocturnal migrants in Illinois by means of radar has shown that they have an average ground speed of 36.3 knots per hour. It is rather interesting to note that speed does not increase in proportion to the speed of favorable winds. Thus for each ten-knot increase in wind force, the ground speed increases only 3.2 knots. These figures were arrived at as a result of records of four thousand nocturnal migrants.[24]

Villa-R. and Cockrum estimate that the guano bat (*Tadarida brasiliensis*) in its southward migration from western United States to central Mexico travels at a rate of twenty or more miles per night.[25] The northward migration in spring is thought to be more leisurely.

Davis and Hitchcock indicate that common little brown bats (*Myotis lucifugus*) move rapidly from their wintering caves to the summer colonies after coming out of hibernation in New England.[26] One banded female was found to have traveled eighty miles in the course of three nights, thereby averaging about twenty-seven miles per night.

The speed of migrating humpback whales is regarded as being fairly constant. Based on catching records over the years of humpbacks passing New Zealand, Norfolk Island, and Tonga, the mean overall progression

[23]Meinertzhagen, R. 1955.
[24]Bellrose, F. C. 1967.
[25]Villa-R., B., and E. L. Cockrum. 1962.
[26]Davis, W. H., and H. B. Hitchcock. 1965.

is approximately fifteen degrees per month, according to Chittle-borough.[27] This amounts to 220 nautical miles per month. There are, however, periods of rest and periods of continuous migration. Sometimes individual whales will remain in the same locality for a number of days. On the other hand, Chittleborough reported two marked individuals that traveled sixty miles in twenty-four hours, and another that traveled five hundred miles north in six days.[28]

The sei whales (*Balaenoptera borealis*) in the South Atlantic are estimat-ed by Best to cover approximately sixteen hundred miles in six months.[29] This means they travel about 267 miles a month. The southward move-ment past the coast of South West Africa to the Antarctic reaches its peak in spring between August and October. The peak in the Antarctic occurs in March. The average speed, therefore, is 0.37 knots. These figures tell little of the actual speed of individual whales but indicate rather that of populations over a long period of time.

There is one record of a blue whale (*Balaenoptera musculus*) that covered nineteen hundred miles in the Antarctic in forty-seven days.

HEIGHT OF FLIGHT OF AERIAL MIGRANTS

Most migrating insects fly within a few feet of the ground, rarely going above eight or ten feet. There are exceptions, however. Migratory locusts in Africa are capable of rising to great heights and have been recorded as much as seven thousand feet above ground level. Recent studies on migrating desert locusts (*Schistocerca gregaria*) around Delhi, India, by means of radar, have shown that these insects may fly at heights of up to five thousand feet above the ground. A South American butter-fly, *Ascia monuste*, is said to be abundant up to heights of three thousand feet during migration. Monarch butterflies regularly move at heights of up to three hundred or four hundred feet.

During migration it is often necessary to cross high mountain ranges, which necessitates flight at great altitudes, although not necessarily far above ground level. Some of the most remarkable altitude records are made by the cabbage butterflies (*Pieris brassicae*) and tortoise shells of the genus *Aglais*. Members of the former species have been found at twelve thousand feet in the Alps and the Himalayas, and tortoise shells

[27]Chittleborough, R. G. 1959.
[28]*Ibid.*, 1959.
[29]Best, P. B. 1967.

have been recorded flying at nineteen thousand feet over Zemu Glacier in Sikkim, according to Williams.[30]

Much information has been gathered by various means on the altitudes at which various birds fly while migrating. Earlier observations were made by watching birds in flight, with or without the use of optical instruments. Some information was obtained from records of birds that crashed into lighthouses and beacons at night, although the conclusion from such data that birds migrated within a few hundred feet of the ground was erroneous. Records of sightings from airplanes flying at known altitudes have been of some value but fail to provide sufficient data for any statistical analysis. These various methods, however, do permit ornithologists to draw certain general conclusions. Sea birds such as shearwaters, loons, grebes, alcids, and scoters rarely fly more than a few hundred feet above the sea in migrations. In fact, they often fly just above the crest of the waves.

Large birds such as many kinds of hawks, vultures, and storks usually wait until the heat of the day has produced thermals before they take to the air. They then spiral in these updrafts to gain considerable altitude before gliding in the direction in which they are migrating.

Storks have been noted gliding from one thermal to another, losing altitude between each one but regaining the lost height by riding the succeeding thermal upward. In North Africa, migrating white storks (*Ciconia ciconia*) have been observed by plane as they moved northward in spring at altitudes of over ten thousand feet. In the Himalayas there are records of storks flying at altitudes estimated to be close to twenty thousand feet. Such remarkably high-flying individuals are the exception, however, rather than the rule. The highest record known is that of geese that were seen at Dehra Dun, India, flying at an altitude of 29,500 feet.

Most passerine birds migrate within several thousand feet of the ground. An excellent summary of the earlier studies and records of the height at which birds migrate is given by Meinertzhagen.[31] According to that author, most diurnal passerine migrants fly at less than two hundred feet above ground during migration. If the weather is stormy, the flights are even nearer the ground. The altitudes at which larger birds fly are considerably more variable. The highest records listed are for choughs (*Pyrrhocorax graculus* and *P. pyrrhocorax*) at twenty-one

[30]Williams, C. B. 1958.
[31]Meinertzhagen, R. 1955.

thousand feet, wall creeper (*Tichodroma muraria*) at twenty-one thousand feet, lammergeier (*Gypaetus barbatus*) and condor (*Vultur gryphus*) at 19,800. These birds were not necessarily migrating, and the records were obtained in high mountainous regions where the ground level was not too much less than the flight height of the birds. There is one record of a linnetlike bird, presumably *Carduelis* sp., observed flying at ten thousand feet over France.

Great advances and refinements in our knowledge of the exact altitudes used in migration have been made by the use of radar. This has made it possible to determine the precise height of migrants above the ground during flight for considerable distances at night as well as during the day. The major contributions in this field have been made by Sutter, Harper, Lack, Nisbet, Bellrose and Graber, and Eastwood and Rider.[32] The last two workers named showed that British birds tend to migrate at somewhat higher altitudes at night than they do during the day. The median altitude from daytime measurements is eighteen hundred feet, whereas at night it is two thousand feet. Likewise, there is a difference between spring and autumn, with spring migrants averaging about a hundred feet higher than fall migrants both by night and by day. Nisbet's observations by use of radar over Cape Cod, Massachusetts, indicate that nocturnal migrants fly mostly between 1,500 and 2,500 feet at the peak of the night flight, which is three or four hours after sunset.[33] These were mostly passerine species. He estimated that 90 percent of all the migrants were below five thousand feet and 99 percent below ten thousand feet. His highest altitudinal records were fifteen thousand to twenty thousand feet. These were thought to be either transatlantic migrants or birds arriving from South America and the Lesser Antilles. Nisbet's instrument was useful above six hundred feet. Below this altitude the echoes from the ground and sea overlapped those of low-flying birds. However, he concluded that only 10 to 20 percent of the birds observed during forty-five nights were flying below the six-hundred-foot level. It is interesting to note that the average height of migration was 10 percent higher at 10 P.M. than at 8 P.M.

Lack's figures in general indicate that the migration heights are higher, at least over northern Europe, than those Nisbet recorded over Cape Cod, although most of the passerines were recorded below five thousand

[32]Sutter, E. 1957; Harper, W. G. 1958; Lack, D. 1960; Nisbet, I. C. T. 1963a, 1963b; Bellrose, F. C., and R. R. Graber. 1963; Eastwood, E., and G. C. Rider. 1965.
[33]Nisbet, I. C. T. 1963a.

feet. The highest passerine recorded was at twenty-one thousand feet. This was in September. Lack also notes that in autumn the migration flight tends to be higher than it is in the spring.

Observations made by radar from an aircraft carrier in the Mediterranean Sea by Casement showed that most echoes of migrant birds there were at 4,000 to 6,000 feet.[34] Radar studies by Graber indicate that most migrants passing over the Champaign area of Illinois at night fly at altitudes of between 2,200 and 3,200 feet.[35]

There appears to be little difference in the altitudinal distribution of birds on clear and overcast nights. Studies by radar in Illinois have shown that most birds migrate beneath the cloud cover when the skies are overcast.[36] Other observations, made at Cape Cod in Massachusetts, have also shown that nocturnal migrants do not attempt to climb through a cloud cover unless it is low. Among diurnal migrants, however, weather may definitely influence the height at which certain birds fly. Feeny et al., in their studies of autumn migration in the south Caspian Sea region, noted that swifts, bee-eaters, and swallows showed an increased visible migration during bad weather.[37] This, in their opinion, suggested that most of these birds fly too high to be seen when the weather is good.

Just how migratory birds maintain fairly constant altitudes during migration is not known. Daytime migrants do have landmarks that may serve as guides, but this is not true for nocturnal migrants. It has been suggested that perhaps the ear of a bird serves as an altimeter, but this has yet to be demonstrated.

ORIENTATION

The ability of living organisms to travel in a specific direction or to return to their home base after being displaced to a distant point is one of the most interesting aspects of migration. In subsequent chapters this will be considered for the various groups of vertebrates, but the ability to orient in relation to the environment goes back as far as one-celled organisms. Certain protozoans show a definite phototaxis that, as pointed out by Birukow, is part of their circadian rhythm.[38] From a simple mechanism of orientation like this, it is not a long step to phototactic

[34]Casement, M. B. 1966.
[35]Graber, R. R. 1968.
[36]Bellrose, F. C. 1967.
[37]Feeny, P. P., et al. 1968.
[38]Birukow, G. 1963.

orientation of the type exhibited by planarians, or by many insect larvae. More complicated is the orientation of amphipods, isopods, and certain spiders, which may make use not only of the sun but also of the polarization pattern of the sky. Some can orient by means of the moon, as does the amphipod *Talitrus saltator*. A few years ago von Frisch showed that bees use polarized light in determining their direction.[39] He also demonstrated that they have the ability to use compass orientation by combining fixed periods of time with the sun's azimuth. It is possible that this sort of orientation on the part of invertebrates led to the use of celestial features by vertebrates in making extensive migratory movements.

Orientation to a photostimulus, whether received by a single-celled organism or by a nocturnally migrating bird with a photoreceptor composed of millions of cells, is but one of a number of ways that directive movements are effected. Many kinds of animals orient by means of chemoreceptors. It may be a simple positive or negative reaction as in a protozoan, or it may involve many complicated factors, including special olfactory organs, imprinting, and physiological conditioning, as in certain migratory movements of salmon. Orientation is also often effected by sounds. These may be pulses reflected back from objects in the environment by animals that make use of echolocation, or they may be communicative sounds such as the vocalization of male frogs at a breeding pond to attract females, or the chirps of members of a flock of birds trying to retain a definite spatial relation to each other while migrating at night. As will be seen, there are other senses in addition to those related to sight, olfaction, and sound reception that animals make use of in order to carry out directive movements. These may even include reaction to water currents and electrical impulses. Some of these orientation mechanisms will be considered in the following chapters.

[39]Frisch, K. von. 1950.

12

ORIENTATION IN FISHES

The means by which migratory animals navigate with accuracy has long been a mystery as well as a source of considerable speculation. It is only within very recent years that advances in scientific methodology have produced some explanations.

As a background for studies on orientation it was first necessary to gather accurate data on the migratory movements of the animals concerned. This began with the banding of birds so that individuals could be recognized when recaptured. Marking techniques were subsequently developed to follow the movements of fishes, mammals, amphibians, reptiles, and even certain invertebrates. Data on fishes, such as salmon, showed that individuals traveling long distances from the sea to spawn in small streams at the headwaters of river systems did not migrate in a random manner. Salmon coming to a particular stream were the same individuals that had hatched there several years before and then migrated to the sea. Investigation of the orienting methods that these organisms use to guide themselves while in transit has barely begun, but nonetheless some remarkable discoveries have been made.

OLFACTORY ORIENTATION

When an animal lives in an environment where visibility is limited, it must make use of other methods to find its way if it is to make a long trip. One of these, which is available to all vertebrate animals, even though it is rather poorly developed in birds, is the sense of smell. In our own brain, the lobes concerned with olfaction are among its smallest major components; but in cartilaginous and most bony fishes, the lobes are the largest and among the most important components. The significance of this anatomical feature in the brain of fishes and fishlike vertebrates and its possible use in migratory species was not realized until a few years ago. Great credit must be given to Dr. Arthur D. Hasler of the University of Wisconsin and his associates for discovering the use of olfactory organs by salmon in their migratory movements.

The various species of salmon spawn in the smaller tributaries of waterways that empty into the northern Atlantic and Pacific oceans. In the process, the fish gather in shallow water, where the bottom is sand or gravel. Here the female digs a depression, called a redd, in which she sheds her eggs, and the male deposits milt to fertilize them. She then goes upstream and disturbs the sand or gravel so that it rolls down and covers the eggs. In all species of Pacific salmon (*Oncorhynchus* spp.) the adults subsequently die, but the Atlantic salmon (*Salmo salar*) and the steelhead (*Salmo gairdneri*) may return to the sea and come back another season to reproduce.

Studies on salmon have rather clearly shown that small fry have the odor of the home stream imprinted in them. This odor is the result of chemicals in the water that are primarily organic substances, although inorganic salts cannot entirely be ruled out. The drainage basin of a stream has certain minerals in the soil as well as specific plant communities, all of which may contribute to produce a characteristic odor in the water that is not exactly the same as that of other streams. This distinctive feature of the home stream is learned and remembered by the fish even though it may spend some years in the sea, where the chemical composition of the environment is very different.

A most interesting series of experiments demonstrating the role of olfaction in the homing of salmon was made by Wisby and Hasler.[1] This research was on the coho or silver salmon (*Oncorhynchus kisutch*) in western Washington at the confluence of two streams, Issaquah Creek and its East Fork. Salmon were known to spawn in both branches of this stream and fish ascending either branch were captured a mile to a mile and a half above the point at which the streams separated. Out of a total of 302 fish captured and tagged, 153 had their olfactory organs occluded by cotton plugs so that water was prevented from entering the pits. The remaining 149 were controls. All were taken downstream below the fork and released from this displaced position. All the control fish from the Issaquah Creek that were released after this tagging and displacement below where the streams forked returned to the original point of capture. Seventy-six percent of the controls from the East Fork returned to their

[1]Wisby, W. J., and A. D. Hasler. 1954.

point of capture. On the other hand, 23 percent of the salmon originally captured in Issaquah Creek that had their olfactory pits occluded before subsequent release below the forks entered the East Fork in their attempt to return to the point of capture. Of the salmon captured at East Fork and then displaced downstream after olfactory occlusion, only 16 percent returned to East Fork. There seemed to be little question here as to the significant role of olfaction in the detection of the home stream. A number of subsequent experiments on silver salmon have shown similar results.

Olfaction has also been shown to be important in the homing of the kokanee salmon (*Oncorhynchus nerka kennerlyi*).[2] Unlike most of the other Pacific salmon, the kokanee is not anadromous and spends its life in fresh water. The adults live in lakes and when sexually mature move into their home streams to spawn in the months of August and September. Migrating kokanee swim along shore until they arrive at the mouth of the stream in which they were hatched. When this occurs, they turn abruptly and move into the delta of the stream, where they stop until ready to enter.

Samples of kokanee that had entered their home stream were trapped in a series of experiments. The nasal rosettes were destroyed by cauterization in the experimentals. These, along with an equal number of controls, were then taken and released about 150 meters from the mouth of the home stream. A fair percentage of the controls were recaptured at the original site of capture, but none of those whose nasal rosettes were completely destroyed were subsequently taken, in two series of experiments. There is the possibility, however, that the traumatic effect of cauterization may have been a factor in altering the migratory response.

One of the most remarkable accounts of the homing of silver salmon concerns a fourteen-inch male of this species that was raised in a hatchery in Humboldt County, California.[3] This individual, as well as a number of others, was removed from the hatchery at one year of age and released in another nearby coastal stream. The following year at spawning time this male was found back in the hatchery tank. To get there it had to come in from the sea and up the home stream for five and a half miles, follow a rivulet across porous ground, and travel under U.S. Highway 101 through a one and a half foot culvert and into a storm sewer. From there it was necessary to jump into another smaller culvert and up eighty feet to a flume. Once in the flume, the only way for the salmon to

[2]Lorz, H. W., and T. G. Northcote. 1965.
[3]Regan, C. 1965.

get to the rearing tank was through a four-inch drainpipe that had a ninety-degree bend in it. The pipe rose vertically two and a half feet from the bend to enter the tank. The outlet also had a screen cap covering the top and was surrounded by a square box of wire netting. The square was open at the top and only slightly higher than the water level in the tank. This fish had made this remarkable journey through the culverts and pipe and had knocked off the screen cap to the drain and leaped over the wire netting surrounding the drain. It was aptly christened "Indomitable." Further investigation revealed seventy-two other salmon that had taken the same course had become stranded in the flume.

It is generally believed now that for salmon the major determinant in finding the home stream is the imprinting of the young with the odor of that stream. The eggs of salmon along the Pacific coast have been removed from the parental stream and hatched in a new watercourse. The young when a year old migrated to the sea and subsequently returned to the new stream rather than the parental stream to spawn.[4] This would seem to indicate a conditioned reflex rather than a genetic factor that controls homing.

The time or age at which imprinting takes place varies with the species of salmon. Along the Pacific coast of North America it is believed that imprinting occurs at an early age, possibly within one week of hatching in some members of the genus *Oncorhynchus*. With the Atlantic salmon (*Salmo salar*) this may occur at a considerably later age. It has been shown in Scandinavia that salmon transported from their home stream at one year of age will subsequently, after returning from the sea, go to the new stream to which they were transplanted.

Olfactory orientation as a result of chemical imprinting of the home stream odor presents a plausible explanation of the manner in which these fish return to the same locality where they were hatched. This odor, though very dilute, may still be detected far downstream or even in the major rivers of which these streams are tributaries. It has been demonstrated that fish can detect chemicals that are greatly diluted. Studies on the olfactory organs of eels have shown that dilutions of β-phenylethyl alcohol equivalent to half a teaspoonful in a volume of water the size of Lake Constance can be detected by these fish.[5] This is equivalent to only two or three molecules of this chemical contacting the olfactory epithelium at any one time.

[4]Donaldson, L. R., and G. H. Allen, 1958.
[5]Teichmann, H. 1957.

Each year about 3,000 chinook salmon (*Oncorhynchus tshawytscha*) migrate from the sea to Lake Union and then, by means of a ladder, to the small pond seen in the center of the picture in front of the University of Washington College of Fisheries, in Seattle. *Photograph by James O. Sneddon, courtesy University of Washington.*

A chinook salmon moving up the ladder from Lake Union to the pond in front of the University of Washington School of Fisheries, where it had hatched a previous year. *Photograph by James O. Sneddon, courtesy University of Washington.*

OTHER SENSORY FACTORS

Other sensory factors, however, may play some role in salmon migration, even after the fish have entered fresh water. The memory of some edaphic features such as the type of bottom, temperature, volume of flow, or even speed of current may be of some significance. It has been shown by Stuart that salmon also make use of currents and sound vibrations in their timing when ascending waterfalls.[6]

Downstream orientation by young salmon is very different from that employed by adults returning to spawn. Pink salmon (*Oncorhynchus gorbuscha*) and chum salmon (*O. keta*) tend to spawn in the lower parts of streams, usually no more than one hundred miles from the sea. When hatched, the fry stay hidden in the gravel bed, coming out only briefly to secure food. When they are only a few weeks old, they begin their downstream migration. This seems to be controlled partly by light and partly by current. During the daytime they stabilize their position, usually by burrowing into the sand or gravel at the bottom of the stream. When night comes, they rise and drift with the current until daylight. In this way the ocean is reached in a very few days.

A different sort of downstream migration is engaged in by other Pacific salmon, including the chinook or king salmon (*Oncorhynchus tshawytscha*), the coho or silver salmon (*O. kisutch*), the sockeye (*O. nerka*), and also by the Atlantic salmon (*Salmo salar*). In these species, spawning takes place at a considerably greater distance inland. Like the pink and chum salmon, the young of these species tend to avoid light and stay hidden on the bottom of the parent stream during the daytime. At night they emerge and drift with the swift current until they reach a lake into which the stream flows. Here they remain for a year or so until they have attained what is termed the smolt stage, at which time they begin moving to the outlet of the lake. Some of these lakes are very large. Johnson and Groot, in their study of the migration of young sockeye salmon through a large, complex lake system in British Columbia, concluded that the smolts made use of sun-compass orientation to arrive at the outlet.[7] Furthermore, they found that the salmon changed their migratory direction as the season progressed and the position of the sun changed. To see if the sun was the guiding factor, the investigators

[6]Stuart, T. A. 1962.
[7]Johnson, W. E., and C. Groot. 1963.

captured smolts and placed them in containers, where their movements were recorded at noon each day. Under these conditions the fish showed the same directional orientation as those in the lake as well as the same directional changes as the season progressed.

As a result of further studies on sockeye smolts, Groot came to the conclusion that in addition to sun-compass orientation, young salmon make use of polarized light from the blue sky.[8] Their migratory movements occur primarily during the twilight periods of the evening and morning. This is the time when neither the sun nor the stars are visible. However, the polarization of the light from the sky is most pronounced then.

Placing a polaroid filter over an experimental tank which had the horizon blocked off appeared to have little effect on the direction of orientation of smolts at noon. When this was performed at dusk, a marked effect was noted. In twelve out of sixteen smolts, menotaxis in relation to the plane of polarization was indicated. Groot also concluded that orientation under these conditions was not to horizontal light intensity patterns resulting from polarized light but directly to the polarized light itself. He further found that sockeye salmon (*Oncorhynchus nerka*) often reverse their migratory direction by 180 degrees under experimental conditions. This sort of bipolar orientation along the proper axis has also been noted in the southern cricket frog (*Acris gryllus*) in experimental tanks.

Once young salmon have reached the mouth of the river to which their home stream is a tributary, they begin to show increased tolerance to salt water, in which they will be living for the next two or three years. Pacific coast salmon range widely over the North Pacific Ocean during these years in search of food. Individuals that have been tagged off Baranof Island in Alaskan waters have subsequently been taken in the Columbia drainage. The greatest concentrations of these fish are found in the Gulf of Alaska.

Less is known regarding the orienting mechanism used by adult salmon to find the entrance to the home river system. Currents or odors seem unlikely to be able to guide these fish across hundreds of miles of open sea. It has been suggested that they may make use of sun-compass orientation, but this theory has yet to be proved. Much of the time the sun is obscured by clouds and fog in the North Pacific, and it is also known that salmon move by night as well as by day. Some sensory

[8]Groot, C. 1965.

process, however, guides them accurately and will ultimately be discovered.

Sun-compass orientation has been clearly demonstrated in the white
bass (*Roccus chrysops*) by Dr. Hasler and his associates.[9] Lake Mendota,
Wisconsin, where this work was undertaken, has a shoreline of 32.4 km.
and a surface area of 39.4 square km. There are only two sites in the lake
where white bass spawn. Both are along the north shore. Here the bass
congregate in late May and early June upon moving in from the open
water. Studies were made over five spawning seasons on the effect of
displacement. Fish were captured at the two shoreline localities, marked
with Peterson disks, and transported to release points 2.4 km. from each
spawning ground. Releases were made during daylight hours and records kept of sun visibility. Each fish had a float attached to its back by
means of a nylon thread so that its course could be traced. Fish so displaced moved in a northerly direction, provided their eyes were un-
covered and the sky was not obscured by clouds. Once the shoreline was
reached, it appeared that both visual clues in the immediate environment
and olfaction aided in finding the spawning area. Fish with opaque
plastic cups covering their eyes moved at random when so displaced.
Likewise, no directional orientation was evident when displaced fish
were released under overcast skies. The fact that white bass could maintain a constant compass direction when the sun was visible, irrespective
of the time of day, led Dr. Hasler to conclude that they also have an
internal biological clock that enables them to compensate for the changing solar azimuth.

Visual orientation, not necessarily celestial, has been demonstrated in
other freshwater fishes, including largemouth bass (*Micropterus salmoides*)
and green sunfish (*Lepomis cyanellus*).

[9]Hasler, A. D., *et al.*, 1958; Hasler, A. D. 1966.

13

ORIENTATION IN AMPHIBIANS
AND REPTILES

AMPHIBIANS

In early spring the calls of frogs and toads emanate nightly from swamps and ponds where these amphibians gather for breeding purposes. Many tailed amphibians also move to streams and ponds to lay their eggs, though they remain silent. As spring progresses, these adults move away from the water, not to return until the next year. The eggs hatch and the young tadpoles grow until they complete their metamorphosis, at which time they too move onto land and begin a new manner of life.

The movements of amphibians involve very small distances, in contrast to the migrations of other kinds of vertebrates, but it has been discovered that they use some of the same means of orientation. Sun- and stellar-compass cues are employed by many, perhaps most, anurans in their seasonal travels to and from their breeding ponds. The young likewise make use of these methods in locating shorelines. It is likely that amphibians, like some fishes, have been using celestial orientation for long periods of time, probably since before birds and mammals made their appearance in the world.

Vocalization also functions as a means of orientation in anurans. In most species the males call at the breeding sites during the breeding season. This serves, in part, to attract and guide females as well as other males to these locations. Vocalization, of course, serves other purposes. It seems to function as an isolating mechanism and may stimulate reproductive activity. Recently it has been shown that olfaction too plays an important part in the orientation of some caudate amphibians.

ANURANS. Bogert some years ago, in his study of the Carolina toad (*Bufo t. terrestris*), summarized most of what was known up to that time about the homing activities of amphibians.[1] He indicated that, in his opinion, vocalization was the most important clue in orienting the Carolina toad to the breeding ponds. Later, Jameson published an account of a two-year project involving the displacement of Pacific tree frogs (*Hyla regilla*) as well as the seasonal return of marked individuals in western Oregon.[2] His results showed that most males return not only to the same pond each breeding season but also to the same part of the pond in which they had territories the previous year. In one experiment 414 frogs were moved from their breeding pond and released one thousand yards away in another pond containing a breeding chorus. One month later none of the frogs was found in the release pond, but 5 of the 414 were back at the home pond. In this locality the male tree frogs go to the breeding areas in January or February and some males are still present after the breeding season is over. Warm rains apparently stimulate the females to move to where the males are calling, although they leave after the eggs are laid. Homing is not attributed to any one factor. It has been suggested that olfactory, auditory, and kinesthetic senses may contribute to this response in Pacific tree frogs.

On Barro Colorado Island in the Canal Zone, during the nonbreeding season, displaced giant toads (*Bufo marinus*) have been found to return invariably to their original stations of capture.[3] At this time of year there is no vocalization by the males. In most of the experiments the displaced individuals were captured near lights outside of buildings and when subsequently released were still able to see the lights. Visual clues were therefore thought to function for orientation. In instances where released toads were unable to see their home lights, their return was thought to be a result of retention of previously learned topographic clues, although celestial navigation was still considered as a possibility.

Fowler's toad (*Bufo fowleri*) occurs in the Mississippi Valley and Great Lakes region. A three-year study carried on at State College, Mississippi, where this toad is abundant, indicated that both auditory and celestial cues may function for orientation.[4] Toads could be diverted from their course toward breeding sites by calls from other directions. Furthermore, they were found to aggregate for breeding at new ponds less than one year old.

[1]Bogert, C. M. 1947.
[2]Jameson, D. L. 1957.
[3]Brattstrom, B. H. 1962.
[4]Ferguson, D. E., and H. F. Landreth. 1966.

To test possible compass orientation based on celestial clues, a circular test pen sixty feet in diameter was constructed seventy-five yards from shore in water about four feet deep. The plastic walls of the pen extended two feet below the surface of the water, and only the sky and the walls of the pen were visible from the surface. Recently transformed young toads were subjected to a variety of conditions. These included individual tests, group tests, the testing of two groups from different shores at the same time, and long-distance displacement. Some toads were transported from the site of capture along shore to the test pen in light-proof bags from which they were released after surface disturbance in the water had ceased. Others were transported in full view of the sky.

In general the results showed that the young toads able to see the sun in the test pen oriented in a direction corresponding to a line bisecting the home shoreline at right angles. This was referred to as the Y-axis. There was little or no orientation under closed cover. Individuals displaced as much as ninety-one miles displayed the same Y-axis orientation. Unlike adults, young toads did not rely to any great extent on stellar orientation. The authors conclude that orientation to a Y-axis compass course is probably imprinted on the toads around the time of metamorphosis. Since they are largely diurnal until they attain a body length of thirty-eight to forty-five millimeters, solar orientation is most effective in assisting them to find the shoreline even when they cannot see it. In the toads tested it was found that directive orientation persisted in individuals maintained in total darkness for seventy-two hours, indicating an internal clock mechanism.

Adult toads are largely nocturnal and appear to depend to a large extent on celestial signs, especially in the nonbreeding season when there are no auditory clues for orientation.

Ferguson, Landreth, and Turnipseed conducted a series of orientation tests with the southern cricket frog (*Acris gryllus*) at Bluff Lake in Mississippi.[5] Frogs were captured and placed in a circular plastic pen in the water where they could not see landmarks on the horizon. When released under the sun in the pen, they swam in a direction that would have taken them to land had they been thrown into the lake off their home shore. The behavior was the same whether they were transferred to the experimental pen in view of the sky or in a darkened container. Similar results were obtained with frogs released under a full moon and

[5]Ferguson, D. E., H. F. Landreth, and M. R. Turnipseed. 1965.

starlit sky. When released under a moonless but starry sky, they showed a bipolar orientation along the proper axis, with some going in the direction of the home shore and others going in exactly the opposite direction.

When frogs were released between sunset and the appearance of the moon or stars, their directional movements appeared to be of a random nature. This was also true when clouds obscured the sky.

Similar experimental studies have been done with northern cricket frogs (*Acris crepitans*).[6] When removed from shore and placed in a circular offshore pen, these frogs orient on a compass course that is at right angles to the shoreline. There was no difference noticed in the orientation of individuals moved while in view of the sky and those moved in covered containers. Likewise, when the frogs were displaced as much as 115 miles to the east in lighttight containers, the orientation was in the same direction.

CAUDATE AMPHIBIANS. Caudate amphibians do not vocalize; therefore, auditory clues, at least from their own kind, cannot serve these animals as a means of orientation. Furthermore, the ear of caudate amphibians has not advanced to the stage found in anurans. There is evidence, however, that olfaction may be of considerable importance in the movements of some species of newts and salamanders.

Some of the most significant experiments on orientation in these animals have been carried on in western North America on the western red-bellied newt (*Taricha rivularis*), which occurs in the redwood belt of northwestern California.[7] During the dry summer months these amphibians remain underground. When the rains come in October or November, they emerge and live under rocks and logs until it is time to move to nearby streams or ponds to breed. In one series of experiments numerous males were marked by amputating one or both hind feet. These are regenerated but do not attain full size for four or five years. The marked newts were captured in a stream and displaced for distances ranging from one to over two and a half miles. The foreign sites at which they were released were either in the same stream or a different one, and the displacement was made within one or two days of capture. Out of 564 individuals captured at one station and displaced about one and a half miles down the same stream, 58 percent were recaptured during the succeeding three breeding seasons. The great majority returned to their

[6]Ferguson, D. E., H. F. Landreth, and J. P. McKeown. 1967.
[7]Twitty, V. C. 1959; Packer, W. C. 1963; Twitty, V., D. Grant, and O. Anderson. 1964.

original point of capture, with a small number remaining in the new locality. Essentially none was found in the intervening portion of the stream. In another experiment 692 males were marked and transported over rough terrain from the home stream to one that was approximately two miles away. The two watercourses were separated by a ridge. During the following three breeding seasons, 77 percent of the displaced newts were found to have returned to the original site of capture. Twitty at that time was inclined to believe that olfactory clues played a major part in the orientation of these salamanders. This conclusion was based in part on the fact that blinded salamanders were able to home successfully.

Subsequently Grant, Anderson, and Twitty carried on another series of experiments which indicated that olfactory clues were definitely used by newts in homing.[8] These studies were made on the same species, *Taricha rivularis*, and also involved displacement from the home area. Such displaced individuals returned directly to their home regardless of compass direction or the character of the intervening terrain. Blinded individuals accomplished this as well as those with their vision unimpaired. Newts with their olfactory nerves surgically impaired, however, did not return when similarly displaced unless the nerves had regenerated. This species does most of its migrating to breeding sites during cloudy or rainy nights when celestial clues are unavailable but olfactory clues are present.

In another experimental study Landreth and Ferguson showed that rough-skinned newts (*Taricha granulosa*), while in the process of migration as well as at the breeding ponds, are capable of celestial orientation by day and by night.[9] Both migrating and breeding newts were captured and placed in circular arenas with walls about two meters high that obscured the landscape but permitted them to see the sky. On both sunny days and moonlit nights, they so oriented in these arenas that their courses would have intersected the shoreline of the breeding pond at right angles. Migrating individuals released 27.6 kilometers from the point of capture maintained the same compass course, essentially precluding the possibility of olfactory orientation. Under cloudy skies this compass orientation was not maintained. However, blinded individuals showed the same sun-compass orientation as those with unimpaired vision, which the experimenters suggest presents evidence that there may

[8]Grant, D., O. Anderson, and V. Twitty. 1968.
[9]Landreth, H. F., and D. E. Ferguson. 1967.

The rough-skinned newt (*Taricha granulosa*) exhibits a remarkable homing ability. *Photographed in Marin County, California, by Robert T. Orr.*

be alternative light receptors associated with the optic tectum.

Displacement experiments of a similar nature, but not involving such distances, have been made on several other kinds of salamanders.[10] Female green salamanders, *Aneides aeneus*, of southeastern United States when displaced for distances up to three times the length of the home range are able to return to their nests within twenty-four hours. Similar results have been obtained with the dusky salamander, *Desmognathus fuscus*. Furthermore, when dusky salamanders are displaced at right angles to a stream, the percentage of returns decreases markedly with the increase in distance and seems dependent on a moist substrate. When females are displaced with their eggs, they remain with them and exhibit no homing behavior. One might conclude from this that chemical stimuli in some way may play a part in homing.

As a result of marking spotted salamanders (*Ambystoma maculatum*) in

[10]Gordon, R. E. 1961; Dennis, D. M. 1962; Rose, F. L. 1966.

a breeding population in two small ponds in Kingston, Rhode Island, it was found that 76 percent returned to the same breeding site within two years.[11] The annual migration from areas where these salamanders hide during the nonbreeding season to the breeding ponds probably does not involve more than one thousand feet each way.

REPTILES

SEA TURTLES. Very extensive studies have been made on green turtles (*Chelonia mydas*) by Dr. Archie Carr of the University of Florida.[12] Green turtles are found in the tropical and subtropical parts of oceans around the world. They are limited to the north and south by temperature, generally not occurring in waters that are colder than 68° Fahrenheit.

The breeding areas and the feeding grounds of green turtles are quite different. The females lay their eggs on the sandy beaches of remote oceanic islands and bury them above high tide. The males do not come on the beach but may mate with the females just off shore. It is believed that these matings do not serve to fertilize the eggs that the females are about to lay, as many of them have shells at this time, but are for the fertilization of eggs to be laid in the next two or three years. Some females have a two-year cycle, and others produce eggs every third year.

Each female lays eggs from three to seven times, with an interval of about twelve days between successive visits to the beach. About one hundred eggs are laid each time. The laying season varies in different parts of the world and in some regions may occur at any time of the year. The eggs, which are encased in a tough, leathery shell, are about two inches in length and require nearly two months of incubation in the warm sand before they hatch.

Outside of the reproductive period, the adults move to areas where turtle grass, their principal food, is abundant. These grazing areas are, for the most part, off continental coasts.

The question as to where the turtles that breed on these remote oceanic islands or isolated beaches migrate from has long been a puzzle. The first clues to this were the result of a tagging program by Dr. Carr and his students. During an eight-year period they tagged over three thou-

[11]Whitford, W. G., and A. Vinegar. 1966.
[12]Carr, A. 1965.

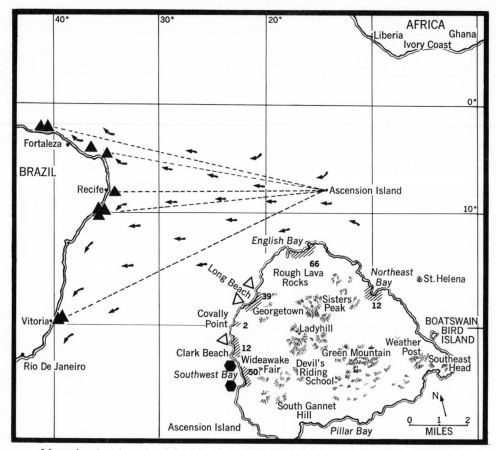

Maps showing Acension Island in the mid-Atlantic where green turtles were banded, and the possible routes followed to points of subsequent recovery along the coast of Brazil. (After Carr, A., 1967)

sand adult green turtles at Tortuguero Beach on the Caribbean coast of Costa Rica. One hundred twenty-nine of them were recovered subsequently by turtle hunters. Although most of the recoveries were made along the coast of Nicaragua, there were records of captures made off Cuba, Florida, Yucatan, and as far south as the coast of Venezuela. This project proved that there was a wide dispersal of turtles following the breeding season, although it did not prove that there was any definite migratory pattern. The dispersal could easily be a random one.

To prove that green turtles have definite migratory movements, Dr. Carr and one of his graduate students, Harold Heath, decided to band turtles on Ascension Island. This tiny landmass is located in the middle of the South Atlantic Ocean, approximately fourteen hundred miles east of Brazil. It is about seven miles in greatest breadth, and the highest peak, named Green Mountain, has an elevation of five thousand feet. A turtle swimming could see Ascension Island only from within a few miles.

Green turtles come to this isolated oceanic island to lay eggs each year between February and June. The nearest feeding grounds where turtle grass is abundant are along the west coast of Africa and the Brazilian coast, where these animals are very abundant. The tagging program was started on Ascension Island in 1960. Some of those tagged that year were recovered two years later when they returned to lay, and the following year three of the 1960-tagged individuals were recorded. In 1964 two, that had returned in 1962, again came back to the place where they had been tagged in 1960. This indicated a probable two- or three-year cycle. The most important discoveries, however, were made by Brazilian fishermen, who up to 1965 had captured nine of the marked Ascension Island turtles along their own coast.

Although this does not positively prove a migratory pattern, it strongly indicates that one exists. The question as to how green turtles that spend most of their lives along the Brazilian coast find a small mid-Atlantic island is an interesting one on which to speculate. Ascension Island is in the path of the South Equatorial Current, which travels at the rate of three to four miles per hour to the west. Young turtles leaving the island can drift until they reach the South American coast, but the return trip as an adult that may weigh as much as five hundred pounds and that has to swim fourteen hundred miles or more against a four-mile-an-hour current is another matter. Obviously this must be done, but there is still the tiny island to find in a large sea in which visible landmarks are lacking. The possibility of olfactory orientation has been suggested, but it seems unlikely that chemical substances exuding from this island could be detected at such great distances. The current itself is doubtless a broad guiding factor, but much more precise information is required to locate so small a mass of land as an island only seven miles in diameter that must, in addition, be seen from the surface of the sea.

The most plausible explanation as to how green turtles from the east coast of South America swimming eastward against the South Equatorial Current find Ascension Island is that they make use of sun-compass orientation. This, of course, has yet to be proved, but Dr. Carr and his associates are endeavoring to find the answer.

On hatching, young green sea turtles orient toward the sea. Once in the sea, they swim away from shore until they are picked up by ocean currents. This behavioral pattern gets them under the protection of water and away from the threat of predation by sea birds as soon as possible. Experiments performed by Dr. Carr involving the transportation by plane of young turtles from the Caribbean side to a Pacific coast beach of Costa Rica showed that the young in this new environment immediately went toward the sea when released. In this instance the direction of the sea was the opposite of that in the area from which they had been removed, showing that they were not depending on a sun compass for this purpose. It was suggested at the time that perhaps the quality of light over open water was the orienting factor. In young turtles kept in captivity this tendency to orient toward the sea disappears after several months.

Later, in a series of controlled experiments by Ehrenfeld and Carr, it was found that sea-finding by the adult females after laying and by the young turtles after hatching appears to be primarily a visual process involving inspection of the beach horizon and landscape features.[13] They found no evidence of an innate compass direction preference based on celestial information. Blindfolded turtles were unable to find the sea except accidentally. Young placed in a low-walled container with full view of the sky went toward land 50 percent of the time, whereas those in an unwalled area went toward the sea, even though it could not be seen. Turtles with green filters or neutral density filters and depolarized diffusion filters over the eyes, to which they had become adapted, oriented as well as those with clear filters. Red, blue, and 0.4 neutral density filters decreased orientation ability.

Research continues on the movements of adult and young green turtles, whose amazing migrations still prove to be a puzzle to scientists.

TERRESTRIAL REPTILES. Unlike amphibians, terrestrial reptiles do not need to move to ponds or streams, nor to the land like marine turtles. As was pointed out in an earlier chapter, however, some tortoises and snakes do make seasonal movements to winter dens and summer

[13]Ehrenfeld, D. W., and A. Carr. 1967.

feeding areas. Perhaps the nearest approach to a true migration is that of female Galapagos tortoises (*Testudo elephantopus*), which are reported to come down from the highlands of certain islands to lower coastal areas. There they dig holes in the soil and deposit their eggs.

Experiments have been made on the homing ability of a number of kinds of lizards and snakes, but as yet there is little evidence to show that they make use of any celestial clues. In a study of the movements and seasonal activities of the side-blotched lizard (*Uta stansburiana*), Spoecker found that homing occurred only when individuals were displaced no more than 400 feet from the original point of capture.[14] This would seem to indicate that familiarity with the area is a prerequisite to homing. Since every individual that was displaced less than 250 feet from the point of capture returned, it was concluded that the familiar home territory for these lizards consisted of an area about 500 feet in its smallest diameter.

[14]Spoecker, P. D. 1967.

14

ORIENTATION IN BIRDS

CELESTIAL ORIENTATION

For many years those who kept migrating songbirds in captivity were aware that some species exhibited nocturnal restlessness during the migration period. German ornithologists used the word *Zugunruhe* to describe this phenomenon. The significance of nocturnal migratory restlessness, however, was not clearly known until Gustav Kramer presented evidence to show that it was directionally oriented.[1] He worked primarily with three species of European birds that were known to be night migrants. One of these was the red-backed shrike (*Lanius collurio*), which breeds in Europe and western Asia and winters in southern Africa. The other two were Old World warblers, the whitethroat (*Sylvia communis*) and the blackcap (*Sylvia atricapilla*). Both nest throughout most of Europe and winter principally in tropical Africa, although some blackcaps winter in southern Europe around the Mediterranean. When these birds were kept in circular cages where they could see the sky without the distraction of city lights, at night in the fall of the year they faced toward the south and all of their orientation was in this direction. The reflection of city lights disrupted this orientation and caused them to orient toward the light.

This was a great step forward, but it did not explain how birds were able to determine direction at night. Subsequently Kramer studied the starling (*Sturnus vulgaris*), a species that is essentially sedentary in western Europe but migratory in much of central Europe.[2] The fall migration is to the southwest, to southwestern Europe and northern Africa. Starlings, unlike many other passerines, are diurnal migrants. Kramer kept starlings in circular cages similar to those he used for night migrants and

[1]Kramer, G. 1949, 1950.
[2]Kramer, G. 1951.

found that during the day they oriented in spring to the northeast and in autumn to the southwest. He concluded that they obtained their bearings from the sky, since this was all they could see, and that their directional orientation was the same as that of free-flying migrants. He then built cages with six windows, each having a movable shutter permitting the window to be closed. Above each shutter was a mirror that allowed light to enter the cage at a definite angle. Observations on the positions or orientation of a bird in such a cage were made from below through a Plexiglas bottom. Even with most of the sky obscured, the starlings were able to orient themselves in the proper direction. Furthermore, Kramer found that shifting, by means of a mirror, the angle of the rays of light coming from the sky near the sun caused the birds to reorient accordingly. A shift of ninety degrees in the sky caused the starlings to shift ninety degrees. This was fairly conclusive proof that the birds were using the sun as a compass. Since starlings migrate for about six hours after daybreak and the sun changes position during this same time, Kramer postulated that the birds have a built-in time clock that compensates for the changing position of the sun, which in six hours has changed position by ninety degrees.

Matthews in England came to essentially the same conclusions as Kramer although his explanation was quite different.[3] Kramer's hypothesis was based on the belief that direction on the part of a diurnal migrant was obtained by determining the angle of the sun above the horizon. Matthews, on the other hand, concluded that the migrating bird was familiar with the path the sun takes through the sky and consequently with the sun's position on its arc at any one time. When a bird is migrating over an unfamiliar area, it has to reconstruct the whole arc on the basis of the sun's movement over a small part of that arc. Thus, by means of extrapolation to determine the maximum altitude, plus a knowledge of the angle of the horizon, a comparison with the home situation latitude can be determined. Longitude is obtained by comparing the position of the sun in relation to the highest point in the arc with the corresponding home position as indicated by the internal time clock of the bird.

To test Kramer's theory, Schmidt-Koenig devised a series of experimental studies on homing pigeons at the Max-Planck-Institut in Wilhelmshaven, Germany, and at Duke University in North Carolina.[4] He postulated that if the "internal clock" of these pigeons was reset by a

[3]Matthews, G. V. T. 1955.
[4]Schmidt-Koenig, K. 1960.

time-shifted sequence of day-night cycles, they would be misled in their orientation in a predictable way when released. Accordingly, over a period of four years he carried on three groups of experiments, each involving about eighteen experimental and eighteen control birds.

In each of the experiments all birds were kept in lightproof rooms in which an artificial day-night cycle could be provided. In group A the experimental birds had the light switched on and off six hours before natural sunrise and sunset. In group B the experimental birds had the light switched on and off six hours later than natural sunrise and sunset. For group C the time schedule was shifted twelve hours, so as to reverse completely the natural time of sunrise and sunset. Groups A and B were subjected to the time shift of six hours for four days before being released, and group C was maintained for seven days under the twelve-hour shift. All of the controls were kept on the natural day-night schedule.

The birds in all groups, both experimentals and controls, were displaced in various directions and at distances varying from 5.5 to one hundred miles on their release. Furthermore, it was so planned that each release would occur during the period of natural daylight. Birds were released singly, with experimentals alternating with controls. Each bird was followed with binoculars until it was out of sight, and records were kept on the times of arrival in the home lofts.

It was expected that those birds whose time clock had been advanced six hours would deviate approximately 90 degrees to the left of the controls and those whose time clock had been retarded six hours would deviate 90 degrees to the right. The birds whose day was reversed should shift 180 degrees from the controls. The actual results, while not exactly as predicted, came close. The experimental birds in group A had a mean deviation of 72 degrees to the left. Those in group B had a mean deviation of 93 degrees to the right. The birds in group C had a mean deviation of 168 degrees to the right of the controls.

An explanation of the orienting mechanism used by nocturnal migrants still remained to be discovered. It had been shown by Drost and others that the moon has no significant effect on migratory birds.[5] Migration occurs at the same rate with or without the moon and irrespective of its phases. It remained for Franz Sauer and his wife Eleanore, through a series of unique experiments, to present an almost unbelievable explanation.[6]

[5]Drost, R. 1935.
[6]Sauer, F., and E. Sauer, 1955; Sauer, F. 1956, 1957, 1958.

The Sauers worked on Old World warblers of the genus *Sylvia* and employed circular cages very similar to those used by Kramer. The birds, therefore, had a clear view of the sky above. Observations were made from beneath through a Plexiglas bottom to the cage so that the directional orientation of a bird in a cage at night could be noted. As had previously been determined by Kramer, the warblers oriented in a northeast or north-northeast direction in April and in a southwest or south-southwest direction from late August until October. However, it was found that directional orientation ceased when the sky was overcast, and movements were then of a random nature.

From these studies Sauer concluded that these nocturnal migrants must make use of stars or star patterns for orientation. To prove this, the experiments were transferred to the Olbers Planetarium in Bremen. In a planetarium, by the use of a projector the appearance of the sky at night can be projected onto a dome. The projector may project the stars and planets as seen at any desired time of night and at any location on the earth at any time, past, present, or future. Here was a tool that would prove or disprove Dr. Sauer's hypothesis. Although the Olbers Planetarium was a small one with a dome only about twenty feet in diameter, when the birds were placed under the dome in diffused light, their nocturnal movements were of a random nature. This was done to be certain there were no landmarks of which they might make use. When an artificial spring night sky was projected to these migrants in the spring, they immediately oriented northeast to north-northeast. This was evidence that these birds were making use of celestial clues for direction.

A number of other experiments were carried out to present further proof of this discovery. Several species of warblers of the genus *Sylvia* were taken in autumn from Europe and transported to their wintering grounds in Africa. There, when placed in the experimental cages and exposed to the night sky, they first directed their activities to the south but soon ceased exhibiting nocturnal restlessness. The winter sky pattern apparently inhibited further *Zugunruhe*.

Other workers meanwhile were contributing to the significance of celestial navigation in avian migration. Frank Bellrose, working on mallards (*Anas platyrhynchos*) in Illinois, found that these ducks, when displaced at distances ranging from eleven to thirty-three miles and released, would immediately head in the correct direction for home on clear nights.[7] He was able to follow them for some distance by illumina-

[7]Bellrose, F. C. 1958b.

tion from small flashlights that were attached to their feet. On cloudy nights the movements of the ducks on being released appeared to be random ones.

A very interesting series of observations was made by Hamilton and Hammond on the migratory impulse in pinioned Canada geese (*Branta canadensis*) that were released or escaped from several wildlife refuges south of their natural breeding areas.[8] The birds were trapped in Missouri and taken to the Dakotas, Minnesota, and Nebraska. Those that were released or escaped in their new environment in spring during or even after the normal time of northward migration moved overland in a northward direction. The greatest distance traveled by any one goose was 24.8 air miles. The speed of travel was fairly uniform throughout the season and ranged from .31 to .74 miles per day. The observers intimate that orientation may have been influenced to some extent by wild migrants flying overhead. However, they point out that northward overland migration on the part of pinioned birds continued for some time after the end of the normal period of migration, indicating the possible use of celestial clues.

In California extensive experiments on the nocturnal orientation of captive sparrows of several species belonging to the genus *Zonotrichia* have been made in recent years by Dr. L. Richard Mewaldt of San Jose State College and some of his associates.[9] The forms used included two races of the white-crowned sparrow: *Zonotrichia leucophrys gambelii*, which breeds from Alaska east to Hudson Bay and south to north central Washington, and *Zonotrichia leucophrys pugetensis*, which breeds along the Pacific coast from southwestern British Columbia to northwestern California. Some populations of both winter in central California. In addition, the golden-crowned sparrow (*Zonotrichia atricapilla*) and the white-throated sparrow (*Zonotrichia albicollis*) were used. The golden-crowned sparrow breeds mainly in western Canada and Alaska and winters in California, and the white-throated sparrow breeds in Canada and northeastern United States. A few birds of the latter species winter in central California. The response of these four wintering populations to the night sky was recorded. The birds, which were captured and maintained at San Jose, were exposed to the sky at various times of the year, although most of the data, which involved 140,000 bird hours and over a million perch hours, were obtained during the migration periods. The cages used were circular and had eight activity-sensitive perches around the

[8]Hamilton, W. J. III, and M. C. Hammond. 1960.
[9]Mewaldt, L. R. 1964.

periphery. When a bird landed on the perch, it depressed the arm of a microswitch and closed the circuit, which was connected to an Esterline-Angus 20-pen recorder. The closure of the circuit resulted in a pen mark on the paper of the rotating drum of the recorder. The results of over four years of recording were published by Mewaldt, Morton, and Brown.[10] The birds of all four populations showed a northward orientation in the spring and a southward orientation in the autumn. In the spring the restlessness occurred mainly before midnight, whereas in the autumn it was principally between midnight and dawn. The strongest spring northern and autumn southern *Zugunruhe* was shown by *Zonotrichia l. gambelii*, with *Z. atricapilla*, *Z. l. pugetensis*, and *Z. albicollis* showing progressive decrease in the strength of their responses, in this order. In some birds the light from the city or the moon was found to overwhelm the orientation mechanism at times. It was suggested that night restlessness and directional choice may be separate components. Furthermore, *Zugunruhe* may develop before the sense of orientation does. In these captive birds the migratory restlessness in spring extended beyond the migratory period.

Further evidence of the use of star patterns by nocturnal avian migrants was provided by a study of bobolinks (*Dolichonyx oryzivorus*) conducted by W. J. Hamilton III.[11] The bobolink is a transequatorial migrant whose breeding range is confined to the grasslands of northern United States and southern Canada. It winters in southern Brazil, Uruguay, and northern Argentina. This involves an annual round trip of over twelve thousand miles, which exceeds the distance traveled by any other passerine bird in the Western Hemisphere. So far as is known, most of the migrants pass through Florida in both spring and fall. A few seem to move down the western American coast and even reach the Galapagos Islands.

Most of Dr. Hamilton's birds were captured in North Dakota during the breeding season and maintained in San Francisco, California, on local time either indoors or under natural sky. Circular cages with peripheral perches attached to automatic registering devices and sides that prevented visual detection of the horizon were used in his experiments. At night when exposed to a clear sky in autumn, these birds took a migratory course which was parallel to that taken by wild migrants going from North Dakota to Florida. On moonlit nights the birds directed their activities toward the moon, which interfered with orienta-

[10]Mewaldt, L. R., M. L. Morton, and I. L. Brown. 1964.
[11]Hamilton, W. J. III. 1962a.

White-crowned sparrows (*Zonotrichia leucophrys*) at Point Reyes Bird Observatory, Marin County, California. *Photograph by William K. Kirsher.*

tion, and on overcast nights directional response was lacking and activity waned markedly. Young birds that had never migrated showed the same response as adults. Some experiments were made with New York-taken birds that indicated a preferred migration course somewhat different from that of North Dakota birds. This would be expected under natural conditions if they were to arrive in Florida.

Experiments of the same type made in spring with Florida-caught birds showed a wide variation in directive responses, but all were east of north. The birds were assumed to come from a heterogeneous migra-

tory population, most of which nest in various parts of eastern North America.

In addition to the use of automatic recording devices, electrically operated, and perches with microswitches attached to them, a very simple method was suggested by Emlen and Emlen.[12] To determine the direction of orientation in captive migrants, the birds are placed in a small cage whose sides are sloping or funnel-shaped. These sloping sides

[12]Emlen, S. T., and J. T. Emlen. 1966.

are covered with blotting paper, and a moist ink pad is glued to the bottom of the container so that the birds' feet contact the ink. The top of the funnel has a covering of quarter-inch wire screen to prevent the birds from escaping and is surrounded by a circular opaque screen to obscure the horizon. The captive, therefore, can observe the sky above but cannot see various surrounding landmarks. Each time a bird hops up the sloping sides, it leaves the track of its footprints on the blotting paper before it slides back down to the bottom. The direction of its activity during the night as well as the number of hops is recorded very simply and can subsequently be evaluated statistically.

In the fall of 1964 and the spring and fall of 1965, Stephen Emlen made a series of tests, both out of doors under a natural sky and in a planetarium, on the indigo bunting (*Passerina cyanea*).[13] This is a species that breeds over much of the eastern half of the United States and winters in some of the islands of the West Indies as well as from southern Mexico to Panama. The migration route of some individuals of this species may involve distances of up to 2,500 miles each way. Evidence seems to indicate that the indigo bunting is probably a trans-Gulf migrant.

In the experimental studies on this species, birds were collected in the spring of 1964 in Michigan and in the spring of 1965 on the coast of Alabama. During the summer and fall they were maintained in outdoor cages near Ann Arbor, Michigan, where they had a continuous view of the sky and were, therefore, subject to the normal photoperiods for that locality. Most but not all of the birds displayed *Zugunruhe* from late September to early November, which covers the fall period of migration for this species. Following this, the birds were kept indoors in a windowless room where they were subjected to the same photoperiods as would occur at 15° N. latitude in their wintering range. *Zugunruhe* behavior was noted in thirteen of thirty-two birds in the spring between mid-April and early June. This is the normal time of northward migration. *Zugunruhe* in any one migration season was present for only five or six weeks, in contrast to considerably longer periods of nocturnal restlessness generally observed in other caged migrants. Nocturnal activity extended from shortly after dark until a few hours before sunrise.

When indigo buntings were placed in test cages that permitted a view of the overhead sky but blocked the horizon up to thirty-eight

[13]Emlen, S. T. 1967a, b.

degrees, the majority exhibited a southward oriented *Zugunruhe* in the autumn and a northward directed activity in the spring on moonless nights. The intensity of nocturnal activity was found to decrease as the cloud cover increased, although it was found that a few birds were able to show directional activity when there was a nine-tenths cloud cover and only a few stars were visible.

When the test cages containing the experimental birds were placed in a planetarium at night, those individuals showing directional preferences oriented correctly when the stars were projected onto the dome with the Spitz projector. When the north-south axis was reversed 180 degrees, the birds reversed their direction, and all signs of orientation disappeared when the projector was turned off and the dome was illuminated with diffused light.

These observations tend to support Sauer's theory of star orientation by nocturnal migrants.

The fact that some species at least can properly orient themselves with only a small portion of the sky visible suggests that birds may make reference to star patterns rather than single stars or planets. Emlen has made some studies on this possibility with indigo buntings.[14] By using a planetarium sky with captive birds, he was able to block out certain portions of the sky. He found that during the spring migration period the northern sky alone was sufficient for directional orientation. The elimination of the Big Dipper or the North Star did not interfere with directional determination, thus indicating that sufficient information for proper orientation was present in their absence. There was some indication, however, that the circumpolar area within thirty-five degrees of the North Star may be essential to orientation.

The Sauers, in their earlier studies, previously referred to, found that Old World warblers of the genus *Sylvia* became completely disoriented when exposed to skies that were not characteristic of the migratory season. When the sky of the opposite migratory season was presented to them, they displayed a bimodal orientation between north and south. This suggests a stellar stimulation producing a northward directional response in the spring and the reverse in the fall. Emlen did not find this to be true of the indigo bunting. Most of his captive birds maintained the normal directional orientation for spring under skies that were shifted six or twelve hours. Retarding or advancing the sky six hours relative

[14]Emlen, S. T. 1967b.

to local time presents conditions as they would be found three months earlier or later. A shift of twelve hours produces the sky as it would be seen six months later at the same local time. Emlen suggests, therefore, that the north-south reversal in avian migration direction is dependent upon physiological changes within a bunting and not upon celestial stimuli produced by seasonal changes in the sky pattern.

EFFECTS OF OVERCAST AND WIND

The possible effect of overcast skies on the orientation of nocturnal avian migrants has already been indicated in Chapter 3. Nisbet and Drury, in their studies of migrants along the Massachusetts coast at night by means of radar, concluded that orientation was unimpaired by overcast.[15] On twelve out of fifty-two nights the sky was overcast, and on an additional eight nights the average cloud cover was eight-tenths or more. No statistical differences were noted between migratory orientation on these nights and orientation on the other thirty-two nights.

Dr. Frank Bellrose, in a paper presented at the 14th International Ornithological Congress held at Oxford University in 1966, gives an excellent summary of the effect of overcast skies on nocturnal migrants.[16] His radar studies in Illinois showed that there were extensive movements of birds on nights when celestial clues were obscured, although the magnitude of such movements was somewhat less than that on clear nights. Birds can navigate and make a successful flight, at least for one night, without the aid of any celestial clues, but their course is not quite as accurate as it is when these clues are available. It is possible, however, that they could not navigate successfully without celestial clues for many nights. Furthermore, Dr. Bellrose's observations confirm the general belief that nocturnal migrants pay little attention to features in the landscape. Since migration may occur on overcast nights without celestial clues, and although birds may refer to major geographical features, they do not rely upon the landscape. Bellrose and his associates are of the opinion that at these times wind turbulence is the clue. Radar findings show that birds migrate on nights when and at altitudes at which the wind is blowing in a favorable direction and at a favorable speed. Likewise, they are able to compensate rather accurately for wind drift. This does not mean that celestial clues are not of great importance. Probably

[15]Nisbet, I. C. T., and W. H. Drury, Jr. 1967.
[16]Bellrose, F. C. 1967.

all nocturnal migrants make use of stellar patterns, but they are not so dependent on these clues that migration ceases when it is overcast. At such times other means of orientation are employed.

Lack supposed that passerine migrants leaving England for continental Europe in a southeasterly direction, even though they would ultimately arrive on the Iberian Peninsula, did not compensate for wind drift in flight.[17] This matter of a directional shift in migration is by no means confined to European birds. Studies made on waterfowl in North America show similar examples. During the fall most ducks arrive in the upper Mississippi River drainage on a broad front from the northwest. Their flight direction from the nesting areas in the Canadian Prairie Provinces has been to the southeast to enter the Mississippi Flyway. On leaving the upper Mississippi and Illinois river valleys, however, they shift direction to the south or southwest. Lack presumed that they came to ground before either changing their course to southwest or compensating for drift. Evans holds a somewhat different view.[18] He points out that some passerine migrants maintain a sustained flight until their energy reserves are depleted. If these migrants do not change their course while in flight or compensate for drift, they will be far off course when they alight and in areas where food is scarce.

Eric Eastwood, in his interesting book *Radar Ornithology*, agrees with Lack that birds are drifted by the wind during migration.[19] He therefore differs with most American ornithologists, who contend that avian migrants compensate for wind in flight.

There seems to be little doubt now that many kinds of birds, particularly nocturnal migrants, depend upon celestial bodies or patterns to determine their migratory course. Visual detection of the sun, stars, or planets is essential. This, of course, does not mean that other methods of orientation are not employed in navigation. Much remains to be learned, however, about the use of celestial bodies by birds as well as by other organisms. How, for example, are birds of the Northern Hemisphere able to reverse their direction of orientation between spring and autumn? Some species essentially backtrack in autumn over the course they followed in the spring, while others use entirely different routes. Many factors in the physiological activity of an organism must figure in this reversal of behavior pattern.

[17]Lack, D. 1962.
[18]Evans, P. R. 1966.
[19]Eastwood, E. 1967.

GEOGRAPHICAL ORIENTATION

There has been an inclination to consider migration routes as tending to follow river systems or to parallel other geographic features such as mountain ranges. In the continent-wide study on four nights in October, 1952, that has been summarized by Lowery and Newman, some of the assumptions were shown to be incorrect.[20] There was no evidence that the migrants observed on these nights tended to follow river systems, although, as pointed out, this does not preclude the possibility that some nocturnal migrants do. A fair number of birds were found to detour around the Great Lakes, although it is known that some species fly directly over these bodies of water.

As regards diurnal migrants, there is little reason to believe that geographic features are not important in orientation. Even nocturnal migrants may make use of such clues during the early evening and early morning hours when there is some visibility. Radar studies cited by Bellrose have shown that most waterfowl migrating at night ignore major river systems, but before dark or after it becomes light in the morning, such features seem to be followed.[21]

What is termed leading lines are regarded as important visual clues for migrants. These are generally long, narrow topographical features such as valleys, ridges, rivers, or coasts. Frequently a leading line represents a border condition between a favorable and an unfavorable habitat. For a prairie-inhabiting bird, the junction of the prairie with a forest would constitute a leading line. The same might be true for a forest-dwelling species. Each tends to keep to its favored habitat even during migration.

Coastlines are most important leading lines for both land and marine species. Many kinds of land birds fly down continental coastlines, which provide an obvious directional course to follow. These species adhere closely to the coast. Similarly, water birds often make use of the same leading lines. Loons, scoters, and many other birds that winter in coastal waters fly north and south in spring and autumn within sight of the coast. Brown pelicans, many kinds of gulls, and jaegers seem also to follow coastlines in their movements.

[20]Lowery, G. H., Jr., and R. J. Newman. 1966.
[21]Bellrose, F. C. 1967.

DISPLACEMENT

A number of experiments have been made on the ability of birds to return to their winter homes after being artificially displaced. Such evidence as is available indicates that the capability for this sort of homing exists. Mewaldt carried on experiments involving the displacement of wintering sparrows of the genus *Zonotrichia*. In the 1961–1962 winter season, 411 birds representing the golden-crowned sparrow (*Zonotrichia atricapilla*) and two migrant subspecies of the white-crowned sparrow (*Zonotrichia leucophrys gambelii* and *Z. l. pugetensis*) were transported from their wintering area in San Jose, California, to Baton Rouge, Louisiana, by aircraft. The displacement was 2,900 kilometers. The golden-crowned sparrow nests in Alaska and Canada. One race of the white-crowned sparrow (*gambelii*) has a similar breeding range. The other (*pugetensis*) breeds in Washington and British Columbia in the vicinity of Puget Sound. In the 1962–1963 winter season, 26 of these birds were recaptured at the banding station in San Jose. This was 21 percent of the 123 that would have been expected had they not been displaced. During this same winter period, 660 birds of the same kinds trapped at San Jose were flown to Laurel, Maryland, which is 3,860 kilometers distant. Twenty-two of these were individuals that had been displaced to Baton Rouge the previous year and recaptured in San Jose in 1962–1963. In the 1963–1964 winter season, 15 of these 660 birds were recaptured at San Jose, and among this number were 6 of the 22 individuals that had been displaced to Maryland after returning to San Jose from Louisiana the year before.

In all of these displacement experiments Dr. Mewaldt and his associates found that the percentage of returns after displacement was higher for *Zonotrichia atricapilla* and *Z. leucophrys gambelii* than for *Z. l. pugetensis*. The last-named bird does not migrate as far from the nesting to the wintering area as do the other two.

The homing ability of certain migratory sea birds on being displaced is perhaps even more remarkable than that of land-dwelling species. In 1957 Karl Kenyon and Dale Rice carried out a series of experiments on the Laysan albatross (*Diomedea immutabilis*) on Midway Atoll in the Pacific.[22] The results were published the following year. Eighteen adults

[22]Kenyon, K. W., and D. W. Rice. 1958.

that were either incubating eggs or brooding newly hatched young were captured and transported by plane to six localities in the North Pacific Ocean. Each bird had a numbered United States Fish and Wildlife Service aluminum band and a colored plastic tag attached to it and also had the body plumage marked with an alcohol-soluble red dye. The time involved from capture on Sand Island until release in a distant location ranged from 11 hours at Guam to 105 hours at Whidbey Island along the coast of Washington. Fourteen of the 18 birds returned to their

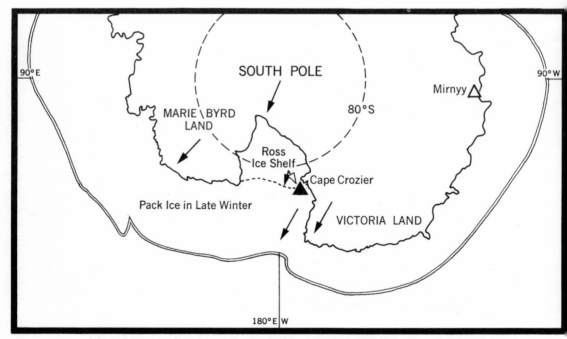

Mean departure directions taken by Adélie penguins released singly on featureless snow-ice surfaces at various points on the Antarctic continent and on the offshore pack ice. Data include both 1962 and 1964 observations. The solid arrows show the directions selected by birds from Cape Crozier; the open arrow that taken by birds from Mirnyy shortly after transport. (After Penny, R. L., and Emlem, J. T., 1967)

nests. The greatest distance covered was by one released from Sangley Point in the Philippine Islands. It made the return trip to Midway Atoll, which is 4,120 miles away, in 32 days. Two birds released along the Washington coast returned a distance of 3,200 miles in 10 and 12 days, respectively. The average distance traveled per day for these two birds was 317 and 264 miles. Five of the birds were released at Kwajalein Atoll, which is south of the known range of the species and 1,665 miles from Midway. All 5 returned in from 8 to 12 days.

Shearwaters, like albatrosses, appear to have a remarkable homing ability. A Manx shearwater (*Puffinus p. puffinus*) that was flown from its nest along the coast of Wales and released near Boston, which is 3,400 air miles away, was found back in its nest 12½ days afterward.

Adélie penguins (*Pygoscelis adeliae*), when removed some distance from their rookeries in Antarctica and released at the South Pole, move in a north-northeasterly direction. This is true of juveniles removed from their crèches as well as of adults. Penney and Emlen consider that the northern directional component serves to take the birds toward open water and the eastern component compensates for a westward drift caused by coastal currents.[23] For those birds that move from the nesting area to the home coast, a circadian rhythm that is in phase with the local longitude serves to guide the birds. Displaced birds may require a few weeks to have their circadian rhythm reset to the solar cycle in the new location.

Bellrose displaced juvenile and adult drake mallards (*Anas platyrhynchos*) from Illinois to refuges in Utah, a distance of more than one thousand miles, and released them in November, 1953.[24] Both age groups stayed in the Utah refuge area the first winter, even though the mallards that normally nested in Utah moved south along the Pacific Flyway. Bellrose suggests that "the failure of mallards from Illinois to move far from the point of release in Utah during the first fall is attributed either to an awareness of their displacement in longitude, or to confusion resulting from the unfamiliar landscape." During the subsequent two years, however, indirect recoveries indicated that about two-thirds of the adults and one-third of the juveniles returned to the Mississippi Flyway. It was presumed that the displaced young and adults went north from Utah in spring with other mallards to Alberta and Saskatche-

[23]Penney, R. L., and J. T. Emlen. 1967.
[24]Bellrose, F. C. 1958a.

wan, where they were closer to their former territory. On their way south, a certain number moved over to the Mississippi Flyway once again.

DELAYED MIGRATION

Experimental studies have been made on delaying young birds in their migration as well as displacing them. Early studies of this sort were made on storks in eastern Europe. Schüz retarded the southward migration of young white storks (*Cicona ciconia*) until one or two weeks after the adults had left and found that most of them took the correct route for this species by way of the Black Sea, although a few went farther west to Greece and Italy.[25]

Bellrose, in later experiments in the United States, detained juvenal blue-winged teal (*Anas discors*) that had been trapped and banded in September in Mason County, Illinois, for varying periods after the normal time for fall migration.[26] Adults also were captured and banded in September, but released immediately. Groups of juvenals ranging from 393 down to 45 individuals were released periodically from November 11 to December 8. The adults had all left Illinois by the time the first releases of the juvenals were made, and by the time the last juvenals were released, the adults had left the United States. Some of the released young stayed near the release site for two or more weeks, while others moved to southern United States in a few days. Subsequent recoveries of banded birds showed that the young migrated in the same direction as the adults but certainly without the benefit of any adults to guide them.

Among herring gulls (*Larus argentatus*) there is a strong tendency for the birds to return to their natal colony. This has been demonstrated by banding large numbers of chicks.[27] Some of the most extensive work on this subject was done by Ludwig, who, with other members of his family, banded sixty thousand downy young of this species over a period of Thirty-two years at colonies in Lakes Huron, Michigan, and Superior.[28] An analysis of his results showed that of those recovered as presumably breeding adults, 40.4 percent were retaken in the same colony, 32.1 per-

[25]Schüz, E. 1934.
[26]Bellrose, F. C. 1958a.
[27]Gross, A. O. 1940; Paynter, R. A., Jr. 1947; Tinbergen, N. 1953.
[28]Ludwig, J. P. 1963.

cent in the same area, and 27.5 percent in a different area from where originally banded.

Ludwig is of the opinion that herring gulls normally attempt to return to their natal colony to breed but may be prevented if the site proves to be unsuitable or if it cannot be used because of population pressure. If a bird is forced to breed for the first time in a new site, it will probably return to this site in subsequent years. This dispersal of displaced birds involves individuals, not groups.

A somewhat different sort of displacement occurs in certain terns. Oliver L. Austin presented the results of twenty years of banding common terns (*Sterna hirundo*) at Cape Cod, Massachusetts. During this time, 47,409 adults and 165,610 chicks were banded.[29] There were 31,867 returns and recoveries on the breeding grounds. Austin found that within the larger tern colonies there exist smaller associations of up to one hundred or more birds that act more or less in unison. When displaced, the birds move as a group, unlike gulls. When large numbers are forced to move, they also move as a body. This group adherence continues even on the wintering grounds of this species in the West Indies, the Caribbean coast, and the east and west coasts of South America, as indicated by banding returns from some of these areas.

GRAVITATIONAL AND MAGNETIC FIELD THEORIES

There have been several interesting theories that relate avian orientation during migration to certain mechanical and electrical forces of the earth. One of these, proposed by Ising, suggests that birds make use of the Coriolis force and in flight may determine direction by the change in gravitational pull, depending upon whether they are flying with or counter to the direction of the earth's rotation. On the equator a bird flying east, which is the direction in which the earth is rotating, would weigh less by one part in two thousand at forty miles per hour than it would traveling west at the same speed.[30]

Ising's theory proposes that perhaps some type of receptor in the circulatory system may be able to detect changes in pressure resulting from the earth's rotation. We know that such sensory receptors do exist, but it is questionable if they would be able to detect such minute changes.

[29]Austin, O. L. 1951.
[30]Ising, G. 1946.

Man is able to detect an increase in weight of one part in one hundred, which is an increase twenty times greater than that which Ising's theory would have birds able to perceive.

For nearly one hundred years there has been a recurring theory that birds may have a special sense that enables them to detect the earth's magnetic field and its polarity. This might presume that a bird has a built-in compass or that the bird builds up an electrical charge as a result of flying through a magnetic field which it is capable of detecting and using as an orienting mechanism. This idea was given some impetus a few years ago by Yeagley, a physicist.[31] Yeagley proposed that birds not only make use of the Coriolis force to navigate, as suggested by Ising and others, but also are capable of detecting and measuring the earth's magnetic fields.

During World War II observations made by Knorr showed that radar seemed to have an effect on certain birds.[32] Scoters and scaup were observed to become bewildered and fall out of flock formation when a radar beam was directed at them. When the beam was turned away, the birds regrouped and continued on their course. Knorr (p. 264) suggested that "one cannot help but wonder if the behavior described above does not support the theory that birds indeed perceive the earth's magnetic field. In flight the crossing of these lines of force may result in the production of phosphenes, or perhaps the answer lies in the setting up of tiny oscillating currents somewhere in the animals' central nervous system." Other observations of this same type had been made earlier by Drost.[33]

The effect of strong radar beams at short range on these birds is probably somewhat similar to the disturbing effects on parts of the human nervous system when a person is close to a very strong magnetic field. Relatively little evidence has been brought forth so far to show that birds have any sensory mechanism to detect very weak electrical fields, although the possibility still exists that they might. Recently Wiltschko has provided some experimental evidence that European robins (*Erithacus rubecula*) are capable of choosing normal migratory direction in a room devoid of environmental clues but having the earth's normal magnetic field.[34] When the magnetic field was doubled artificially, the orientation became random or at least different from the correct direc-

[31]Yeagley, H. L. 1947.
[32]Knorr, O. A. 1954.
[33]Drost, R. 1949.
[34]Wiltschko, W. 1968.

tion of orientation. If the direction of magnetic north was artificially changed, there was a corresponding change in the direction of migratory activity. The significance of these results has yet to be analyzed.

Electroreceptors are known in certain fishes and in some are capable of detecting very slight changes in the electrical field surrounding them. This is true of some of the gymnotids and mormyrids. The latter group occur in the fresh waters of tropical Africa and show a marked enlargement of the cerebellum. The electroreceptors are called mormyomasts and are associated with the nerves of the lateral line organs. The lateral line system, however, has disappeared in all vertebrates above the amphibians.

ECHONAVIGATION

Echolocation as a means of orientation and navigation is best known among bats and toothed cetaceans, but there are certain birds that have been found to possess this ability. Although the species involved are essentially nonmigratory and there is no evidence that such an orienting mechanism would be of value in any extensive flight, nevertheless a brief account of the use of echonavigation by some birds seems appropriate.

The first bird that was found to emit sound pulses whose echoes served for orientation was the oilbird or guacharo (*Steatornis caripensis*) of South America and Trinidad.[35] This is a member of the order Caprimulgiformes, which includes the nightjars, goatsuckers, whippoorwills, and their relatives. The oilbird is nocturnal and lives in caves. In flight, it relies largely on acoustical orientation.

Subsequently it was discovered that certain swifts of the genus *Collocalia* of southeastern Asia also echonavigate.[36] These birds roost and nest deep in caves where there may be total darkness or, at best, very poor light. Both *Collocalia unicolor* and *C. fuciphaga* have been shown to produce high-frequency sounds and to fly in total darkness without hitting obstacles. The latter species produces sounds ranging in frequency from 1.5 to 4.5 kilocycles per second at a rate of nine or ten pulses per second.

[35]Griffin, D. R. 1958.
[36]Novick, A. 1959; Medway, Lord. 1967.

15

ORIENTATION IN MAMMALS

Migration among mammals is confined almost entirely to certain species of bats, cetaceans, pinnipeds, and large herbivores of several orders. Homing ability, however, has been shown to exist in other kinds of mammals even though they do not normally engage in seasonal population movements.

Although the means by which mammals are able to follow definite migratory routes have barely been touched upon by investigators, it appears that visual, olfactory, and auditory clues are all employed. Deer, elk, and caribou, as well as other big game species, usually tend to follow trails that are used year after year. It would seem likely that use of the trails, combined with a knowledge of the terrain from past experience, is sufficient to enable animals such as elk or deer to find their way from a high summer range to lower winter quarters in many areas. Olfaction too may play a very important role in these movements. Most big herbivores have interdigital as well as tarsal glands that produce a scent which, deposited on or along such trails, may persist for long periods of time.

Olfaction obviously is of no assistance to migrating cetaceans or pinnipeds, but vision, possibly sound, the awareness of temperature gradients, and even ocean currents may all be directional aids.

Occasionally during migration gray whales raise their heads nearly vertically out of the water, as though to get their bearings. This sort of behavior, called spyhopping, is noticed most often in immature animals that are migrating alone, especially when they get into coastal kelp beds and are confused. One also frequently observes gray whales spyhopping in the calving lagoons. Other species of whales have been observed peering out of the water in the same manner in the Arctic and the Antarctic when they were swimming among ice floes.

Some species of pinnipeds regularly stay within a few miles of shore during their migrations. Distinctive geographical features such as headlands may provide important clues to location. The presence of rivers flowing into the ocean may also aid coastal migrants.

Many cetaceans and some pinnipeds winter in ocean waters that are markedly different in temperature from those they inhabit in the summer. Most whales, for example, reproduce in subtropical or tropical parts of the sea in the winter season and spend the summer in polar waters where food is more abundant. Temperature, possibly combined with familiarity with ocean currents, may provide them with the necessary directional clues.

ECHOLOCATION

Echolocation has been shown to be an important navigational aid for several different groups of mammals as well as certain other kinds of animals. It might be defined as the detection by an organism of the echoes of self-produced sounds, these echoes being reflected from an object or objects in its environment, thereby enabling the organism to utilize this information to orient itself in relation to the object or objects. In other words, it is essentially a sonar mechanism. This, however, is an oversimplification, as will be shown.

The discovery of echolocation starts back in the last decade of the eighteenth century with the discoveries of an Italian scientist named Lazaro Spallanzani. He noted that bats could fly about in a dark room at night without crashing into anything. In a long series of experiments he began blinding bats and found that individuals so mutilated could fly without hitting objects just as well as controls that had not been so treated. Subsequently he used various types of hoods on the heads of bats. As a result, he found that their ability to avoid obstacles was impaired only when the ears or the mouth were covered. Although he was unable to explain what this "sixth sense" that bats possessed was, he was certain that they were able to "see with their ears." Unfortunately, neither he nor anyone else for nearly a century and a half subsequently suspected that bats were capable of detecting sounds that are inaudible to the human ear. It remained for Dr. Donald R. Griffin to make this discovery. As he modestly explains in his book *Listening in the Dark*, in 1938 he persuaded physics professor G. W. Pierce at Harvard to use some of his equipment, which was capable of detecting high-frequency pulses, on

Elk or wapiti (*Cervus canadensis*) migrating essentially in single file along a trail in the snow in Idaho. *Photograph courtesy Idaho Fish and Game Department.*

Gray whales (*Eschrichtius gibbosus*) occasionally raise their heads out of the water. *Photographed at Scammons Lagoon, Baja California, Mexico, February 1968 by George E. Lindsay.*

some live bats.[1] It soon showed beyond a doubt that these animals could produce such sounds.[2] This had been postulated, but never proved, back in 1920 by an English physiologist named Hartridge. In 1939, Dr. Griffin joined forces with Robert Galambos, who was interested in the physiology of hearing. They repeated the experiments that Spallanzani had carried out by obscuring the vision of bats with darkened collodion eye plates that could later be removed. Bats so treated would avoid wires strung in a room. They also plugged the ears of flying bats and observed that they were unable to detect wire obstacles that blindfolded bats with unplugged ears could avoid. The sonic detector for high-frequency pulses that Professor Pierce had developed was used in these experiments to show that the bats were emitting sounds above the range of human audibility.[3] The next step was to show that when bats were prevented from emitting high-frequency sounds, they would be unable to avoid hitting obstacles in flight. Accordingly, Griffin and Galambos sealed the lips of some bats with collodion after tying their jaws and found that their ability to avoid objects was lost. Since then many experimental studies have been made on the use of high-frequency sounds by bats in orientation.

The advantages of a built-in sensory sonar system to an animal navigating in darkness are obvious. When the animal itself is small—and one of the functions of this system seems to be the location of small night-flying insects for food—the use of high-frequency sounds that do not carry very far but are of very small wave length and therefore can echo back from small objects is of great adaptive value. The possible significance of this sensory system in more extensive navigation such as migration will be considered a little farther on in this chapter.

Just as visual orientation at night is difficult and not the most efficient, so also is orientation in water. Among mammals, the cetaceans show the greatest adaptation to life in the sea, with pinnipeds next, followed by sirenians. Most cetaceans are marine, but a few are found in large river systems where the water is very turbid. Even in the ocean visibility is poor and, at most, limited to short distances. Studies in recent years have shown that these animals locate food and avoid hitting obstacles and running aground also by the use of echolocation. Research with the use of a hydrophone has shown that toothed cetaceans produce many complex underwater sounds, which have been described as squeals, clicks,

[1]Griffin, D. R. 1958.
[2]Pierce, G. W., and D. R. Griffin. 1938.
[3]Galambos, R., and D. R. Griffin. 1940; Griffin, D. R., and R. Galambos. 1941.

groans, and whistles. They exhibit an ability to produce a much wider range of frequencies than do bats. The upper limit recorded appears to be near 300,000 cycles per second. Less is known about sound production in the baleen whales, but some of these species have been shown to produce underwater sounds, and it is possible that all do so.[4] This, however, does not mean that they use echolocation as the odontocetes do.

Sound production and sound reception by mammals under water is very different from that which occurs in the air.[5] In water, sound travels about four times as fast as in air; therefore an echo bounced off an object returns much more rapidly. Furthermore, the ear of a land mammal is not well suited to the reception of sounds in water. It is said that the human ear under water is about as efficient as one in air with the chain of auditory ossicles not functioning and the tympanic membrane punctured.

One of the major problems involved in underwater sound reception is related to insulation. Flesh and bone is much more dense than air, and sound waves do not pass readily from a lighter to a denser medium. In a land mammal, sound waves pass into the external auditory meatus and impinge upon the delicate tympanic membrane, thereby setting up vibrations which are transmitted across the three auditory ossicles to the inner ear. In our own body the ears are separated from each other by the head, which serves as a sound insulator and assists in directional hearing. If we face the source of a sound, it will arrive in both ears at the same time and in the same intensity. If, however, we are not facing toward the sound, the intensity will be greater in the ear nearer the source, thus providing directional orientation. This "air type" of directional orientation is lost in the water because of the relative ease with which sound passes from water into the body, which is of nearly the same specific gravity.

Cetaceans seem to have solved this problem, at least in part, by the development of insulation for the ear. The tympanic bone, which houses the inner ear, is suspended from the skull by ligaments and is surrounded by cavities filled with air or foam. (In our own ear the tympanic bone is fused to the skull.) The result of this insulation suggests that sound received by a cetacean under water comes to each ear from the side on which the ear is located, thus providing the possibility of directional orientation similar to that available to land mammals.

In land mammals the external auditory meatus is the channel through which sound waves are funneled from the external environment to the

[4]Schevill, W. E. 1964.
[5]Orr, R. T. 1963.

tympanum. There they set up vibrations of varying frequencies that are transmitted across the chain of auditory ossicles in the middle ear to the cochlea. In cetaceans the external auditory canal is greatly reduced in diameter and may not be the main channel by which sound waves are transmitted to the tympanic bulla. Norris, Purves, and other workers recently have suggested that the lower jaw of odontocetes may serve for the passage of sounds from the water to the tympanic bulla.[6] The jaw in these toothed cetaceans, unlike the jaw of baleen whales, is composed of very thin bone, and each ramus is filled with fat. Some experimental studies have shown that the area of the jaw that covers the mandibular fat body is several times as sensitive to high-frequency sounds as the area over the external auditory meatus. Furthermore, two other areas of the head that are almost equally as sensitive to sound as the lower mandibles are situated on either side of the fatty prominence on the forehead, which is often referred to as the melon. There exists therefore the possibility that there may be four reception points on the head, each of which is several times more sensitive to the reception of sound than are the two external auditory canals.[7] Their sensitivity, however, decreases as the frequency of sound decreases. Such receptive channels are unknown in terrestrial mammals. A porpoise, therefore, when moving its head about while scanning the environment, has the advantage of multiple receptive channels.

Directional orientation in cetaceans may also possibly be effected by means of frequency modulation. These animals produce sound of a wide range of frequency over a period of very short duration. When the receptors are not the same distance away from the object from which sounds of this sort are reflected back, there will be a difference in the frequency received by each ear. By turning until the frequency received in both ears is synchronized, the animal can determine the direction of the echo.

The production of sound by cetaceans appears to differ considerably from the means employed by land mammals. In the latter, the larynx with its vocal cords is the principal source of sound. In odontocetes, the significance of the larynx in sound production has been questioned. Most students of cetacean sound are of the belief that the pulses produced by these animals come from nasal diverticula.[8] The larynx itself lacks vocal

[6]Norris, K. S. 1964; Purves, P. E. 1966.
[7]Norris, K. S. 1966.
[8]Norris, K. S., et al. 1961; Evans, W. E., and J. H. Prescott. 1962.

cords. Sound produced in these nasal diverticula seems to emerge from the melon. These sounds seem to be projected in a relatively narrow beam and appear to be highly directional. This is especially true of the higher-frequency sounds, which are recorded only directly in front of the animal.

After the discovery that cetaceans produce underwater sounds, there remained the problem of showing that these were used in navigating.[9] A great deal of experimental work was subsequently done on captive bottlenosed porpoises (*Tursiops truncatus*). At Marineland of the Pacific, Palos Verdes Estates, California, Dr. Kenneth Norris and his associates blindfolded these animals, using latex suction cups.[10] It was shown that a blindfolded dolphin could easily avoid obstacles, locate food, and even distinguish small pieces of food from other objects of the same size and weight.

Presently it would appear that several species of pinnipeds that have been subjected to experimental studies also depend upon echolocation under water to locate food and to navigate when the light intensity is low.[11] The clue that led Dr. Thomas C. Poulter of Stanford Research Institute to suggest that sea lions echolocate was discovered in an interesting way. He and the author were carrying on a population study on several species of pinnipeds that occur on an island along the coast of central California. Large numbers of male California sea lions were found to arrive here in August or early September of each year, presumably from breeding colonies several hundred miles to the south where they join with the females in June and July. Some of these males were found to be totally blind but were in good condition. This led to the hypothesis that they might be able to secure their food by echolocation.

Recently it has been discovered that at least one sirenian, the manatee (*Trichechus manatus*), also produces underwater sounds.[12] It is likely that other species of this group do likewise, although it remains to be demonstrated that such sounds are utilized in navigation.

We now know that bats, cetaceans, and pinnipeds produce sounds of varying frequency whose echoes they are able to detect and utilize in the location of food in air or in the water. This mechanism can also be

[9]Kellogg, W. N. 1961.
[10]Norris, K. S., *et al.* 1961.
[11]Poulter, T. C. 1963; Schevill, W. E., *et al.* 1963.
[12]Schevill, W. E., and W. A. Watkins. 1965.

used to navigate and avoid obstacles, judging from the experimental evidence. We do not know, however, how important this acoustical system is in migratory orientation. Undoubtedly bats come to know the echoes of the immediate environment of their roosts and must use echolocation as a means of avoiding obstacles and each other during migration. Migrating cetaceans and pinnipeds may also make use of this sensory system for the same purposes, but for long-range navigation its function is yet to be demonstrated. Quite possibly whales that follow coastlines or migrate in waters of certain depth might make considerable use of a sonar system.

DISPLACEMENT AND HOMING

BATS. Because of their remarkable locomotor capabilities as well as the fact that a number of species are migratory, bats have been the subject of a good many homing experiments. Most of these have involved capturing individuals in summer roosts, transporting them varying distances, banding the animals, and then releasing them. Some remarkable returns involving hundreds of miles of travel have been made by both European and American bats. Most of the species experimented with have been members of the family Vespertilionidae, but there is evidence that homing capabilities occur in members of other families.

Although it has long been known that bats make use of echolocation as a navigational aid, the actual use of this sensory mechanism has not yet been shown in long-distance orientation. In fact, very little is known about the means by which this is accomplished by these mammals. There is little doubt that echolocation is of considerable importance for orientation over short distances. The evidence so far tends to indicate that familiarity with the home terrain is of primary importance. Familiarity with geographic features such as river systems is probably a major factor for orientation in some species. The greater the distance of the point of release from the home roost, the lower the percentage of returns. The return of individuals after extensive displacement may be the result of random flight until a familiar landmark is found. From then on, both sight and echolocation may be used. As a result of experiments on blindfolded bats, Davis[13] concluded that the return of such individuals to their home roost after displacement may possibly be the result of random

[13]Davis, R. 1966.

flight, with some of the individuals ultimately coming into areas with which they are familiar and where they then may make use of echolocation for locating a specific place such as a roost. The distances away from a roost that a bat may be familiar with may be considerable if this is true. In an experiment, two out of eighteen blinded bats returned to the site of capture from a release point thirty-two miles away. The elapsed time was five days. Out of eighteen controls released at the same time and place, three returned to the home roost. There is the possibility that the blinded bats may have followed the controls in this sort of experiment. A point of interest was the fact that a third blinded bat was discovered six miles from the home roost on the same day as the other two returned. This individual was found in an unoccupied roost that was said to be almost identical in construction to the home roost. The implication is that if the bat were depending on echolocation, it may have become confused by the similarity of the structure to that with which it was familiar.

Mueller and Emlen have also shown that some bats, when blindfolded with eye caps made of lampblack and collodion and removed at distances varying from five to sixty miles from their roost, were able to return home.[14] However, the percentage of returns decreased as the distance increased. There was a 72 percent return from those displaced five miles, whereas the return of those displaced sixty miles was only 6 percent. The homing speed averaged ten miles per hour, although the maximum speed was nineteen miles per hour.

One of the earliest experiments on homing in bats was made on the big brown bat (*Eptesicus fuscus*), a species of very widespread occurrence over North America. Big brown bats range from southern Canada south to central Mexico and from the Pacific to the Atlantic coasts. They are not known to be migratory in the sense that they move south to warmer winter quarters, but they do move to certain caves to hibernate in winter. In the summer of 1921 the late A. Brazier Howell and Luther Little banded five big brown bats that they had captured at Covina in southern California.[15] These were released twenty miles away. Nearly two years later, two of the displaced bats were retaken near the original site of capture.

More recently, extensive displacement experiments were carried out

[14]Mueller, H. C., and J. T. Emlen, Jr. 1957.
[15]Howell, A. B., and L. Little. 1924.

on this species in Ohio.[16] One hundred and fifty-five bats were captured on July 20 in Cincinnati and released the following evening at Pilgrim, Michigan, which is 450 miles to the north. When the home roost was checked on August 24, three of the displaced bats were found to have returned. Four more were recovered there on October 26. All were adult females, although two-thirds of the displaced bats were juveniles. Another group of eighteen bats captured in Cincinnati on July 31 was released two days later about 340 miles to the southwest, at Redfoot Lake, Tennessee. On August 17, two of these bats were recaptured at the home roost. The percentage of return for those displaced 450 miles was 4.6, with a minimum of one month required. Of those displaced 340 miles, 11 percent returned, with a minimum of two weeks required.

One of the most rapid returns of a displaced bat was reported by Cockrum.[17] This related to twelve cave bats (*Myotis velifer*) that were captured at Colossal Cave southeast of Tucson, Arizona. After having been banded, they were released between 1:00 and 1:30 A.M. on May 3 at a point about twenty-eight miles from the cave. On the afternoon of May 3 a net was placed across the cave from which they had been removed earlier, and just after dark two of the banded individuals were taken as they tried to leave the cave. Apparently they had returned before daylight that morning. This would mean a return from a distance of twenty-eight miles in not more than four hours.

Davis and Hardin recorded capturing three silver-haired bats (*Lasionycteris noctivagans*) in New Mexico on June 6.[18] These were taken to the Southwestern Research Station of the American Museum in Arizona and released on June 8 after having been banded. One of the banded individuals was taken eighteen days later within one mile of the original site of capture and 107 miles north-northeast of the point of release.

The little brown myotis (*Myotis lucifugus*) of North America is known to return to the home roost after considerable displacement. Smith and Hale recorded the return of two out of seventy-seven little brown myotis that were captured near Wilmington, Ohio, and released near Jamestown, Pennsylvania.[19] One of the bats was recaptured at the home site one year later, and the other, two years later. The percentage of recaptures at this distance was 2.6 (two out of seventy-seven).

[16]Smith, E., and W. Goodpaster. 1958.
[17]Cockrum, E. L. 1956.
[18]Davis, W. H., and J. W. Hardin. 1967.
[19]Smith, E., and K. Hale. 1953.

Williams and Williams attached radio transmitters to a species of phyllostomid bat in Trinidad and found a high rate of return for individuals displaced from five to ten kilometers from their home roosts if their vision was unimpaired.[20] The species used was *Phyllostomus hastatus*, which is one of the largest bats in the Western Hemisphere, weighing up to one hundred grams. The radio transmitter used weighed about seven grams, measured one by three centimeters, and had an antenna made of piano wire that extended back twenty-five centimeters. The movements of the displaced bats were followed by a receiver with a directional antenna. Bats released at greater distances showed a lower percentage of returns. From eleven to thirty-four kilometers, 57 percent returned. Those released from forty to fifty-three kilometers had a 26 percent return. The minimum speed of flight, calculated on the basis of distance and time involved, of several bats released thirty-two kilometers from their home roost was eleven kilometers per hour. The authors speculate that these flights were either highly oriented at this speed or else the result of only slightly oriented wanderings at higher flight speeds.

In Europe a number of displacement experiments have been carried out with bats of the genera *Nyctalus*, *Pipistrellus*, and *Myotis*. Eisentraut had one large mouse-eared bat (*Myotis myotis*) return a distance of almost 94 miles from its home colony.[21] Casteret had some remarkable returns from bats of the same species that were displaced from Tignahustes Cavern in Hautes-Pyrénées.[22] There were a few returns from releases made at distances up to 165 miles away at Sète, 125 miles at Moliets, and 112 miles at Saint-Jean-de-Luz. In general, species that engage in extensive migrations appear to be better able to return from more distant displacement sites than those that engage only in local movements. It is possible that familiarity with a considerably larger area may be an important factor.

RODENTS. Certain European studies, notably those of Lüters and Birukow, have indicated that some small rodents appear to make use of a sun compass in orientation.[23] This has been shown in the wood mouse, *Apodemus agrarius*. On the other hand, it has been rather clearly demonstrated that while homing is accomplished after displacement in many species, it results either from a prior knowledge of the area or through

[20]Williams, T. C., and J. M. Williams. 1967.
[21]Eisentraut, M. 1943.
[22]Casteret, N. 1938.
[23]Lüters, W., and G. Birukow. 1963.

random wandering. Robinson and Falls made a very extensive study of homing ability in the meadow vole (*Microtus pennsylvanicus*) and found that the percentage of mice homing decreased as the distance of displacement increased.[24] No mice returned from distances in excess of fourteen hundred feet. Their general conclusion was that homing was dependent upon familiarity with the territory in which the mice were displaced. Fisler, in his work on the California vole (*Microtus californicus*) and the western harvest mouse (*Reithrodontomys megalotis*), likewise concluded that there was no evidence that these rodents could orient by means of celestial clues.[25]

Experiments performed on harvest mice indicate a homing ability. Fisler moved western harvest mice for distances up to one thousand feet from their home areas.[26] The less the distance displaced, the greater the percentage of returns. However, one out of six individuals displaced the maximum distance returned to its original site of capture. It was believed that homing was accomplished by nonrandom movements over known terrain.

[24]Robinson, W. L., and J. B. Falls. 1965.
[25]Fisler, G. F. 1967.
[26]Fisler, G. F. 1966.

16

HAZARDS OF MIGRATION

Migration is a means of benefiting a species through the movement of populations. The movement may be toward suitable breeding areas at the proper time of the year or at the appropriate period in the life of the individual. It may be governed by seasonal climatic conditions. It may also take populations into regions where there is suitable food and habitat available at certain seasons of the year. Despite these obvious benefits, migration is hazardous. For species that engage in long migrations it may be a great strain on the bodies of the participants. There may be extended periods without food as well as long hours of travel. Sudden unfavorable climatic conditions may at times result in heavy mortality to migrants. Attrition through predation may be higher during migration. For example, it has been estimated that the Eleonora's falcon (*Falco eleonorae*) captures close to one million passerine birds migrating over the Mediterranean in the autumn (see Chapter 8).

There are some species whose life terminates on completion of the migration. Pacific salmon of the genus *Oncorhynchus* are among these. The only exception to this rule occurs in chinook salmon (*O. tshawytscha*), among which certain precocious males may survive and return to the sea. Six environmental and physiological factors are considered to contribute to the eventual death of Pacific salmon after their return migration to their spawning ground. These are as follows: (1) the change involved in moving from a saltwater to a freshwater environment, (2) a frequently lengthy freshwater migration, (3) bodily infections, (4) increased water temperature, (5) lack of food, and (6) body depletion resulting from sexual maturation.[1]

The hazards to migrating salmon are numerous. Man himself rates high in this regard. Schools of these fishes congregated at the mouth of bays and rivers are seined by commercial fishermen and trolled for by

[1]McBride, J. R., *et al.* 1965.

sportsmen. In many of the larger rivers, salmon must face obstacles such as rapids and waterfalls. Pollution and siltation are further complications of this century. There are natural predators, both birds and mammals, that seek migrating salmon as food.

MORTALITY

FROM NATURAL ENVIRONMENTAL FACTORS

Drowning may be an important mortality factor in the migrations of caribou in the Arctic. Mass drowning has been reported during river crossings in times of high water. There is one instance recorded where over five hundred individuals died on a single crossing.

There are many instances of sudden lowering of the temperature having a catastrophic effect on migrants. One of the greatest examples of the effect of a sudden freeze on avian migrants occurred in 1907. A rapid fall in temperature in Minnesota resulted in heavy snowfall and icing conditions during the migration of large numbers of Lapland longspurs (*Calcarius lapponicus*). In a short time dead birds were reported over an area of more than 1,500 square miles. On two small lakes alone approximately 750,000 dead longspurs were recorded.

Wind sometimes contributes directly or indirectly to mortality during migration. There are records of large flocks of eagles grounded and exhausted as a result of sandstorms.[2] This occasionally happens in Asia Minor. Eagles from Europe as well as Asia Minor, in their migrations to Africa to winter, avoid water-crossings and stay largely over desert, where they may make use of thermals. When caught in high winds producing sandstorms, they are forced down in areas where food and water are lacking. Wind may also blow them off their course.

Although we are finding out that migrant species have developed very accurate methods of navigation, there are some individuals that get lost. Whales following coastlines occasionally come into bays where they become confused and even stranded. More often under such circumstances they are hit by ships or become entangled in docking areas. Several such occurrences have been reported in San Francisco Bay in recent years.

There is little information on the losses that occur as a result of exhaustion and drowning among terrestrial organisms that engage in extensive

[2]Mackintosh, D. R. 1949; Marchant, S. 1963.

flights over water or get lost at sea during coastal migrations. Some evidence of this potential source of mortality, however, is derived from ships and observations on offshore islands. For example, the painted lady butterfly (*Vanessa cardui*), which is a rather cosmopolitan species, is sometimes found a long way from land. Migrant individuals have been noted in the mid-Atlantic over one thousand miles from shore.

Along the Pacific coast of North America it is not uncommon for coastal boats to have small passerine migrants come aboard, especially during periods of heavy fog. A good example of this is described in a letter from Mr. Anthony Mercieca to Dr. George E. Lindsay, the director of the California Academy of Sciences. In the latter part of May, 1967, Mr. Mercieca was en route in a small boat from San Diego, California, to the Coronado Islands, which are about ten statute miles southwest of the United States–Mexican boundary in the Pacific Ocean. The day was very foggy and "on the way we noticed that quite a few different kinds of warblers were migrating and . . . a lot of them were getting lost and dying. Some of the birds were coming to rest on the boat, others sat on the little dinghy we were towing behind for use in landing. Most of the birds that alighted on the boat went to sleep right away, others ran around the boat trying to get something to eat. Some, after resting awhile, tried to fly away, but most returned to the boat while still others fell into the water. I watched a few birds getting tired, fall into the water and I noticed that they did not come out. One missed the boat by a couple of inches, and tried frantically for a few seconds to get out of the water. Some of the birds stayed on the boat until it was a short distance from land and then took off for the Island. Some of the birds went to sleep and when we got back to the boat the Captain told us the birds had died in their sleep and he had thrown them away.

"The birds that came to rest on the boat were Wilson's warblers, yellow warblers, Townsend's warblers and MacGillivray's warblers also a pewee. . . . The birds that died on the boat and those falling in the water were mostly Wilson's and yellow warblers."

There are many other instances of passerine birds becoming lost in fog or low overcast during coastal migration and landing aboard offshore boats and on small islands. The Farallon Islands, situated about twenty-seven miles west of San Francisco, California, have long been an area for recording migrants, especially warblers, from far outside their normal range. Recently several additional species, including a Connecticut warbler (*Oporornis agilis*), a chestnut-sided warbler (*Dendroica pensylvanica*), an ovenbird (*Seiurus aurocapillus aurocapillus*), and a red-eyed vireo (*Vireo olivaceus*), were taken in mid-June on these islands during a period of continuous fog.[3] This was the first record for the Connecticut warbler for California, and the other species were previously known from California by from one to three records.

Sometimes small land birds get even farther off their course. There are records for the latter part of October for the Tennessee warbler (*Vermivora peregrina*), the bay-breasted warbler (*Dendroica castanea*), and the summer tanager (*Piranga rubra rubra*) from Clipperton Island, which is a coral atoll in the eastern Pacific situated about six hundred miles southwest of the coast of Guerrero, Mexico.[4] These are all species of eastern North America that winter in Central and South America and were far off their course. There are two records of the bay-breasted warbler being found at sea off the west coast of northern Baja California and extreme southern California at distances up to forty-five miles from the mainland, and there is another record of this species from Isla San Benedicto of the Revilla Gigedo group, which is approximately three hundred miles west of the mainland of Mexico and over two hundred miles south of Cape San Lucas at the tip of Baja California.[5]

There are also instances in which sea birds become confused and lose their directive orientation in heavy fog during migration along a seacoast. Sometimes tragic results follow. Early in the morning of August 18, 1961, thousands of sooty shearwaters (*Puffinus griseus*), believed to have become confused from the lights of coastal communities shining through fog, flew ashore in central California. This event took place at the north end of Monterey Bay between the towns of Capitola and Seacliff. Some birds were injured and many perished because of their seeming inability to take off from land.

There have been a number of records of migratory bats, apparently lost at sea, that have taken refuge on vessels. Most of these instances have occurred off the coast of eastern North America, and the species involved are the red bat (*Lasiurus borealis*) and the silver-haired bat (*Lasionycteris noctivagans*). Griffin mentions a red bat that landed on a ship inbound from Africa but still three days out of Philadelphia, as well as another bat of unknown species noted flying near a ship five hundred miles from

[3]Bowman, R. I. 1961.
[4]Howell, T. R. 1959.
[5]Hubbs, C. L., and R. C. Banks. 1966; Arvey, M. D. 1957; Brattstrom, B. H., and T. R. Howell. 1956.

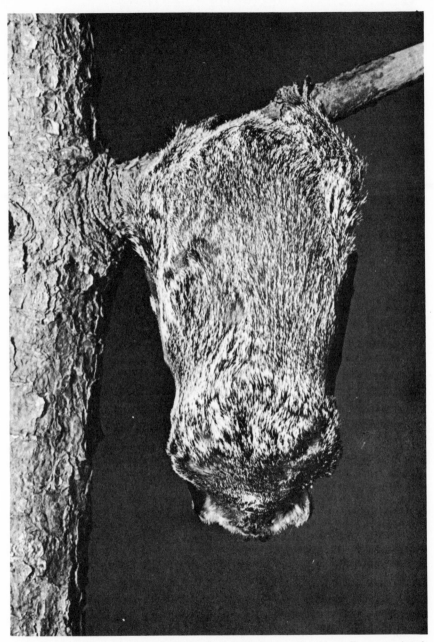

The hoary bat (*Lasiurus cinereus*) of North and South America is a solitary species that engages in extensive seasonal migrations. Its frosted color blends well with the bark and lichens. *Photographed November 2, 1955, by Robert T. Orr.*

land off the coast of Nova Scotia.[6] Flights of hoary bats (*Lasiurus cinereus*), red bats, and silver-haired bats have been reported at the Bermuda Islands, which are six hundred miles off the east coast of the United States. It seems doubtful that this represents a regular migratory pattern. More likely they were individuals lost or blown off course along the mainland. A summary of these records is given by Mackiewicz and Backus, who add several new records of red and silver-haired bats that landed on the rigging of a research vessel ninety to ninety-five miles off Long Island, New York. The great majority of the records are for early autumn.[7]

Recently an account was published of the occurrence of hoary bats in late August and early September as well as in April on the Farallon Islands off the central California coast.[8] As many as twenty-one individuals were observed in a single day. A stunted pine and two cypresses provided the only significant roosting sites on the barren, rocky islands for these migrants. The nearest land is Point Reyes, a long promontory that projects out to sea about twenty miles to the north. It is possible that these rocky islands provide a regular resting site for those bats that migrate along the coast and make it unnecessary for them to detour eastward around the San Francisco Bay region. However, the area is subject to heavy coastal fogs at times, and the possibility of getting lost at sea seems considerable.

MORTALITY FROM MAN-MADE HAZARDS

Among many other man-made hazards to avian migration are airport ceilometers. These are aeronautical instruments to determine the cloud level, or ceiling, in the vicinity of airports. A ceilometer projects a beam of light upward toward the cloud level. Under certain circumstances, especially on nights when there are low clouds, such a light beam confuses migrant birds that may be passing over and causes some of them to crash into nearby structures or even onto the ground. In recent years, however, the use of filters that produce a blue or purple light has greatly decreased the danger from this source. Seemingly these colors either are poorly seen or do not attract birds.

The first recorded avian tragedy from an airport ceilometer was in

[6]Griffin, D. R. 1958.
[7]Mackiewicz, J., and R. H. Backus. 1956.
[8]Tenaza, R. R. 1966.

1948 at the Nashville Airport in Tennessee.[9] On the night of September 9, a member of the airport staff heard birds passing overhead at 11:30 P.M. The night was cloudy but the ceiling at that time was 4,200 feet and visibility ten miles. Within an hour, birds began to fall and continued to do so until 4:30, September 10, at which time the ceiling was nearly ten thousand feet. Most of the birds, however, had fallen during the first hour, and the majority were within fifty to one hundred feet of the ceilometer. In the morning the total number of dead or injured birds was approximately three hundred, of which 248 were collected and taken to a local children's museum. Thirty-three species, ranging from six pied-billed grebes (*Podilymbus podiceps*) to a Savannah sparrow (*Passerculus sandwichensis*), were represented, but the majority of the birds were warblers, with twenty-one species recorded. There was also heavy mortality among red-eyed vireos, with ninety-five birds being counted. At this time no plausible explanation could be found to account for these birds' fatal plunge to the ground. Ceilometers had been in use for some years at this and other airports.

Tall man-made structures such as monuments, buildings, and towers have long been a source of mortality to migrant birds. In Washington, D.C., the Washington Monument, an obelisk 555 feet high, was reported in 1938 to have caused an average yearly mortality of 328 since 1932.[10] On the night of September 12, 1937, an unusually high kill occurred, and 576 birds, principally vireos and warblers, were found dead at the base of the monument the next morning. All had died from hitting the obelisk between 10:30 P.M. and midnight. There were no unusual local weather conditions except for a slight mist at the top of the shaft at the time of the tragedy.

A somewhat similar holocaust occurred in New York City shortly after midnight on September 11, 1948, when many hundreds of birds crashed into the 1,472-foot Empire State Building. Over twenty-five species, principally warblers, were identified, but an exact count of the number of casualties could not be made, as the bodies were swept away with hoses and shovels at an early hour. Dr. Richard H. Pough suggested a plausible explanation for this tragedy.[11] The birds were probably flying with a mass of cold air that was also moving south. In the vicinity of New York City a mass of warm air was moving north. The cold air was

[9]Spofford, W. R. 1949.
[10]Overing, R. 1938.
[11]Pough, R. H. 1948.

forced below the warmer, rising air, and the flight level of migrant birds was lowered to the point where they would collide with tall objects such as the Empire State Building.

The significance of weather conditions as a major factor causing nocturnal birds to collide with man-made objects was seen in late September and early October, 1954, in the eastern half of North America when a series of major casualties occurred. All seemed to be associated with cold fronts and stationary fronts that caused rain, fog, and cloud ceilings as low as eight hundred to one thousand feet. Such cold fronts moving down from the north push the warm, moisture-laden air up higher until it cools and forms clouds and rain. Furthermore, the cold front with its reduced temperature is a stimulus to migration. The cold front that caused the series of major casualties in 1954 moved into the New York area on the night of October 5 and reached southern United States by the night of October 7–8. It was estimated that on these three nights alone (October 5, 6, and 7) at least 100,000 birds were killed by flying into man-made objects.[12] Hundreds struck the Empire State Building in New York City on October 5. Several thousand were killed the same night at two United States Army Air Force airfields by being attracted to ceilometers, and hundreds more died at other airports as a result of the attraction of ceilometers. Larger numbers of migrants were killed the following night because of airport ceilometers or because of collisions with radio or TV broadcasting towers. Mortality was recorded from North Carolina, South Carolina, Tennessee, Mississippi, Missouri, and Kansas. The greatest tragedies took place on the third night in southeastern United States. At four airport ceilometers alone in Alabama and Georgia an estimated 75,000 birds perished. Most of the birds killed were warblers, thrushes, vireos, catbirds, tanagers, and sparrows.

During this general period a careful study was made of nocturnal migrants striking a newly erected television tower one mile west of Topeka, Kansas.[13] The tower was 950 feet high and situated on a hill about a thousand feet above sea level. The first casualties were noted on September 7, and the last for that autumn on October 23. The major accidents took place on the nights of September 24–25, September 30–October 1, October 5–6, and October 6–7. A total of 1,090 birds, which represented nearly all of the casualties, was collected. There were sixty-one species identified, although the major mortality occurred among

[12]Terres, J. K. 1956.
[13]Tordoff, H. B., and R. M. Mengel. 1956.

warblers, thrushes, vireos, and sparrows. On all the nights that the casualty rate was high there was either a cold front or stationary front over eastern Kansas with rain, fog, and a low cloud ceiling.

Television towers continue to be a source of high mortality to nocturnal migrants. Caldwell and Wallace made a summary of the number of birds killed in Michigan at three towers in spring from 1962 to 1964 and seven towers in autumn from 1959 to 1964.[14] Over 7,000 avian victims were found. Sixty-five percent of these were wood warblers, 22 percent thrushes, 6 percent vireos, and all of the other species constituted 7 percent. Even greater was the mortality noted at a single television tower at Eau Claire, Wisconsin, on two consecutive nights in September, 1963. On the night of September 19–20, 5,595 dead birds were collected, and on the following night, 4,600, making a total of 10,195. As usual, warblers and vireos suffered the most. Magnolia warblers constituted 15.2 percent of the total kill on the first night, and on the second night 17.4 percent of the casualties were red-eyed vireos.[15] At this same tower on the morning of September 20, 1957, an estimated 20,000 birds had been found dead.

In the earlier days of television, the transmission towers were in the range of 500 feet. Presently many towers are 1,000 feet or more in height. There are at least two in the United States that are approximately 1,600 feet high. With increased height, the mortality to nocturnal avian migrants also increases.

A very interesting compilation of data was made by Stoddard and Norris on mortality at a television tower about twenty miles north of Tallahassee, Florida, over a period of eleven years.[16] When the study started in 1955, there was a 673-foot TV tower. In 1960 it was replaced by a 1,010-foot tower. During the eleven years, 29,451 dead birds were picked up beneath the structures. In addition, there were many cripples, and it was believed that predators had removed others. It is interesting to note that only one of the nearly 30,000 birds handled was banded.

For many years before the advent of television towers and even skyscrapers, one of the most important man-made hazards to nocturnal avian migrants was lighthouses. These coastal beacons, usually situated on promontories, periodically flash a powerful beam concentrated by prisms or other means so that it will carry far to sea. As with airport

[14]Caldwell, L. D., and G. J. Wallace. 1966.
[15]Kemper, C. A. 1964.
[16]Stoddard, H. L., and R. A. Norris. 1967.

ceilometers, the light from these objects seems both to attract and to confuse migrating birds at night and cause them to collide with the source of the beam.

Even lower man-made objects can be hazardous to migratory birds at night. There are reports of birds killed by wires along railroad lines in southeastern U.S.S.R.[17] The danger is particularly great in the steppes, where there are no trees. Low-flying birds such as short-toed larks, skylarks, partridges, and quail suffered the highest mortality. Very few casualties were noted during daylight hours.

Banding itself has inadvertently been responsible for avian mortality. Some years ago a group of uninformed but well-meaning residents in eastern Canada's province of Quebec gained the impression that the United States Fish and Wildlife Service wanted reports on all banded birds. Unfortunately they shot large numbers of nesting birds to gain these data. The numbers were carefully noted and sent to Washington and the bands made into such items of jewelry as watch chains and bracelets by the local collectors. By the time these mistakes were discovered, bands had been collected from 270 evening grosbeaks and two purple finches that had been shot. A detailed account of this tragedy is given by Parks and Parks.[18]

[17]Beeb, H. 1955.
[18]Parks, G. H., and H. C. Parks. 1963.

17

METHODS OF STUDYING MIGRATION

Many methods, some simple, others very complex, have been employed in recent years to determine the movements of both individual organisms and populations. These range from field observations to the use of modern instrumentation.

FIELD OBSERVATION

The seasonal movements of some animals can readily be observed. This is especially true of many kinds of birds. The movements of fishes, amphibians, reptiles, and most mammals are less easily seen, although there are many exceptions. Most easily observed are the migrations of locusts and butterflies. Salmon, steelhead, and certain other species of fish that spawn in fresh water are often conspicuous in their passage, although mechanical counters are almost essential in order to obtain accurate data on numbers. The movements of most marine fishes are not easily seen, even though in some instances the spawning activities may be spectacular. The seasonal spawning of the grunion along the coast of southern California and northwestern Mexico can hardly escape notice, nor can that of certain smelts and herrings that perform this activity in shallow water where they attract large numbers of gulls.

Occasionally one sees overland movements of large numbers of amphibians, usually young that have recently completed metamorphosis, but more often frogs and salamanders move singly, quietly, and at night. One usually becomes aware of the presence of anurans at a breeding pond by their vocalization. The movements of marine turtles between their marine pastures and the remote beaches where the females lay their eggs are still much of a mystery.

Birds lend themselves to field studies on migration better than any other group of organisms. Because of their size, movement, and the environments they occupy, their presence or absence can usually be determined by the amateur as well as by the professional. Censuses taken at different seasons of the year and in many locations on land as well as at sea have provided much of the basic information relative to the nesting range, winter range, and migration route for many species. In any such field studies the value of the data is dependent upon standardized methods. In order that censuses may be compared for any one location from day to day or between seasons, it is necessary that recordings be made under essentially similar conditions as regards habitat, time of day, and weather. The equipment necessary for such studies consists simply of census sheets, a pen, and binoculars. Good vision and hearing combined with quick recognition are essential qualities for a field observer. In studies on large flocking birds, especially waterfowl, visual sighting from small aircraft that may actually follow flocks has proved an extremely accurate method of studying migration pathways.

The movements of some mammals such as deer and bats occur principally at night and do not lend themselves to simple observation. These animals can be seen on their arrival at their summer or winter quarters, but their actual travels en route usually must be determined by other means. On the other hand, the seasonal migrations of certain whales that follow coastlines as well as some of the larger herbivores like caribou in arctic North America or springbok in southern Africa are spectacular to watch. Most of our current knowledge on the migrations as well as numbers of these animals has been obtained solely by observation.

Observations may sometimes be indirect. In the case of some big game animals in the north, where snow is often present in spring and autumn during the migration period, track counting may be an effective means of determining population movement. Edwards and Ritcey made daily track counts of moose crossing a snowshoe trail in British Columbia in their studies on the migration of these animals.[1] Similar techniques have been used in determining deer movements.

MOON WATCHING

Since the latter part of the nineteenth century there have been occasional recordings by ornithologists and astronomers of birds seen passing across the face of the moon when it was viewed through a moderately

[1]Edwards, R. Y., and R. W. Ritcey. 1956.

low power telescope during the full periods. No effort was made to use this system for the scientific study of migration, however, until almost the middle of the twentieth century.

Credit for the development of this method for making a quantitative study of nocturnal bird migration must go to Dr. George H. Lowery, Jr., of Louisiana State University, who was later joined by Dr. Robert J. Newman. Dr. Lowery was seeking a means whereby he could make a comparison of nocturnal migrations occurring at different times and in different places. Dr. W. A. Rense, an associate of Dr. Lowery in the department of physics and astronomy at Louisiana State University, showed that a mathematical procedure could be used to analyze counts made of birds observed crossing the face of the moon, which counts would then serve as an index.[2] With this information a very important phase in the study of bird migration began.

In brief, the technique involves the use of a 20-power telescope that is mounted on a tripod and focused on the moon. Observations are made on the four or five nights that center about the period of the full moon during the spring and fall migrations. Records are kept of all birds seen crossing the rim of the moon from twilight to dawn. The moon as viewed through the telescope is regarded as the face of an upright clock, and each object passing across it is identified in terms of the numbers on the clock. For example, a bird may enter at 4:30 and leave at 2:15, in which instance it would have passed over only one side of the moon's image, or it might enter at 6 and leave at 12, thereby going across the center of the moon. The various coordinates for each locality, each representing birds crossing the moon during a given period, such as an hour, must then be plotted so as to cross through the center of a circle representing the moon. Since many will likely be parallel to one another, they can be expressed by one line with a small mark or marks to indicate the number of observations.

A triangle from the telescope or observer to the moon represents the lunar cone. The triangle from the observer to the flight ceiling of the birds is referred to as the cone of observation. Since the observer will start recording when the moon is low on the horizon and will continue as the moon rises to its zenith and then goes down toward the western horizon, the cone of observation will change greatly in length during the course of the night. The more nearly the lunar cone comes toward a vertical position, the shorter the cone of observation becomes. This is

[2]Rense, W. A. 1946.

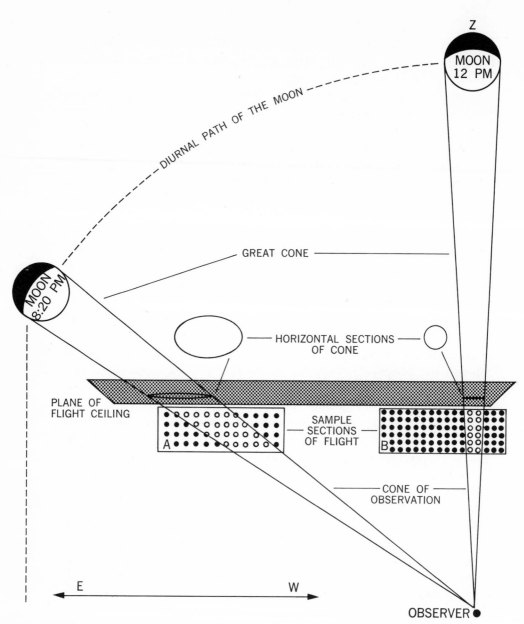

Temporal change in the effective size of the field of observation. The sample sections, A and B, represent the theoretical densities of flight at 8:20 and 12:00 P.M., respectively. Though twice as many birds are assumed to be in the air at midnight when the moon is on its zenith (Z) as there were at the earlier hour, only half as many are visible because of the decrease in size of the cone of observation. (After Lowery, G. H., Jr., 1951)

because the flight ceiling is closest to the observer directly overhead. Since the diameter of the viewing area increases with distance, the observer is likely to see more birds in the early evening when the moon is low and the cone of observation is longer than he will see later when the moon is overhead. This, however, does not mean that fewer birds are passing over at the later time but means rather that fewer can be seen because of the shorter observation cone and smaller viewing diameter. The diameter of the cone is obtained, approximately, by multiplying the distance by .009. At a distance of 1,000 feet the diameter is 9 feet, whereas at 10,000 feet it would be 90 feet. Account must be taken not only of the changing position of the moon during any one night but also of its changing position in the sky on different nights and in different localities.

Lunar observations through a telescope have certain drawbacks. One is limited to studying migration on nights when the moon is full, or at least fairly full. We know that moonlight appears to have little effect on migration, as the phenomenon continues on moonless nights. Another problem involves identification. There are occasions when a bird can be identified as to species when its silhouette is momentarily seen crossing the moon. Generally, however, this is not possible. More often the identification is of a general nature, such as waterfowl, shorebirds, herons, small passerines, and the like.

These imperfections in the method, nevertheless, do not detract from the great amount of valuable information that has been acquired in the past twenty years from coordinated observations on birds seen through a telescope while passing across the face of the moon. From twilight on October 1 to dawn on October 5, 1952, a continent-wide observing of this sort was carried on in North America. Two hundred sixty-five observation stations at 235 localities in Canada and the United States were manned by 1,391 observers. During the period of observation, the silhouettes of 35,407 birds were recorded. This mass of data was analyzed by Lowery and Newman to show the computed amounts and directional trends over the United States and southern Canada on these four nights in October, 1952.[3]

The results of such coordinated studies over a wide area of both latitude and longitude have been not to determine the number of birds engaging in migration but rather, as pointed out by Lowery and Newman (p. 244), "to reduce all observations to an equal comparative basis. . . ."[4]

[3]Lowery, G. H., Jr., and R. J. Newman. 1966.
[4]Lowery, G. H., Jr., and R. J. Newman. 1955.

MARKING

Field observations, even with species that lend themselves best to this kind of study, provide only quantitative data on population movements. Where it is desirable to follow the movements of individuals, a method of recognition must be employed. Sometimes an individual of a species is distinguished by an unusual feature such as a scar or an abnormality in color pattern or some other such character, but, for the most part, recognition by such means is not possible.

Many different ways of marking animals, however, have been devised to permit the recognition of individuals of a population. The principal methods are by mutilation and by tagging or color marking.

Mutilation involves the destruction or scarring of some part of the body. The area so treated is small and usually causes only minor and at most very temporary discomfort to the animal. Removal of a part or all of a fin may serve to distinguish one population of fish from others of the

Schematic drawing of feet to show system of assigning serial numbers. (From Martof, B. S.: *Ecology*, Vol. 34, 1953)

An electric flash brand being applied to a subadult male northern elephant seal (*Mirounga angustirostris*). *Photograph by Richard Jennings.*

same species. The excising of particular scales or groups of scales in various combinations has been used to mark certain fishes as well as reptiles. For amphibians, some reptiles, and even small mammals, toe clipping is a common means of marking individuals. Since most of these animals have five toes on each foot, it is not difficult to work out a system whereby, with the removal of one or two toes in various combinations, many thousands of individuals can each be recognized. One system is to number the toes so that those on the left hind foot are one to five, those on the right hind foot 10 to 50, those on the left front foot 100 to 400, and those on the right front foot 800 to 3,200. This presumes only four toes on each front foot, which is the common number for most frogs and toads. If five are present, a greater number of combinations is possible. By removing no more than two toes on each foot, 6,399 individuals can be marked in series.

A northern elephant seal bull that has been flash-branded. *Photograph by Richard Jennings.*

Ear notching or punching has long been used to mark mammals both large and small. Although notching is best suited to marking populations and has been employed for generations by cattle ranchers to mark their stock, the use of this in combination with punches that will make small round holes in the cartilaginous pinna of each ear can permit recognition of a large number of individuals. Fur clipping and tail docking are other means of marking mammals.

A very practical method of mutilation that has been employed with success in marking elephant seals is branding. This involves the use of an electric branding iron that has sex symbols and changeable numbers. The iron sears the skin and produces a permanent scar that denotes the sex and number of the animal.

Tagging involves the attachment of some device to the body of an animal. Metal or plastic strips or disks are most commonly employed for this purpose. In fishes strap tags with data are sometimes attached to the jaws, the operculum, or the preopercle. These tags are generally made of Monel metal. Cellulose nitrate tags, known as Petersen disks, placed on each side of the dorsal part of the caudal peduncle or on either side of the base of the dorsal fin are commonly used. The disks are connected to one another by means of monofilament nylon leader through the bony base of the fin. Such disks bear numbers as well as the correct address to which the finder may send them.

In order to follow the direction taken by white bass that were removed from their spawning area along the shore of Lake Mendota, Wisconsin,

Largemouth bass, showing method of attaching the float which was used as an aid to tracking the course of the fish after displacement. A nylon thread connects the bobber and hook. (After Hasler, A. D., 1966)

U. S. Fish and Wildlife Service bands. *Photograph by Robert T. Orr.*

Illustrating a band attached to the leg of a fox sparrow (*Passerella iliaca*). *Photographed at Point Reyes Bird Observatory, Marin County, California, by Robert T. Orr.*

and released some distance away, Dr. Hasler attached small yellow floats or bobbers to them.[5] The bobbers were sixty-four millimeters in diameter and were attached to the bass by means of two- to five-meter lengths of monofilament nylon line. Although the fish could not be seen once they were released, their movements could be followed easily.

Sea turtles are usually banded with Monel metal clips on which a serial number and adequate data for their return are stamped. These clips are generally attached to the back edge of the front flipper.

The banding of birds with metal tags has been carried on for the past half century. These bands, which have serial numbers on them and instructions to the finder to notify the proper authorities, are attached to the leg in such a way as not to injure the bird. They are made of soft, lightweight metal and come in various standard sizes. In the United States, the Fish and Wildlife Service has jurisdiction over bird banding and provides those who have the proper permits with serially numbered bands of the sizes needed.

Recently a cooperative project to mark dolphins, both *Lagenorhynchus obliquidens* and *Delphinus delphis*, has been undertaken off the coast of southern California by the United States Naval Undersea Warfare Center at Point Mugu and Marineland of the Pacific. This involves the capture and subsequent release of dolphins after a white plastic spool has been attached to the dorsal fin. Later observation or capture of marked individuals may give considerable information on the movements of these cetaceans.

In any tagging or banding operation it is necessary to capture the animal and have it in hand. Various kinds of nets and traps are used in the capture of fishes for marking. These range from dip nets to large trawls. Hatchery-raised fry are marked or tagged before being released. With large species such as marlin, sailfish, and even tuna the fish may be caught with hook and line in order that a tag may be attached to its body.

Many kinds of traps have been developed for use in bird banding. For many years wire traps were used almost exclusively for taking small species, principally sparrows and finches. These depend principally on bait. Sometimes the presence of a captive bird in one compartment serves as an attractant. Water-drip traps also have been used very successfully in certain regions.

The problem of catching small insectivorous species and shorebirds

[5]Hasler, A. D. 1966.

Wire trap commonly used for capturing small ground foraging birds. Traps are usually set near numbered stakes and a marker is attached to a nearby shrub or tree. *Photographed at Point Reyes Bird Observatory, Marin County, California, February 27, 1967, by Robert T. Orr.*

as well as bats was solved to a large extent by the development of the Japanese mist net, which requires no bait whatsoever. Mist nets are made of fine black silk or nylon thread that is made into a mesh. The standard is three-quarters of an inch, although a larger mesh of one and one-quarter inches is sometimes used for larger birds. Mist nets are generally from thirty to thirty-eight feet in length and from three to seven feet in height. The netting is attached rather loosely on horizontal lengths of twine about eighteen to twenty-four inches apart. A bird hitting a net, therefore, falls downward in the mesh, which then forms a sort of pocket hanging from the taut horizontal lengths of twine. Each end of a mist net is attached to tree trunks or poles. Hollow aluminum poles that come in sections are commonly used by many banders because of their lightness, strength, and the ease with which they may be transported.

The principle of the mist net is that it is invisible until a bird or bat is almost in it. As soon as it hits the net, it becomes caught in a pocket of mesh from which escape is not readily made. With a little experience the bander can quickly remove a netted individual with no injury to the captive.

Mist nets properly placed in weed patches are satisfactory for finches, siskins, and buntings. Forest-dwelling birds, such as many kinds of warblers, thrushes, flycatchers, and grosbeaks, are easily taken by placing mist nets in flyways between the trees, across paths, and at the edges of woodlands. Mist nets are also useful at times in taking shorebirds.

Mist nets have partly solved the problem of capturing birds that live high in tropical forests. Such birds may not leave this canopy to come to the middle or lower forest levels, and their presence as well as seasonal movements therefore goes unnoticed. Recently, Humphrey *et al.* developed a method of raising a series of mist nets placed one above the other on rigging so as to penetrate the forest canopy to heights of over seventy-five feet.[6] Their experiments with this technique were carried on in a rain forest near Belém, Brazil. The nets were lowered by pulleys every

[6]Humphrey, P. S., *et al.* 1968.

Heligoland trap set up to catch migrant land birds on South Farallon Island off the central California coast by members of the Point Reyes Bird Observatory. *Photographed April 1967 by Fred Sibley.*

thirty to forty-five minutes. During periodic netting over two months, they captured fifty species of birds, of which about one-third had never been captured in the area at ground level. Some species had not even been seen in the area before.

The cannon trap is a device to shoot a large net out over a group of birds as they are feeding. It is used most often for waterfowl that have been lured to the net site by bait.

Birds should be removed from the trap or net as soon as possible. Those in traps are usually removed and processed one at a time. If a flock is caught in a mist net, it is advisable to remove all the individuals to a small retaining sack made of netting so that they will not injure themselves. After a bird is removed, it is examined and the following data are recorded: the species and, if positively determined, the subspecies; the American Ornithologists' Union number of the species for those banding in North America; the age (whether adult, immature, juvenal, etc); the sex, if possible; the date banded; the flyway; the station; the latitude and longitude; and of course the number of the band that is attached. Those making special studies of a particular species may even weigh the bird and record certain measurements such as the length of the wing. After these data are recorded, the bird is released. Each year the results of banding by various individuals are sent to the Patuxent Wildlife Research Center maintained by the United States Fish and Wildlife Service in Laurel, Maryland. In Canada such data are sent to the Chief, Canadian Wildlife Service, Ottawa, Ontario.

Other methods are used to mark birds so that particular individuals can subsequently be recognized and their band number determined without their being captured. This involves use of bands or rings of various colors. Such bands are made of plastic and can easily be attached to one or both legs. By using various combinations of colors, it is possible to band a number of individuals of the same species and be able to recognize each one at a distance.

The use of color in marking birds has not been restricted to attaching color bands to the legs. Recently, dyes have been employed in coloring feather patches, thereby making it possible to detect marked individuals at a considerable distance. This method was first employed extensively in the United States on snow geese so that their movements could be followed. Subsequently it has been used on other kinds of birds with successful results. On South Georgia Island a number of wandering albatrosses (*Diomedea exulans*) were dyed by using rhodamine B in an alcohol and water mixture. This was applied to the back, wings, and undersides and was found to last at least twelve months. Individuals so marked were sighted as far away as New South Wales in Australia.[7]

A novel method of following the movement of captured migratory waterfowl upon their being released at night was used by Dr. Frank Bellrose of the Illinois Natural History Survey.[8] In order that the initial direction of flight of migrant ducks might be recorded, he attached small pen flashlights to their legs. These could be seen for several hundred yards by one person and followed farther by the proper positioning of several persons. Such marking devices are so attached that they do not remain permanently on the leg, thus being good for only one time.

Bands, tags, and other marking devices have been used extensively on migratory mammals to follow the movements of both populations and individuals. The same general type of band that is used on birds is employed in marking bats. Soft metal cylinders are generally attached to the forearm in such a way that the flight membrane is not injured and no pressure is produced. If they are attached too tightly, bats bite the bands, which results in the serial numbers becoming illegible and the flesh growing over the bands in time. Hundreds of thousands of bats have been banded in recent years, principally in their winter quarters during hibernation. Adults as well as young can also be banded in nursery colonies.

For large herbivores such as antelopes, deer, moose, elk, and caribou, plastic disks are sometimes attached to the ears. Colored streamers are also occasionally used and may be placed around the neck or attached to horns or antlers. Serially numbered boxcar seals have been used in deer studies. Bucks trapped on their summer range are so marked, and the shed antlers, when found late the following winter, provide evidence of seasonal movement.

Seals and sea lions are sometimes tagged with noncorrosive strips of metal on which serial numbers and data for their return are stamped. These strips are best attached to the proximal posterior edge of one of the front flippers. They are clamped through the skin and flesh so that their removal by the animal is difficult. Sometimes plastic disks are attached to the hind flippers, but there is a greater chance that they will be torn off in time.

The marking of whales was started about 1920 by the Norwegians. It was soon taken up by the British Discovery Committee and carried out by members of the royal research ship *Discovery* and subsequently by

[7]Tickell, W. L. N. 1968.
[8]Bellrose, F. C. 1958b.

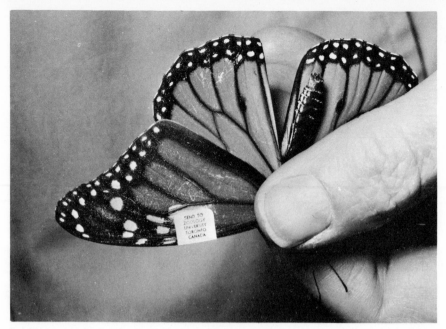

Small tags attached to the leading edges of the wings of monarch butterflies have provided much information on the movements of this species. *Photograph by Edward S. Ross.*

Discovery II in the Southern Hemisphere. The most satisfactory marking technique involves the use of a stainless steel tube about ten and a half inches long that has a blunt head and is fired into the blubber by means of a specially modified harpoon gun. A number is inscribed on the tube as well as instructions to the finder as to where to send it. No damage is done to the whale by firing this into the blubber or muscle, where it is most likely to be found if the whale is subsequently captured and flensed in a whaling station or ship. To reduce any possibility of infection, the tubes are coated with an antibiotic. There are records of these tubes being taken from whales twenty-five years after they were fired into the animals.

Although most banding and marking has been done with vertebrates, there has been some very extensive banding of monarch butterflies in recent years. Much of it has been under the supervision of Dr. F. A. Urquhart of the Royal Ontario Museum in Toronto, Canada. The band consists of a strip of light paper that is attached to the upper surface of the wing. The weight is so insignificant that it in no way hinders flight.

Radioactive isotopes have been experimented with in the tracking of several kinds of vertebrates, including some fishes and small mammals. For fishes, such substances must have a fairly long half-life, and in order that the individual may be recorded, it must pass close to a Geiger counter. Twenty-gauge radioactive gold-198 wire has been used to study the movements of some small mammals. The wire has an activity of 0.7 to 4.5 millecuries and is cut into sections about one centimeter long. These are inserted under the skin of the abdomen by means of a hypodermic needle.

RADIO TRACKING

More recently the use of radiotransmitters has proved effective in following the movements of some mammals and birds. This involves capture of an animal, the attachment of a small transmitter, and then the following of its movements by means of portable directional receivers. Although this method is most useful in studying local movements, and home range or territory, it can provide information on migration. A most dramatic example of the use of radio tracking in the study of migration is given by Graber, who followed the night flight of a gray-cheeked thrush (*Hylocichla minima*) that had a tiny transmitter weighing 2.5 grams attached to the feathers of its back.[9] The bird was captured on University of Illinois property just south of Urbana at noon on May 24, 1965. As soon as the transmitter was attached, the bird was released, and its local activities were followed for the rest of the day by monitors. A light plane was in readiness to follow this night migrant, which took to the air at 7:55 that evening. The thrush was followed successfully and found to take a direct course that took it over Chicago and then over nearly 250 miles of open water to the northwest end of Lake Michigan. It was recorded in the air for more than eight hours of continuous flight, during which it flew nearly four hundred miles. Its ground speed was fifty miles per hour, but its air speed was only thirty-three miles per hour as a result of a strong tail wind.

The use of electronics in tracking the movements and migratory routes of animals is presently moving into an even more advanced stage, thanks to satellites. Electronic packages are being attached to marine animals ranging from sea turtles to whales. These devices are capable of beaming signals to weather satellites at least twice a day. They are accurate to within about one and one-half miles and permit the tracking of the movements of these animals. Such devices are also being used on larger land mammals to study their seasonal movements.

Transmitters have been used recently on whales in the Gulf of California, Mexico. A population of finbacks (*Balaenoptera physalus*) has long been known to occur in this area, but whether they are resident or not

[9]Graber, R. R. 1965.

is yet to be determined. Recently, radio transmitters have been attached
to the backs of some of these animals in the hope that their seasonal
movements may be plotted. Such methods are also being employed in
tracing the movements of dolphins along the California coast.

The radio-tagging of whales presents a number of major problems, as
has been demonstrated by Schevill and Watkins in their efforts to use
this technique in following the migratory movements of the right whale
(*Eubalaena glacialis*) along the east coast of North America.[10] The receiv-
ing set that will follow the movements of radio-tagged whales must
provide a bearing based on the reception of short, intermittent signals
given by a one-milliwatt transmitter. The fact that much of a whale's
time is spent beneath the surface of the sea means that the small trans-
mitting antenna attached to its body gives off signals only during the very
brief periods of surfacing. The time between surfacings in the right
whale was found to vary from thirty seconds to fifteen minutes or longer,
and the maximum period of transmission when the animal was surfacing
was no more than two seconds. This means that a bearing must be obtained very rapidly. Schevill and Watkins, in following by plane or by
ship the signals given off by tagged whales, found that multiple antennae
giving directional coverage over 360 degrees were best suited for this
purpose. Greater bearing accuracy was obtained with a shipboard
system, but because both the receiver and the transmitter were close to
the surface of the sea (the latter under the surface most of the time), reception was limited to about six kilometers. Airborne directional
receivers were found to have a considerably greater range, which varied
from 20 kilometers at 300 m. to 80 kilometers at 1,500 m.

The radio transmitters consisted of 140 Mc one-milliwatt instruments
with quarter-wavelength (50-centimeter) whip antennae. The transmitters were painted orange and attached with darts to the mid-dorsal
surface over the thorax, this being done by hand from low-flying helicopters.

SONAR TRACKING AND AURAL RECORDING

The migratory movements of fishes present numerous problems to the
scientific investigator. For the most part, fishes cannot readily be observed, unlike most amphibians, birds, and mammals. Their environ-

[10]Schevill, W. E., and W. A. Watkins. 1966.

ment is such that visibility is limited to a relatively few feet even in the clearest water. In the turbid waters of the large rivers as well as in the ocean, the detection of population movements is dependent upon the capture of marked individuals or upon the use of modern detecting devices.

Recently, a sonar apparatus in which the echo signals are seen on a Plan Position Indicator (PPI) scope has proved extremely useful. Groot and Wiley have described the use of a time-lapse motion picture camera in connection with such a horizontal echo ranger in tracking fish.[11] The camera is so adjusted that a single frame is exposed during one complete scan of 180 degrees. The shutter then closes as the next frame moves into place. Both the camera lens and the PPI scope are enclosed in a light-proof covering. To determine time, a luminous-dial watch is located below the grid of the scope. When the developed film is run at twenty-four frames per second, it is possible in a few minutes to view movements that have taken place over a twenty-four-hour period. With such an apparatus, information on direction of movement, time of migration, and speed can be obtained accurately.

Aural recording is employed in studying avian migration at night. This was used most effectively by Ball in his work on bird movements on the Gaspé Peninsula in eastern Canada.[12] This is the recording of flight call as migrants pass overhead. It permits identification of some migrants to species, which cannot usually be done in radar tracking or by observing birds through a telescope as they pass across the face of the full moon. It also permits the recording of migrants flying at low elevations as well as on dark nights. Aural recording has the disadvantage, however, of a ceiling limitation because few persons can hear passerines calling when they are more than 1,500 feet overhead. There is also the fact that the recording of migrant calls cannot give an accurate index of the numbers of individuals passing by. Some individuals may utter several "chips" while within earshot of an observer, but a flock composed of many individuals may pass by in silence. There is also the problem of extraneous sounds that may interfere with the use of this technique. The sounds of cities, towns, passing traffic on highways, planes, water flow in rivers and creeks, as well as surf, greatly restrict the places where "chip counting" can be carried on.

A more advanced method of recording passing migrants by flight

[11]Groot, C., and W. L. Wiley. 1965.
[12]Ball, S. C. 1952.

calls was developed by Graber and Cochran.[13] Instead of depending on the human ear, they employed a parabolic reflector with a microphone in the center. The sounds picked up by the microphone were then amplified and recorded on tape for later analysis. The use of these instruments raises the ceiling of reception to over ten thousand feet and permits more accurate directional recording. Furthermore, all calls are recorded and can be studied in the laboratory where they can be identified and the frequency of utterance can be determined.

RADAR TRACKING

The use of radar as a means of studying bird migration was demonstrated by Sutter, who showed that masses of echoes or blips that appeared on radar screens and were referred to as "angels" were really birds.[14] At the height of the migration period the center of the radar screen is completely saturated at times by targets. This is a result of the density of the moving bird population, which may number in the thousands for each square mile. This pattern, however, thins out toward the periphery so that the density of the echoes can be counted. If it is assumed that this reduction in density occurs at the same rate, the peripheral density can serve as an index of the numbers of migrants passing over. It has been found that the density of the angels is halved for every approximately eight-mile increase in distance from the center of the screen.

Following the earlier uses of radar to note migratory movements, Lack, Nisbet, Bellrose and Graber, Nisbet and Drury, and others have used this technique to advance our knowledge of certain facets of migration.[15]

The radar equipment used presently at South Truro, Massachusetts, has a circular screen or map referred to as the PPI on which the bird echoes appear as bright dots.[16] Used in connection with this is an electronic device called the MTI that removes echoes from the screen in the form of a wedge-shaped sector on either side of the center if the birds

[13]Graber, R. R., and W. W. Cochran. 1959.
[14]Sutter, E. 1957.
[15]Lack, D. 1962, 1963; Nisbet, I. C. T. 1963a, 1963b; Bellrose, F. C., and R. R. Graber. 1963; Nisbet, I. C. T., and W. H. Drury, Jr. 1967.
[16]Nisbet, I. C. T., and W. H. Drury, Jr. 1967.

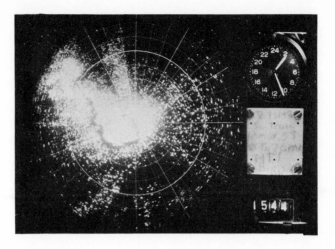

Radar screen showing wedge. *Reprinted by permission of Dr. William H. Drury.*

are all moving in the same direction. This wedge is at right angles to the direction of movement of the birds. It is seen only when the movement is relatively uniform and not with disoriented movement or random flight. A sweep of the radar beam over the screen requires twelve seconds. Each sweep is recorded in slow motion on a single frame of 35-mm. film that can later be projected at a speed sufficient to show the flight pattern and direction as well as spacial distribution of the birds that are recorded.

Recently, Eastwood has written a book on the history of the use of radar in the study of migration with a comprehensive account of the techniques used in this relatively new science.[17]

Radar is being employed also by entomologists to follow the movements of insects. Rainey has described its use in determining the height of flight, population density, and direction of movement of swarms of desert locusts (*Schistocerca gregaria*) in India.[18]

[17]Eastwood, E. 1967.
[18]Rainey, R. C. 1967.

BIBLIOGRAPHY

ALLEN, G. H. 1966. Ocean Migration and Distribution of Fin-marked Coho Salmon. J. Fish. Res. Bd. Canada 23: 1043–1061.

ARVEY, M. D. 1957. Bay-breasted Warbler off California Coast. Condor 59: 268.

AUSTIN, O. L. 1951. Group Adherence in the Common Tern. Bird-Banding 22:1–15.

AUSTIN, O. L., Jr. 1961. Birds of the World. Golden Press, New York. 316 pp.

BAGGERMAN, B. 1957. An Experimental Study on the Timing of Breeding and Migration in the Three-spined Stickleback (*Gasterosteus aculeatus* L.). Arch. Néerlandaise Zool. 12: 105–318.

——— 1960. Salinity Preference, Thyroid Activity and the Seaward Migration of Four Species of Pacific Salmon (*Oncorhynchus*). J. Fish. Res. Bd. Canada 17: 295–322.

BALL, S. C. 1952. Fall Bird Migration on the Gaspé Peninsula. Peabody Mus. Nat. Hist. Bull. 7. vii +211 pp.

BALLANCE, D. K., and S. L. B. Lee. 1961. Notes on Autumn Migration at the Bosphorus and in the Aegean. Ibis 103: 195–204.

BANFIELD, A. W. F. 1954. Preliminary Investigation of the Barren Ground Caribou. Canadian Wildl. Serv., Wildl. Mgmt. Bull., ser. 1, no. 10A, 79 pp., and 10B, 112 pp.

BANNERMAN, D. A. 1953. The Birds of the British Isles. Illustrated by G. E. Lodge. Oliver and Boyd, Edinburgh. Vol. 1, xviii +356 pp.

——— 1963. Birds of the Atlantic Islands. Oliver and Boyd, Edinburgh. Vol. 1, xxxi +358 pp.

BARRINGTON, R. M. 1900. The Migration of Birds as Observed at Irish Lighthouses and Lightships Including the Original Reports from 1888–97, Now Published for the First Time, and an Analysis of These and of the Previously Published Reports from 1881–87 Together with an Appendix Giving the Measurements of about 1600 Wings. R. H. Porter, London. 667 pp.

271

BARTHOLOMEW, G. A., Jr., and C. L. Hubbs. 1952. Winter Population of Pinnipeds about Guadalupe, San Benito, and Cedros Islands, Baja California. J. Mamm. 33: 160–171.

BEEB, H. 1955. Observations on the Autumn Migration in the Area Between the Sea of Azov and the Caspian. Ibis 97: 25–37.

BELLROSE, F. C. 1958a. The Orientation of Displaced Waterfowl in Migration. Wilson Bull. 70: 20–40.

——— 1958b. Celestial Orientation by Wild Mallards. Bird-Banding 29: 75–90.

——— 1967. Radar in Orientation Research. Proc. XIV Internat. Ornith. Congr.: 281–309.

——— 1968. Waterfowl Migration Corridors East of the Rocky Mountains in the United States. Biol. Notes 61, Illinois Nat. Hist. Surv. 24 pp.

BELLROSE, F. C., and R. R. Graber. 1963. A Radar Study of the Flight Directions of Nocturnal Migrants. Proc. XIII Internat. Ornith. Congr.: 362–389.

BENT, A. C. 1937. Life Histories of North American Birds of Prey. Order Falconiformes, Part I. U.S. Nat. Mus. Bull. 167. viii +409 pp.

——— 1940. Life Histories of North American Cuckoos, Goatsuckers, Hummingbirds and Their Allies. U.S. Nat. Mus. Bull. 176. viii+506 pp.

——— 1942. Life Histories of North American Flycatchers, Larks, Swallows, and Their Allies. U.S. Nat. Mus. Bull. 179. xi +555 pp.

BEST, P. B. 1967. Distribution and Feeding Habits of Baleen Whales off the Cape Province. Republic of South Africa, Dept. Commerce and Industries, Div. Sea Fish. Invest. Rept. 57. 44 pp.

BIRUKOW, G. 1963. Time-compensated Sun-Orientation in Animals. Proc. XVI Internat. Congr. Zool. 4: 346–350.

BOGERT, C. M. 1947. A Field Study of Homing in the Carolina Toad. Amer. Mus. Novitates 1355. 24 pp.

BOWMAN, R. I. 1961. Late Spring Observations on Birds of South Farallon Island, California. Condor 63: 410–416.

BRATTSTROM, B. H. 1962. Homing in the Giant Toad, *Bufo marinus*. Herpetologica 18: 176–180.

BRATTSTROM, B. H., and T. R. Howell. 1956. The Birds of the Revilla Gigedo Islands, Mexico. Condor 58: 107–120.

BROEKHUYSEN, G. 1967. Bird Migration in the Most Southern Part of the African Continent. Vogelwarte 24: 6–16.

BROUN, M. 1937. Three Seasons at Hawk Mountain Sanctuary. Emergency Conserv. Com. Publ. 61. 10 pp.

BROWN, D. H., and K. S. Norris. 1956. Observations of Captive and Wild Cetaceans. J. Mamm. 37: 311–326.

BUSSJAEGER, L. J., C. C. Carpenter, H. L. Cleveland, and D. L. Marcinelli. 1967. Turkey Vulture Migration in Veracruz, Mexico. Condor 69: 425–426.

CALDWELL, L. D., and G. J. Wallace. 1966. Collections of Migrating Birds at Michigan Television Towers. Jack-Pine Warbler 44: 117–123.

CALHOUN, A. J. 1952. Annual Migrations of California Striped Bass. Calif. Fish and Game 38: 391–403.

CAMERON, R. A. D., L. Cornwallis, M. J. L. Percival, and A. R. E. Sinclair. 1967. The Migration of Raptors and Storks Through the Near East in Autumn. Ibis 109: 489–501.

CARR, A. 1962. Guideposts of Animal Navigation. Amer. Inst. Biol. Sci. BSCS Pam. 1. 36 pp.

——— 1965. The Navigation of the Green Turtle. Sci. Amer. 212 (5): 78-86.

——— 1967. Adaptive Aspects of the Scheduled Travel of *Chelonia*, pp. 35–55. *In* R. M. Storm [ed.], Animal Orientation and Navigation. Proc. 27th Annual Biol. Coll., Oregon State Univ. Press, Corvallis.

CASEMENT, M. B. 1966. Migration across the Mediterranean Observed by Radar. Ibis 108: 461–491.

CASTERET, N. 1938. Observations sur une Colonie de Chauves-Souris Migratrices. Mammalia 2: 29–34.

CHADWICK, H. K. 1963. An Evaluation of Five Tag Types Used in a Striped Bass Mortality Rate and Migration Study. Calif. Fish and Game 49: 64–83.

——— 1967. Recent Migrations of the Sacramento-San Joaquin River Striped Bass Population. Trans. Amer. Fish. Soc. 96: 327–342.

CHITTLEBOROUGH, R. G. 1953. Aerial Observations on the Humpback Whale, *Megaptera nodosa* (Bonnaterre), with Notes on Other Species. Australian J. Marine and Freshw. Res. 4: 219–226.

——— 1959. Australian Marking of Humpback Whales. Norsk Hvalfangsttidende 48: 47–55.

CLARK, L. B., and W. N. Hess. 1940. Swarming of the Atlantic Palolo Worm, *Leodice fucata* (Ehlers). Pap. Tortugas Lab. 33: 21–70.

CLARKE, W. E. 1912. Studies in Bird Migration. Gurney and Jackson, London. 2 vols., 346 pp.

COCKRUM, E. L. 1956. Homing, Movements, and Longevity of Bats. J. Mamm. 37: 48–57.

COLLMAN, J. R., and J. P. Croxall. 1967. Spring Migration at the Bosphorus. Ibis 109: 359–372.

CONSTANTINE, D. G. 1967. Activity Patterns of the Mexican Free-tailed Bat. Univ. New Mexico Pub. Biol. 7. 79 pp.

COWAN, I. McT. 1936. Distribution and Variation in Deer (Genus *Odocoileus*) of the Pacific Coastal Region of North America. Calif. Fish and Game 22: 155–246.

CRIDDLE, S. 1937. Snakes from an Ant Hill. Copeia 1937: 142.

DAVIS, J., and L. Williams. 1957. Irruptions of the Clark Nutcracker in California. Condor 59: 297–307.

―――― 1964. The 1961 Irruption of the Clark's Nutcracker in California. Wilson Bull. 76: 10–18.

DAVIS, P. 1966. The Great Immigration of Early September 1965. British Birds 59: 353–376.

DAVIS, R. 1966. Homing Performance and Homing Ability in Bats. Ecol. Monogr. 36: 201–237.

DAVIS, W. H., and J. W. Hardin. 1967. Homing in *Lasionycteris noctivagans*. J. Mamm. 48: 323.

DAVIS, W. H., and H. B. Hitchcock. 1965. Biology and Migration of the Bat, *Myotis lucifugus*, in New England. J. Mamm. 46: 296–313.

DELACOUR, J. 1954. The Waterfowl of the World. Country Life, London. Vol. 1, 284 pp.

DENNIS, D. M. 1962. Notes on the Nesting Habits of *Desmognathus fuscus fuscus* (Raf.) in Licking County, Ohio. J. Ohio Herp. Soc. 3: 28–35.

DOLNIK, V. R., and T. I. Blyumental. 1967. Autumnal Premigratory and Migratory Periods in the Chaffinch (*Fringilla coelebs coelebs*) and Some Other Temperature-Zone Passerine Birds. Condor 69: 435–468.

DONALDSON, L. R., and G. H. Allen. 1958. Return of Silver Salmon, *Oncorhynchus kisutch* (Walbaum) to Point of Release. Trans. Amer. Fish. Soc. 87: 13–22.

DORST, J. 1956. Les Migrations des Oiseaux. Payot, Paris. 422 pp.

―――― 1962. The Migrations of Birds. Houghton Mifflin Co., Boston. xix+476 pp.

DOWNS, W. G. 1959. Little Egret Banded in Spain Taken in Trinidad. Auk 76: 241–242.

DROST, R. 1935. Vogelzug und Mondlicht. Vogelzug 6: 26–33.

―――― 1949. Zugvögel perzipieren Ultrakurzwellen. Vogelwarte 15: 57–59.

EASTWOOD, E. 1967. Radar Ornithology. Methuen, London. xii+278 pp.

EASTWOOD, E., and G. C. Rider. 1965. Some Radar Measurements of the Altitude of Bird Flight. British Birds 58: 393–426.

EDWARDS, R. Y., and R. W. Ritcey. 1956. The Migrations of a Moose Herd. J. Mamm. 37: 486–494.

EHRENFELD, D. W., and A. Carr. 1967. The Role of Vision in the Sea-finding Orientation of the Green Turtle (*Chelonia mydas*). Animal Behaviour 15: 25–36.

EISENTRAUT, M. 1934. Markierungsversuche bei Fledermäusen. Z. Morph. Ökol. Tiere 28: 553–560.

―――― 1937. Die deutschen Fledermäuse, eine biologische Studie. Leipzig. Monogr. Wildsäugetiere, no. 2. 184 pp.

—— 1943. Zehn Jahre Fledermausberingung. Zool. Anz. 143: 20–32.

—— 1945. Biologie der Flederhunde (Megachiroptera). Biologia Generalis 18: 327–435.

EMLEN, J. T., and R. L. Penney. 1964. Distance Navigation in the Adelie Penguin. Ibis 106: 417–431.

EMLEN, S. T. 1967a. Migratory Orientation in the Indigo Bunting, *Passerina cyanea*. Part I: Evidence for Use of Celestial Clues. Auk 84: 309–342.

—— 1967b. Migratory Orientation in the Indigo Bunting, *Passerina cyanea*. Part II: Mechanism of Celestial Orientation. Auk 84: 463–489.

EMLEN, S. T., and J. T. Emlen. 1966. A Technique for Recording Migratory Orientation of Captive Birds. Auk 83: 361–367.

ENRIGHT, J. T. 1963. Endogenous Tidal and Lunar Rhythms. Proc. XVI Internat. Congr. Zool. 4: 355–359.

EVANS, P. R. 1966. Migration and Orientation of Passerine Night Migrants in Northeast England. J. Zool., London 150: 319–369.

EVANS, W. E., and J. H. Prescott. 1962. Observations of the Sound Production Capabilities of the Bottlenose Porpoise: A Study of Whistles and Clicks. Zoologica 47: 121–128.

FARNER, D. S. 1955. The Annual Stimulus for Migration: Experimental and Physiological Aspects, pp. 198–237. *In* A. Wolfson [ed.], Recent Studies in Avian Biology. Univ. Illinois Press, Urbana.

FEENY, P. P., R. W. Arnold, and R. S. Bailey. 1968. Autumn Migration in the South Caspian Region. Ibis 110: 35–86.

FERGUSON, D. E., and H. F. Landreth. 1966. Celestial Orientation of Fowler's Toad, *Bufo fowleri*. Behaviour 26: 105–123.

FERGUSON, D. E., H. F. Landreth, and J. P. McKeown. 1967. Sun Compass Orientation of the Northern Cricket Frog, *Acris crepitans*. Animal Behaviour 15: 45–53.

FERGUSON, D. E., H. F. Landreth, and M. R. Turnipseed. 1965. Astronomical Orientation of the Southern Cricket Frog, *Acris gryllus*. Copeia 1965: 58–66.

FINDLEY, J. S., and C. Jones. 1964. Seasonal Distribution of the Hoary Bat. J. Mamm. 45: 461–470.

FISLER, G. F. 1966. Homing in the Western Harvest Mouse, *Reithrodontomys megalotis*. J. Mamm. 47: 53–58.

—— 1967. An Experimental Analysis of Orientation to the Homesite in Two Rodent Species. Canadian J. Zool. 45: 261–268.

FRENCH, N. R., T. Y. Tagami, and P. Hayden. 1968. Dispersal in a Population of Desert Rodents. J. Mamm. 49: 272–280.

FRISCH, K. von. 1950. Bees, Their Vision, Chemical Senses, and Language. Cornell Univ. Press, Ithaca, New York. xiii+119 pp.

GALAMBOS, R., and D. R. Griffin. 1940. The Supersonic Cries of Bats. Anat. Rec. 78: 95.

GENTRY, J. B. 1966. Invasion of a One-Year Abandoned Field by *Peromyscus polionotus* and *Mus musculus*. J. Mamm. 47: 431–439.

GILMORE, R. M. 1958. The Story of the Gray Whale. Privately published, San Diego, Calif. 16 pp.

GOODWIN, D. 1949. Notes on the Migration of Birds of Prey over Suez. Ibis 91: 59–63.

GORDON, R. E. 1961. The Movement of Displaced Green Salamanders. Ecology 42: 200–202.

GRABER, R. R. 1965. Night Flight with a Thrush. Audubon 67: 368–374.

——— 1968. Nocturnal Migration in Illinois—Different Points of View. Wilson Bull. 80: 36–71.

GRABER, R. R., and W. W. Cochran. 1959. An Audio Technique for the Study of Nocturnal Migration of Birds. Wilson Bull. 71: 220–236.

GRANT, D., O. Anderson, and V. Twitty. 1968. Homing Orientation by Olfaction in Newts (*Taricha rivularis*). Science 160: 1354–1356.

GRIFFIN, D. R. 1940. Migrations of New England Bats. Bull. Mus. Comp. Zool. Harvard Univ. 86: 217–246.

——— 1945. Travels of Banded Cave Bats. J. Mamm. 26: 15–23.

——— 1955. Bird Navigation, pp. 154–197. *In* A. Wolfson [ed.], Recent Studies in Avian Biology. Univ. Illinois Press, Urbana.

——— 1958. Listening in the Dark. Yale Univ. Press, New Haven. xviii+413 pp.

——— 1964. Bird Migration. Doubleday and Co., Inc., Garden City, New York. xv+180 pp.

GRIFFIN, D. R., and R. Galambos. 1941. The Sensory Basis of Obstacle Avoidance by Flying Bats. J. Exp. Zool. 86: 481–506.

GRINNELL, J., and T. I. Storer. 1924. Animal Life in the Yosemite. Univ. Calif. Press, Berkeley. xviii+752 pp.

GROOT, C. 1965. On the Orientation of Young Sockeye Salmon (*Oncorhynchus nerka*) during Their Seaward Migration out of Lakes. Behaviour, Suppl. XIV. E. J. Brill, Leiden. 198 pp.

GROOT, C., and W. L. Wiley. 1965. Time-Lapse Photography of an ASDIC Echo-Sounder PPI-Scope as a Technique for Recording Fish Movements during Migration. J. Fish. Res. Bd. Canada 22: 1025–1034.

GROSS, A. O. 1940. The Migration of Kent Island Herring Gulls. Bird-Banding 11: 129–155.

GROSSMAN, M. L., and J. Hamlet. 1964. Birds of Prey of the World. Clarkson N. Potter, Inc., New York. 496 pp.

HALL, J. S. 1962. A Life History and Taxonomic Study of the Indiana Bat, *Myotis sodalis*. Reading Pub. Mus. Art Gal., Sci. Pub. 12. 68 pp.

HAMILTON, W. J. III. 1962a. Bobolink Migratory Pathways and Their Experimental Analysis under Night Skies. Auk 79: 208–233.

———— 1962b. Evidence Concerning the Function of Nocturnal Call Notes of Migratory Birds. Condor 64: 390–401.

———— 1967a. Analysis of Bird Navigation Experiments, pp. 147–178. *In* K. E. F. Watt [ed.], Systems Analysis in Ecology. Academic Press, Inc., New York.

———— 1967b. Social Aspects of Bird Orientation Mechanisms, pp. 57–71. *In* R. M. Storm [ed.], Animal Orientation and Navigation. Proc. 27th Annual Biol. Coll., Oregon State Univ. Press, Corvallis.

HAMILTON, W. J. III, and M. C. Hammond. 1960. Oriented Overland Spring Migration of Pinioned Canada Geese. Wilson Bull. 72: 385–391.

HARPER, W. G. 1958. Detection of Bird Migration by Centimetric Radar—a Cause of Radar "Angels." Proc. Royal Soc. London (B) 149: 484-502.

HASLER, A. D. 1966. Underwater Guideposts. Univ. Wisconsin Press, Madison. xii+155 pp.

HASLER, A. D., R. M. Horrall, W. J. Wisby, and W. Braemer. 1958. Sun-Orientation and Homing in Fishes. Limnol. Oceanogr. 3: 353–361.

HEAPE, W. 1931. Emigration, Migration and Nomadism. Cambridge Univ. Press, Cambridge. 369 pp.

HEARD, W. R. 1966. Observations on Lampreys in the Naknek River System of Southwest Alaska. Copeia 1966: 332–339.

HOAR, W. S. 1958. The Evolution of Migratory Behaviour among Juvenile Salmon of the Genus *Oncorhynchus*. J. Fish. Res. Bd. Canada 15: 391–428.

HÖHN, E. O. 1950. Physiology of the Thyroid Gland in Birds: A Review. Ibis 92: 464–473.

HOLMES, R. T. 1966a. Breeding Ecology and Annual Cycle Adaptations of the Red-backed Sandpiper (*Calidris alpina*) in Northern Alaska. Condor 68: 3–46.

———— 1966b. Molt Cycle of the Red-backed Sandpiper (*Calidris alpina*) in Western North America. Auk 83: 517–533.

HOWARD, W. E. 1960. Innate and Environmental Dispersal of Individual Vertebrates. Amer. Midl. Nat. 63: 152–161.

HOWELL, A. B., and L. Little. 1924. Additional Notes on California Bats; with Observations upon the Young of *Eumops*. J. Mamm. 5: 261–263.

HOWELL, T. R. 1959. Land Birds from Clipperton Island. Condor 61: 155–156.

HUBBS, C. L. 1968a. Black-footed Albatross, Banded at Midway Island, Recovered off Baja California in First Year. Condor 70: 92.

———— 1968b. Dispersal of Cattle Egret and Little Blue Heron into Northwestern Baja California, México. Condor 70: 92–93.

HUBBS, C. L., and R. C. Banks. 1966. Wandering onto the Eastern Pacific Ocean of an Eastern North American Land Bird, the Bay-breasted Warbler. Auk 83: 680–682.

HUMPHREY, P. S., D. Bridge, and T. E. Lovejoy. 1968. A Technique for Mist-Netting in the Forest Canopy. Bird-Banding 39: 43–50.

HUSSELL, D. J. T., T. Davis, and R. D. Montgomerie. 1967. Differential Fall Migration of Adult and Immature Least Flycatchers. Bird-Banding 38: 61–66.

IDLER, D. R., and I. Bitners. 1960. Biochemical Studies on Sockeye Salmon during Spawning Migration. IX. Fat, Protein and Water in the Major Internal Organs and Cholesterol in the Liver and Gonads of the Standard Fish. J. Fish. Res. Bd. Canada 17: 113–122.

IRWIN, M. P. S. 1957. Seasonal Changes in Altitude by Some Southern Rhodesian Birds. Ibis 99: 338–340.

ISING, G. 1946. Die physikalische Möglichkeit eines tierischen Orientierungssinnes auf Basis der Erdrotation. Ark. Mat. Astr. Fys. 32A (18): 1–23.

JAMESON, D. L. 1957. Population Structure and Homing Responses in the Pacific Tree Frog. Copeia 1957: 221–228.

JOHN, T. M., and J. C. George. 1966. Seasonal Variations in the Glycogen and Fat Contents of the Liver and the Pectoralis Muscle of Migratory Wagtails. Pavo 4: 58–64.

—— 1967. Certain Cyclic Changes in the Thyroid and Parathyroid Glands of Migratory Wagtails. Pavo 5: 19–28.

JOHNSON, C. G. 1965. Migration, pp. 187–226. In M. Rockstein [ed.], The Physiology of Insecta, Vol. 2. Academic Press, Inc., New York.

JOHNSON, N. K. 1963. Comparative Molt Cycles in the Tyrannid Genus Empidonax. Proc. XIII Internat. Ornith. Congr.: 870–883.

JOHNSON, W. E., and C. Groot. 1963. Observations on the Migration of Young Sockeye Salmon (Oncorhynchus nerka) through a Large, Complex Lake System. J. Fish. Res. Bd. Canada 20: 919–938.

JOHNSTON, D. W. 1966. A Review of the Vernal Fat Deposition Picture in Overland Migrant Birds. Bird-Banding 37: 172–183.

—— 1968. Body Characteristics of Palm Warblers Following an Overwater Flight. Auk 85: 13–18.

JOHNSTON, D. W., and R. W. McFarlane. 1967. Migration and Bioenergetics of Flight in the Pacific Golden Plover. Condor 69: 156–168.

JOHNSTON, R. F. 1956. Population Structure in Salt Marsh Song Sparrows. Part I. Environment and Annual Cycle. Condor 58: 24–44.

KELLOGG, W. N. 1961. Porpoises and Sonar. Univ. Chicago Press, Chicago. xiv+177 pp.

KELSALL, J. P. 1968. The Migratory Barren-Ground Caribou of Canada. Canadian Wildl. Serv. Monogr. Ser.: 3.

KEMPER, C. A. 1964. A Tower for TV: 30,000 Dead Birds. Audubon 66: 86–90.

KENDEIGH, S. C. 1961. Animal Ecology. Prentice-Hall, Inc., Englewood Cliffs, New Jersey. 468 pp.

KENDEIGH, S. C., G. C. West, and G. W. Cox. 1960. Annual Stimulus for Spring Migration in Birds. Animal Behaviour 8: 180–185.

KENYON, K. W. 1960. Territorial Behavior and Homing in the Alaska Fur Seal. Mammalia 24: 431–444.

KENYON, K. W., and D. W. Rice. 1958. Homing of Laysan Albatrosses. Condor 60: 3–6.

KENYON, K. W., and F. Wilke. 1953. Migration of the Northern Fur Seal, *Callorhinus ursinus*. J. Mamm. 34: 86–98.

KING, J. R., and D. S. Farner. 1963. The Relationship of Fat Deposition to *Zugunruhe* and Migration. Condor 65: 200–223.

KING, J. R., D. S. Farner, and L. R. Mewaldt. 1965. Seasonal Sex and Age Ratios in Populations of the White-crowned Sparrows of the Race *gambelii*. Condor 67: 489–504.

KING, J. R., L. R. Mewaldt, and D. S. Farner. 1960. The Duration of Post-nuptial Metabolic Refractoriness in the White-crowned Sparrow. Auk 77: 89–92.

KLOTS, A. B. 1959. The World of Butterflies and Moths. McGraw-Hill Book Co., Inc., New York. 207 pp.

KNORR, O. A. 1954. The Effect of Radar on Birds. Wilson Bull. 66: 264.

KRAMER, G. 1949. Über Richtungstendenzen bei der nächtlichen Zugunruhe gekäfigter Vögel, pp. 269–283. *In* E. Mayr and E. Schuz [eds.], Ornithologie als biologische Wissenschaft. Carl Winter, Heidelberg.

———— 1950. Orientierte Zugaktivität gekäfigter Singvögel. Naturwissenschaften 37: 188.

———— 1951. Eine neue Methode zur Erforschung der Zugorientierung und die bisher damit erzielten Ergebnisse. Proc. X Internat. Ornith. Congr.: 269–280.

———— 1952. Experiments on Bird Orientation. Ibis 94: 265–285.

———— 1957. Experiments on Bird Orientation and Their Interpretation. Ibis 99: 196–227.

———— 1959. Recent Experiments on Bird Orientation. Ibis 101: 399–416.

LACK, D. 1954. The Natural Regulation of Animal Numbers. Clarendon Press, Oxford. viii+343 pp.

———— 1960. The Height of Bird Migration. British Birds 53: 5–10.

———— 1962. Radar Evidence on Migratory Orientation. British Birds 55: 139–158.

———— 1963. Migration across the Southern North Sea Studied by Radar. Part 4. Autumn. Ibis 105: 1–54.

LANDRETH, H. F., and D. E. Ferguson. 1967. Newts: Sun-Compass Orientation. Science 158: 1459–1461.

LATHBURY, G. 1968. Autumn Migration of Raptors across the Straits of Gibraltar. Ibis 110: 210–211.

LENT, P. C. 1966. Calving and Related Social Behavior in the Barren-Ground Caribou. Z. Tierpsych. 23: 701–756.

LÉVÊQUE, R., R. I. Bowman, and S. L. Billeb. 1966. Migrants in the Galápagos Area. Condor 68: 81–101.

LIDICKER, W. Z., Jr. 1962. Emigration as a Possible Mechanism Permitting the Regulation of Population Density below Carrying Capacity. Amer. Nat. 96: 29–33.

LILLY, D. F., and R. T. Orr. 1959. The Allen Hummingbird—How Many Nests a Year? Pacific Discovery 12 (3): 22–25.

LINCOLN, F. C. 1939. The Migration of American Birds. Doubleday, Doran and Co., New York. xii+189 pp.

———— 1950. Migration of Birds. Circular 16, U.S. Fish and Wildl. Serv., Washington, D.C. 102 pp.

LINT, K. C. 1962. Cattle Egret Expands Range. Auk 79: 483.

LOFTS, B. 1962. Cyclical Changes in the Interstitial and Spermatogenetic Tissue of Migratory Waders "Wintering" in Africa. Proc. Zool. Soc. London 138: 405–413.

LOFTS, B., A. J. Marshall, and A. Wolfson. 1963. The Experimental Demonstration of Pre-Migration Activity in the Absence of Fat Deposition in Birds. Ibis 105: 99–105.

LOFTUS, K. H. 1958. Studies on River-spawning Populations of Lake Trout in Eastern Lake Superior. Trans. Amer. Fish. Soc. 87: 259–277.

LORZ, H. W., and T. G. Northcote. 1965. Factors Affecting Stream Location, and Timing and Intensity of Entry by Spawning Kokanee (*Oncorhynchus nerka*) into an Inlet of Nicola Lake, British Columbia. J. Fish. Res. Bd. Canada 22: 665–687.

LOW, S. H. 1957. Banding with Mist Nets. Bird-Banding 28: 115–128.

LOWERY, G. H., Jr. 1951. A Quantitative Study of the Nocturnal Migration of Birds. Univ. Kansas Publ. Mus. Nat. Hist. 3: 361–472.

LOWERY, G. H., Jr., and R. J. Newman. 1955. Direct Studies of Nocturnal Bird Migration, pp. 238–263. In A. Wolfson [ed.], Recent Studies in Avian Biology. Univ. Illinois Press, Urbana.

———— 1966. A Continentwide View of Bird Migration on Four Nights in October. Auk 83: 547–586.

LUDWIG, J. P. 1963. Return of Herring Gulls to Natal Colony. Bird-Banding 34: 68–72.

LÜTERS, W., and G. Birukow. 1963. Sonnenkompassorientierung der Brandmaus (*Apodemus agrarius* Pall.). Naturwissenschaften 50: 737–738.

McBRIDE, J. R., U. H. M. Fagerlund, M. Smith, and N. Tomlinson. 1965. Post-Spawning Death of Pacific Salmon: Sockeye Salmon (*Oncorhynchus nerka*) Maturing and Spawning in Captivity. J. Fish. Res. Bd. Canada 22: 775–782.

MACKIEWICZ, J., and R. H. Backus. 1956. Oceanic Records of *Lasionycteris noctivagans* and *Lasiurus borealis*. J. Mamm. 37: 442–443.

MACKINTOSH, D. R. 1949. The Use of Thermal Currents by Birds on Migration. Ibis 91: 55–59.

MACLEOD, R. A., R. E. E. Jonas, and E. Onofrey. 1960. A Biochemical Study of Coho Salmon (*Oncorhynchus kisutch*) Maturing Sexually in an Aquarium. J. Fish. Res. Bd. Canada 17: 323–335.

MAHER, W. J., and N. J. Wilimovsky. 1963. Annual Catch of Bowhead Whales by Eskimos at Point Barrow, Alaska, 1928–1960. J. Mamm. 44: 16–20.

MANGALAM, J. J. 1968. Human Migration: A Guide to Migration Literature in English, 1955–1962. Univ. Kentucky Press, Lexington. 194 pp.

MARCHANT, S. 1963. Migration in Iraq. Ibis 105: 369–398.

MARSHALL, A. J. 1952. The Condition of the Interstitial and Spermatogenetic Tissue of Migratory Birds on Arriving in England in April and May. Proc. Zool. Soc. London 122: 287–295.

MATTHEWS, G. V. T. 1955. Bird Navigation. Univ. Press, Cambridge. 141 pp.

MEDWAY, Lord. 1967. The Function of Echonavigation among Swiftlets. Animal Behaviour 15: 416–420.

MEDWAY, Lord, and I. C. T. Nisbet. 1968. Bird Report: 1966. Malayan Nature J. 21: 34–50.

MEINERTZHAGEN, R. 1955. The Speed and Altitude of Bird Flight (With Notes on Other Animals). Ibis 97: 81–117.

MEWALDT, L. R. 1964. California Sparrows Return from Displacement to Maryland. Science 146: 941–942.

MEWALDT, L. R., S. S. Kibby, and M. L. Morton. 1968. Comparative Biology of Pacific Coastal White-crowned Sparrows. Condor 70: 14–30.

MEWALDT, L. R., M. L. Morton, and I. L. Brown. 1964. Orientation of Migratory Restlessness in *Zonotrichia*. Condor 66: 377–417.

MIEGHEM, J. van, and P. van Oye [eds.]. 1965. Biogeography and Ecology in Antarctica. W. Junk, The Hague. xxvii+762 pp.

MILLER, A. H. 1965. Capacity for Photoperiodic Response and Endogenous Factors in the Reproductive Cycles of an Equatorial Sparrow. Proc. Nat. Acad. Sci. 54: 97–101.

MOREAU, R. E. 1966. The Bird Faunas of Africa and Its Islands. Academic Press, Inc., New York. viii+424 pp.

——— 1967. Water-Birds over the Sahara. Ibis 109: 232–259.

MUELLER, H. C., and D. D. Berger. 1967a. Wind Drift, Leading Lines, and Diurnal Migration. Wilson Bull. 79: 50–63.

——— 1967b. Some Observations and Comments on the Periodic Invasions of Goshawks. Auk 84: 183–191.

——— 1967c. Fall Migration of Sharp-shinned Hawks. Wilson Bull. 79: 397–415.

——— 1968. Sex Ratios and Measurements of Migrant Goshawks. Auk 85: 431–436.

MUELLER, H. C., and J. T. Emlen, Jr. 1957. Homing in Bats. Science 126: 307–308.

MÜLLER-SCHWARZE, D. 1967. Tierstrassen in der Antarktis, pp. 120–133. In H. Hediger [ed.], Die Strassen der Tiere. Friedr. Vieweg und Sohn, Braunschweig, Germany.

MURIE, O. J. 1935. Alaska-Yukon Caribou. U.S. Dept. Agric., N. Amer. Fauna 54. 93 pp.

——— 1951. The Elk of North America. Stackpole Co., Harrisburg, Pa., and Wildl. Mgmt. Inst., Washington, D.C. 376 pp.

MURRAY, B. G., Jr. 1965. On the Autumn Migration of the Blackpoll Warbler. Wilson Bull. 77: 122–133.

——— 1966a. Blackpoll Warbler Migration in Michigan. Jack-Pine Warbler 44: 23–29.

——— 1966b. Migration of Age and Sex Classes of Passerines on the Atlantic Coast in Autumn. Auk 83: 352–360.

——— 1967. Dispersal in Vertebrates. Ecology 48: 975–978.

NAIK, D. V. 1963. Seasonal Variation in the Metabolites of the Liver of the Rosy Pastor, *Sturnus roseus* (Linnaeus). Pavo 1: 44–47.

NEAVE, D. J., and B. S. Wright. 1968. Seasonal Migrations of the Harbor Porpoise (*Phocoena phocoena*) and Other Cetacea in the Bay of Fundy. J. Mamm. 49: 259–264.

NEAVE, F. 1964. Ocean Migrations of Pacific Salmon. J. Fish. Res. Bd. Canada 21: 1227–1244.

NEAVE, F., T. Ishida, and S. Murai. 1967. Salmon of the North Pacific Ocean. Part VII. Pink Salmon in Offshore Waters. Internat. N. Pac. Fish. Comm. Bull. 22: 1–39.

NEAVE, F., J. I. Manzer, H. Godfrey, and R. J. LeBrasseur. 1962. High-Seas Salmon Fishing by Canadian Vessels in 1962. Fish Res. Bd. Canada MS Rept. (Biol.) no. 759. 59 pp.

NEWMAN, R. J. 1952. Studying Nocturnal Bird Migration by Means of the Moon. Mus. Zool. Louisiana State Univ. 49 pp.

NEWMAN, R. J., and G. H. Lowery, Jr. 1964. Selected Quantitative Data on Night Migration in Autumn. Spec. Publ. 3, Mus. Zool. Louisiana State Univ. 39 pp.

NICE, M. M. 1937. Studies in the Life History of the Song Sparrow. I. A Population Study of the Song Sparrow. Trans. Linn. Soc. New York 4: 1–247.

NISBET, I. C. T. 1963a. Measurements with Radar of the Height of Nocturnal Migration over Cape Cod, Massachusetts. Bird-Banding 34: 57–67.

—— 1963b. Quantitative Study of Migration with 23-Centimetre Radar. Ibis 105: 435–460.

—— 1963c. Weight-Loss during Migration. Part II: Review of Other Estimates. Bird-Banding 34: 139–159.

NISBET, I. C. T., and W. H. Drury, Jr. 1967. Orientation of Spring Migrants Studied by Radar. Bird-Banding 38: 173–186.

NORRIS, K. S. 1964. Some Problems of Echolocation in Cetaceans, pp. 317–336. In W. N. Tavolga [ed.], Marine Bio-acoustics. Pergamon Press, New York.

—— 1966. The Evolution of Acoustic Mechanisms in Odontocete Cetaceans. Symp.: Evolutionary Processes at the Population Level. Centennial Celebrations of the Peabody Mus. Nat. Hist., Yale Univ. Ms. 37+19 pp.

NORRIS, K. S., J. H. Prescott, P. V. Asa-Dorian, and P. Perkins. 1961. An Experimental Demonstration of Echolocation Behavior in the Porpoise, Tursiops truncatus (Montagu). Biol. Bull. Woods Hole 120: 163–176.

NOVAKOWSKI, N. S. 1966. Whooping Crane Population Dynamics on the Nesting Grounds, Wood Buffalo National Park, Northwest Territories, Canada. Canadian Wildl. Serv. Rept. Ser., 1. 20 pp.

NOVICK, A. 1959. Acoustic Orientation in the Cave Swiftlet. Biol. Bull. Woods Hole 117: 497–503.

ODUM, E. P. 1960. Lipid Deposition in Nocturnal Migrant Birds. Proc. XII Internat. Ornith. Congr.: 563–576.

ODUM, E. P., and C. E. Connell. 1956. Lipid Levels in Migrating Birds. Science 123: 892–894.

ODUM, E. P., D. T. Rogers, and D. L. Hicks. 1964. Homeostasis of the Nonfat Components of Migrating Birds. Science 143: 1037–1039.

OLIVER, J. A. 1955. The Natural History of North American Amphibians and Reptiles. D. Van Nostrand Co., Inc., Princeton, N. J. 359 pp.

ORR, R. T. 1950. Notes on the Seasonal Occurrence of Red Bats in San Francisco. J. Mamm. 31: 457–458.

—— 1954. Natural History of the Pallid Bat, Antrozous pallidus (Le Conte). Proc. Calif. Acad. Sci. (4) 28: 165–246.

—— 1963. Porpoises and Dolphins. Pacific Discovery 16 (4): 22–26.

—— 1966. Vertebrate Biology. 2nd ed. W. B. Saunders Co., Philadelphia. xii+483 pp.

—— 1967. The Galapagos Sea Lion. J. Mamm. 48: 62–69.

ORR, R. T., and T. C. Poulter. 1965. The Pinniped Population of Año Nuevo Island, California. Proc. Calif. Acad. Sci. (4) 32: 377–404.

ÖSTERLÖF, S. 1966. The Migration of the Goldcrest (Regulus regulus). Var. Fagelvarld 25: 49–56. [In Swedish, English summary.]

OVERING, R. 1938. High Mortality at the Washington Monument. Auk 55: 679.

PACKER, W. C. 1963. Observations on the Breeding Migration of *Taricha rivularis*. Copeia 1963: 378–382.

PARKS, G. H., and H. C. Parks. 1963. Evening Grosbeaks Died to Supply Bands for This "Jewelry." Bird-Banding 34: 73–86.

PAYNTER, R. A., Jr. 1947. The Fate of Banded Kent Island Herring Gulls. Bird-Banding 18: 156–170.

PEARSON, O. P. 1950. The Metabolism of Hummingbirds. Condor 52: 145–152.

———— 1953. Use of Caves by Hummingbirds and Other Species at High Altitudes in Peru. Condor 55: 17–20.

———— 1960. Torpidity in Birds. Bull. Mus. Comp. Zool. Harvard 124: 93–103.

———— 1961. Flight Speeds of Some Small Birds. Condor 63: 506–507.

PENNEY, R. L., and J. T. Emlen. 1967. Further Experiments on Distance Navigation in the Adelie Penguin *Pygoscelis adeliae*. Ibis 109: 99–109.

PIERCE, G. W., and D. R. Griffin. 1938. Experimental Determination of Supersonic Notes Emitted by Bats. J. Mamm. 19: 454–455.

PITT, T. K. 1958. Distribution, Spawning and Racial Studies of the Capelin, *Mallotus villosus* (Müller), in the Offshore Newfoundland Area. J. Fish. Res. Bd. Canada 15: 275–293.

POST, P. W. 1967. Manx, Audubon's, and Little Shearwaters in the Northwestern North Atlantic. Bird-Banding 38: 278–305.

POUGH, R. H. 1948. Out of the Night Sky. Audubon Mag. 50: 354–355.

POULTER, T. C. 1963. Sonar Signals of the Sea Lion. Science 139: 753–755.

PURVES, P. E. 1966. Anatomy and Physiology of the Outer and Middle Ear in Cetaceans, pp. 320–380. *In* K. S. Norris [ed.], Whales, Dolphins, and Porpoises. Univ. Calif. Press, Berkeley.

RADFORD, K. W., R. T. Orr, and C. L. Hubbs. 1965. Reestablishment of the Northern Elephant Seal (*Mirounga angustirostris*) off Central California. Proc. Calif. Acad. Sci. (4) 31: 601–612.

RAINEY, R. C. 1967. Radar Observations of Locust Swarms. Science 157: 98–99.

RAMEL, C. 1960. The Influence of the Wind on the Migration of Swallows. Proc. XII Internat. Ornith. Congr.: 626–630.

RAYNOR, G. S. 1956. Meteorological Variables and the Northward Movement of Nocturnal Land Bird Migrants. Auk 73: 153–175.

REGAN, C. 1965. A Salmon Named Indomitable. Pacific Discovery 18 (3): 28–30.

RENSE, W. A. 1946. Astronomy and Ornithology. Pop. Astron. 54: 55–73.

ROBINSON, W. L., and J. B. Falls. 1965. A Study of Homing of Meadow Mice. Amer. Midl. Nat. 73: 188–224.

ROER, H. 1967. Wanderflüge der Insekten, pp. 186–206. *In* H. Hediger [ed.], Die Strassen der Tiere. Friedr. Vieweg und Sohn, Braunschweig, Germany.

Rose, F. L. 1966. Homing to Nests by the Salamander *Desmognathus auriculatus*. Copeia 1966: 251–253.

Rowan, W. 1925. Relation of Light to Bird Migration and Developmental Changes. Nature 115: 494–495.

——— 1926. On Photoperiodism, Reproductive Periodicity, and the Annual Migrations of Birds and Certain Fishes. Proc. Boston Soc. Nat. Hist. 38: 147–189.

——— 1929. Experiments in Bird Migration. I. Manipulation of the Reproductive Cycle: Seasonal Histological Changes in the Gonads. Proc. Boston Soc. Nat. Hist. 39: 151–208.

Ryberg, O. 1947. Studies on Bats and Bat Parasites. Svensk Natur, Stockholm. xvi+318 pp.

Ryder, J. P. 1967. The Breeding Biology of Ross' Goose in the Perry River Region, Northwest Territories. Canadian Wildl. Serv. Rept. Ser., 3, Ottawa. 56 pp.

Safriel, U. 1968. Bird Migration at Elat, Israel. Ibis 110: 283–320.

Sanderson, G. C. 1966. The Study of Mammal Movements—A Review. J. Wildl. Mgmt. 30: 215–235.

Sauer, E. G. F. 1962. Ethology and Ecology of Golden Plovers on St. Lawrence Island, Bering Sea. Psych. Forsch. 26: 399–470.

——— 1963. Golden Plover Migration, Its Evolution and Orientation. Proc. XVI Internat. Congr. Zool. 4: 380–381.

Sauer, F. 1956. Zugorientierung einer Mönchsgrasmücke (*Sylvia a. atricapilla* L.) unter kunstlichem Sternenhimmel. Naturwissenschaften 43: 231–232.

——— 1957. Die Sternenorientierung nächtlich ziehender Grasmücken (*Sylvia atricapilla, borin* und *curruca*). Z. Tierpsych. 14: 29–70.

——— 1958. Celestial Navigation by Birds. Scientific American 199 (2): 42–47.

Sauer, F., and E. Sauer. 1955. Zur Frage der nächtlichen Zugorientierung von Grasmücken. Rev. Suisse Zool. 62: 250–259.

Schevill, W. E. 1964. Underwater Sounds of Cetaceans, pp. 307–316. *In* W. N. Tavolga [ed.], Marine Bio-acoustics. Pergamon Press, New York.

Schevill, W. E., and W. A. Watkins. 1965. Underwater Calls of *Trichechus* (Manatee). Nature 205: 373–374.

——— 1966. Radio-Tagging of Whales. Woods Hole Oceanographic Institution. Ref. 66–17. Ms.

Schevill, W. E., W. A. Watkins, and C. Ray. 1963. Underwater Sounds of Pinnipeds. Science 141: 50–53.

Schmidt-Koenig, K. 1960. The Sun Azimuth Compass: One Factor in the Orientation of Homing Pigeons. Science 131: 826–828.

Schorger, A. W. 1955. The Passenger Pigeon: Its Natural History and Extinction. Univ. Wisconsin Press, Madison. xiii+424 pp.

Schüz, E. 1934. Vom Storch-Versuch 1933 der Vogelwarte Rossitten. Vogelzug 5: 21–25.

Serventy, V. 1965. Budgerygah. Pacific Discovery 18 (3): 23–25.

Shelbourn, J. E. 1966. Influence of Temperature, Salinity, and Photoperiod on the Aggregations of Chum Salmon Fry (*Oncorhynchus keta*). J. Fish. Res. Bd. Canada 23: 293–304.

Simmons, K. E. L. 1951. Raptor Migration in the Suez Area: Autumn 1949–Spring 1950. Ibis 93: 402–406.

Sivertsen, E. 1941. On the Biology of the Harp Seal, *Phoca groenlandica* Erxl. Hvalradets Skrifter 26, Norske Videnskaps-Akad. Oslo. ix+166 pp.

Slijper, E. J. 1962. Whales. Basic Books, Inc., New York. 475 pp.

Smith, E., and W. Goodpaster. 1958. Homing in Nonmigratory Bats. Science 127: 644.

Smith, E., and K. Hale. 1953. A Homing Record in the Bat, *Myotis lucifugus lucifugus*. J. Mamm. 34: 122.

Spoecker, P. D. 1967. Movements and Seasonal Activity Cycles of the Lizard *Uta stansburiana stejnegeri*. Amer. Midl. Nat. 77: 484–494.

Spofford, W. R. 1949. Mortality of Birds at the Ceilometer of the Nashville Airport. Wilson Bull. 61: 86–90.

Stille, W. T. 1952. The Nocturnal Amphibian Fauna of the Southern Lake Michigan Beach. Ecology 33: 149–162.

Stobbe, E. 1966. Tagging the Migratory Monarch. Audubon 68: 343–346.

Stoddard, H. L., and R. A. Norris. 1967. Bird Casualties at a Leon County, Florida TV Tower: An Eleven-Year Study. Tall Timbers Res. Sta. Bull. 8. 104 pp.

Stresemann, E., and V. Stresemann. 1966. Die Mauser der Vögel. J. Ornith. 107 Sonderheft: 1–58.

Stuart, T. A. 1962. The Leaping Behavior of Salmon and Trout at Falls and Obstructions. Freshwater and Salmon Fish. Res., Edinburgh, 28. 46 pp.

Sutter, E. 1957. Radar als Hilfsmittel der Vogelzugforschung. Ornith. Beob. 54: 70–96.

Teichmann, H. 1957. Das Reichvermögen des Aales (*Anguilla anguilla* L.). Naturwissenschaften 44: 242.

Tenaza, R. R. 1966. Migration of Hoary Bats on South Farallon Island, California. J. Mamm. 47: 533–535.

Tennent, J. R. M. 1967. Spring Migration of Birds of Prey near Suez. Ibis 109: 273–274.

Terres, J. K. 1956. Death in the Night. Audubon Mag. 58: 18–20.

Thompson, D. Q., and R. A. Person. 1963. The Eider Pass at Point Barrow, Alaska. J. Wildl. Mgmt. 27: 348–356.

Thomson, A. L. 1926. Problems of Bird-migration. H. F. & G. Witherby, London. xv+350 pp.

——— 1965. The Transequatorial Migration of the Manx Shearwater. Oiseau Rev. Française Ornith. 35, no. spécial: 130–140.

Tickell, W. L. N. 1968. Color-dying Albatrosses. Bird-Banding 39: 36–40.

Tinbergen, N. 1939. The Behavior of the Snow Bunting in Spring. Trans. Linn. Soc. New York 5: 1–94.

——— 1953. The Herring Gull's World. Collins, London. xvi+255 pp.

Tomlinson, R. E., H. M. Wight, and T. S. Baskett. 1960. Migrational Homing, Local Movement, and Mortality of Mourning Doves in Missouri. Trans. 25th N. Amer. Wildl. Conf., Wildl. Mgmt. Inst., Washington, D.C., pp. 253–267.

Tordoff, H. B., and R. M. Mengel. 1956. Studies of Birds Killed in Nocturnal Migration. Univ. Kansas Publ., Mus. Nat. Hist. 10: 1–44.

Twente, J. W., Jr. 1956. Ecological Observations on a Colony of *Tadarida mexicana*. J. Mamm. 37: 42–47.

Twitty, V. C. 1959. Migration and Speciation in Newts. Science 130: 1735–1743.

Twitty, V., D. Grant, and O. Anderson. 1964. Long Distance Homing in the Newt *Taricha rivularis*. Proc. Nat. Acad. Sci. 51: 51–58.

Urquhart, F. A. 1960. The Monarch Butterfly. Univ. Toronto Press, Toronto. xxiv+361 pp.

Villa-R., B., and E. L. Cockrum. 1962. Migration in the Guano Bat *Tadarida brasiliensis mexicana* (Saussure). J. Mamm. 43: 43–64.

Voous, K. H. 1965. Antarctic Birds, pp. 649–689. *In* J. van Mieghem and P. van Oye [eds.], Biogeography and Ecology in Antarctica. W. Junk, The Hague.

Walker, L. W. 1965. Baja's Island of Birds. Pacific Discovery 18 (4): 27–31.

Walker, T. J. 1962. Whale Primer with Special Attention to the California Gray Whale. Cabrillo Hist. Assoc. 58 pp.

Wallraff, H. G. 1966. Über die Anfangsorientierung von Brieftauben unter geschlossener Wolkendecke. J. Ornith. 107: 326–336.

Walter, H. 1968a. Falcons of a Princess. Pacific Discovery 21 (3): 2–9.

——— 1968b. Zur Abhängigkeit des Eleonorenfalken (*Falco eleonorae*) vom mediterranen Vogelzug. J. Ornith. 109: 323–365.

Ward, P. 1963. Lipid Levels in Birds Preparing to Cross the Sahara. Ibis 105: 109–111.

Whitford, W. G., and A. Vinegar. 1966. Homing, Survivorship, and Overwintering of Larvae in Spotted Salamanders, *Ambystoma maculatum*. Copeia 1966: 515–519.

WILKE, F., and K. W. Kenyon. 1954. Migration and Food of the Northern Fur Seal. Trans. 19th N. Amer. Wildl. Conf., Wildl. Mgmt. Inst., Washington, D.C., pp. 430–440.

WILKINSON, D. H. 1952. The Random Element in Bird "Navigation." J. Exper. Biol. 29: 532–560.

WILLIAMS, C. B. 1930. The Migration of Butterflies. Oliver and Boyd, Edinburgh and London. xi+473 pp.

—— 1958. Insect Migration. Macmillan Co., New York. xiii+235 pp.

WILLIAMS, T. C., and J. M. Williams. 1967. Radio Tracking of Homing Bats. Science 155: 1435–1436.

WILLIAMS, T. C., J. M. Williams, and D. R. Griffin. 1966. The Homing Ability of the Neotropical Bat *Phyllostomus hastatus*, with Evidence for Visual Orientation. Animal Behaviour 14: 468–473.

WILSON, A. 1808–1814. American Ornithology; or, The Natural History of the Birds of the United States. 9 vols. Bradford and Inskeep, Philadelphia.

WILTSCHKO, W. 1968. Über den Einfluss statischer Magnetfelder auf die Zugorientierung der Rotkehlchen (*Erithacus rubecula*). Z. Tierpsych. 25: 537–558.

WISBY, W. J., and A. D. Hasler. 1954. Effect of Olfactory Occlusion on Migrating Silver Salmon (*O. kisutch*). J. Fish. Res. Bd. Canada 11: 472–478.

WOLFSON, A. 1940. A Preliminary Report on Some Experiments on Bird Migration. Condor 42: 93–99.

—— 1942. Regulation of Spring Migration in Juncos. Condor 44: 237–263.

—— 1945. The Role of the Pituitary, Fat Deposition, and Body Weight in Bird Migration. Condor 47: 95–127.

—— 1952. Day Length, Migration, and Breeding Cycles in Birds. Scientific Monthly 74: 191–200.

WOOD, J. D., D. W. Duncan, and M. Jackson. 1960. Biochemical Studies on Sockeye Salmon during Spawning Migration. XI. The Free Histidine Content of the Tissues. J. Fish. Res. Bd. Canada 17: 347–351.

YEAGLEY, H. L. 1947. A Preliminary Study of a Physical Basis of Bird Navigation. J. Appl. Physics 18: 1035–1063.

ZAHL, P. A. 1963. Mystery of the Monarch Butterfly. Natl. Geogr. 123: 588–598.

ZWICKEL, F. C., I. O. Buss, and J. H. Brigham. 1968. Autumn Movements of Blue Grouse and Their Relevance to Populations and Management. J. Wildl. Mgmt. 32: 456–468.

INDEX

INDEX

291

Physeter catodon, 66, 84, 162
Picea engelmanni, 170
Pieris brassicae, 182
pigeons,
    homing, 207–208
    passenger, 21
pikas, 32
pinnipeds, 163–168
pintails, 108, 143
Pipistrellus ssp., 237
Pipistrellus pipistrellus, 156
pipit, 8, 130–131
    Sprague's, 130
    water, 130
Piranga flava, 134
Piranga ludoviciana, 134
Piranga olivacea, 76, 107, 134
Piranga rubra, 76, 134, 242
plankton, 2, 89
Platynereis deumerilii, 42
Plectrophenax nivalis, 60, 74
ploceids, 115
plovers,
    American golden, 37, 74, 82, 109, 145
    Eurasian golden, 145
Plusia gamma, 177
Pulvialis, 37, 109
Pluvialis apricaria, 37, 74, 145
Pluvialis dominica, 37, 74, 109, 145
Pluvialis dominica dominica, 82, 109, 145
Pluvialis dominica Fulva, 82, 145
Podiceps caspicus, 117
Podilymbus podiceps, 245
polychaete worms, 42, 89
poorwill, 32
population cycles, *see* irruptions
population movements,
    intraspecific differences, 53–55
porpoises,
    bottle-nosed, 233
    Dall's, 24, 163
    harbor, 163
Progne subis, 128
protozoans, 185
Prunella fulvescens, 117
Prunella immaculata, 117
Prunella rubeculoides, 117
Prunella strophiata, 117
Pteropidae, 158
Pteropus poliocephalus, 158

Puffinus griseus, 141, 242
Puffinus lherminieri, 141
Puffinus puffinus ssp., 138–142, 221
Puffinis tenuirostris, 74, 139
Pygoscelis adeliae, 55–56, 136, 221
Pyrrhocorax graculus, 183
Pyrrhocorax pyrrhocorax, 183

quails, 173, 248
    mountain, 22, 117–118
Quelea quelea, 8, 115

radar effects, 224–225
radar studies,
    birds, 179, 181, 184–185
    insects, 182, 268–269
radar tracking, 175, 268–269
radio tracking, 265–268
rails, 77
Rana clamitans, 100
Rana pipiens, 101
Rangifer tarandus, 169–170
rattlesnakes, 101–102
redd, 188
redstarts, 51
refractory period, 41
refuge,
    Bear River Migratory, 108
    Hawk Mountain Sanctuary, 181
Regulus regulus, 38
Reithrodontomys megalotis, 238
remoras, 172
reproduction, 67–70
Rhynchopsitta pachyrhyncha, 6
Riparia riparia, 51, 127
roadrunners, 123
robins, 54
    European, 224
Roccus chrysops, 95, 194
Roccus saxatilus, 99
rodents, 4, 32, 237–238
rosy pastor, 74
Rubus fruticosis, 78

salamanders, 45, 100, 198–200, 249
    dusky, 200
    green, 200
    hellbender, 100
    spotted, 200–201
Salmo clarki, 33, 44